Mathematical Explorations In Behavioral Science

THE IRWIN-DORSEY SERIES
IN BEHAVIORAL SCIENCE

ARGYRIS *Interpersonal Competence and Organizational Effectiveness*

ARGYRIS, DUBIN, HAIRE, LUCE, WARNER, WHYTE, & STROTHER (ed.) *Social Science Approaches to Business Behavior*

GUEST *Organizational Change: The Effect of Successful Leadership*

KUHN *The Study of Society: A Unified Approach*

LAWRENCE & SEILER with BAILEY, KATZ, ORTH, CLARK, BARNES, & TURNER *Organizational Behavior and Administration: Cases, Concepts, and Research Findings* rev. ed.

MASSARIK & RATOOSH *Mathematical Explorations in Behavioral Science*

ORTH, BAILEY, & WOLEK *Administering Research and Development: The Behavior of Scientists and Engineers in Organizations*

RUBENSTEIN & HABERSTROH (eds.) *Some Theories of Organization*

WHYTE *Men at Work*

WHYTE & HAMILTON *Action Research for Management: A Case Report on Research and Action in Industry*

Mathematical Explorations
in
Behavioral Science

Edited by

FRED MASSARIK
Graduate School of Business Administration, and
Institute of Industrial Relations,
University of California, Los Angeles

And

PHILBURN RATOOSH
San Francisco State College
and Center for Research in Management Science,
University of California, Berkeley

1965 • HOMEWOOD, ILLINOIS
RICHARD D. IRWIN, INC., *and* THE DORSEY PRESS

First Printing, June, 1965

Library of Congress Catalog Card No. 65-17683

PRINTED IN THE UNITED STATES OF AMERICA

Table of Contents

INDEXES

PART I
Mathematics and Behavioral Science: Some Prefatory Thoughts

1   *Introduction*

> Do you seek to walk the infinite?
> All about you explore the finite.
> Do you seek the pleasures of totality?
> Grasp the whole in its minutest part.
>
> GOETHE
> Adapted from *Gott, Gemüt and Welt*, 1815

THIS is the age of the model builder. It is the day of search for understanding of complexity by the development of that rigorous (perhaps even over-rigorous) miniature schema, the mathematical model. Whatever the strengths and limitations of this *nouvelle vague*, rooted in a venerable tradition, it is clear that much is going on these days in the social and behavioral sciences that has to do with mathematics and with their confrontation of the study of man.

This volume seeks to glimpse the rapidly changing panorama of mathematics in behavioral science, evolving in the 1960s. The use of the term *Explorations* in the title is deliberate. Not intended solely as a symbol of reticence or modesty (appropriate though these may be), it reflects our belief that many of the exciting and promising approaches reported still are highly tentative—that they represent snapshots in a rapidly moving picture.

The editors attempted to maintain an exploratory, open approach, extending opportunities to the contributors to amend the ideas they had presented originally, to add "afterthoughts" (or to make deletions) during the period that intervened between the initial preparation of the papers and publication of this volume. Most contributors availed themselves of these opportunities, so that what appears in print is relatively "up to date." But there is little doubt that tomorrow morning, and the day after, even more than in other fields, current experimentation and new reflection may lead to further modification. For some purposes, books such as these might do well in loose-leaf format.

It is noteworthy that, with few exceptions, recent works on mathematical applications in the study of human behavior have been of the "readings" variety, presenting the contributions of a number of authors.[1] We believe that this spirit, considering mathematics in behavioral science through many eyes and from flexible vantage points, is a proper reflection of the current

---

[1] A noteworthy exception: James S. Coleman, *Introduction to Mathematical Sociology* (New York: The Free Press of Glencoe, 1964).

status of the art. We shall need to proceed with a good deal more exploring before comprehensive, unifying theory and research will take hold.

However, this volume was conceived with the view that much needs to be done *now* to close the gap between the abstract, apparently self-sufficient mathematical model and the empirical data needed to breathe life into the model.

With this intent, the Western Management Science Institute of the University of California, Los Angeles, supported by that ubiquitous friend of behavioral science development—the Ford Foundation, invited a group of scholars from fields such as psychology, sociology, business administration, political science, and mathematics to come together for four days of intensive deliberations.[2] Paraphrasing the conference invitation, the desired emphasis was on conceptual innovation, supported by data, rather than on purely formal models or techniques of data analysis; contributions reported empirical findings when available, or indicated possible approaches to the empirical testing of the model or theory.

The conscientious reviewer will observe that not all papers included in this volume meet equally well the constraints imposed by the invitational statement. It became necessary to talk *about* mathematics as well as to speak the language of mathematics itself. In some cases the data were not all that the participating scholars desired, and in others data were but a glint in the researcher's eye. And of course some of the essays, because of their particular histories, reflect later stages of development than others.

A book presenting papers delivered at a conference, perhaps more than most, is an abstraction that does violence to some significant parts of the experience. While verbatim transcripts of discussion often border on the banal, much of what mattered at Cambria Pines is not reflected in the formal papers themselves. Happenings in the bar and in late-night bull sessions under the pines had significant impact.

Let us review post hoc the organization of this book, a kind of content analysis of major rubrics pervading the Cambria Pines sessions. Here is the organizing framework that seemed reasonable to us:

Part I, entitled *Mathematics and Behavioral Science: Some Prefatory Thoughts*, includes these introductory reflections, a chapter expressing an editor's viewpoint concerning conditions in the cultures of mathematics (and the hope for a mathematical humanism) (Chapter 2), and a conceptual look at some of the models and approaches appearing in the rest of the volume (Chapter 3).

Part II, entitled *Explorations in Philosophy and Method*, contains papers that deal with broad issues in the use of mathematical models in the behavioral sciences (Chapter 4, Churchman; Chapter 5, Hunt; and Chapter 6, Harrah), and a treatment of certain problems of error in diagnostic decision making (Chapter 7, Scheff). The former three are concerned

---

[2] Cambria Pines, California, November 2–5, 1961.

with the nature, integration and evaluation of data rather than reporting empirical research, while the latter addresses itself to conceptual issues and to substantive findings.

Part III, Individual Behavior: The Search for Pattern, contains three papers whose major focus is the behavior of the person as he attempts to detect regularity in his perceptual world (Chapter 8, Attneave), as he conforms or deviates from normative patterns (Chapter 9, Miner), and as he is engaged in therapeutically-relevant free associations (Chapter 10, Colby).

Part IV, Group Behavior: Interaction and Conflict, deals with three group situations that involve interactive and often conflicting relationships, in experimental game situations (Chapter 11, Lieberman), in negotiation (Chapter 12, Bartos), and in the simulation of international relationships (Chapter 13, Guetzkow).

Part V, Group Behavior: Process and Performance, examines in a new light the classic question of the effect of group size on group performance (Chapter 14, Solomon), and the nature of diffusion in systems whose subparts are incompletely connected (Chapter 15, Coleman). It contains two additional chapters, one a substantive presentation, and the other a discussion focusing on the former, both dealing with the response of organizations to being pushed to states of stress by overload of demand on their resources (Chapters 16 and 17, Meier and Churchill).

Part VI, entitled *The Behavior of Large Social Aggregates: Parks, Cities and Society,* moves from the level of the small and medium sized group—whether formal or informal, natural or experimental—to the study of mathematical approaches to broad, relatively diffuse social entities. The notion of social gravitation is examined in two chapters (Chapter 18, Catton, and Chapter 19, Huff). Two chapters focus on inter- and intra-urban phenomena (Chapter 20, Mandelbrot, and Chapter 21, Lazarsfeld and Henry). Finally, a chapter concerning the economics of "learning by doing" (Chapter 22, Arrow) concludes the volume.

It is our hope that these selections represent a diversified (though hardly comprehensive) storehouse of ideas, illustrating the nature of problems faced in mathematical applications in behavioral science, in general philosophy and in specific inquiry, ranging from the individual to large social groupings. The contributions included vary in the degree of formality of their models as well as in their subject matter.[3] Hopefully, this may prove to be a useful feature, making it possible for the instructor to illustrate the rather considerable differences in mathematical strategy and empirical completeness that characterize the field. Some instructors may choose to

---

[3] As to the overworked disclaimer that "only elementary knowledge of mathematics is needed," we shall let the reader arrive at his own judgment. It seems to us that for some chapters little or no formal mathematics is required, but in others a good deal of sophistication and familiarity with fairly advanced mathematics would seem in order.

use the book as a text or as a supplementary reading source in courses on research methods in the behavioral sciences (including psychology, sociology, political science, industrial relations, operations research and administration), providing the student with an opportunity to reflect on the difficulties in the use of mathematical approaches no less than on their power and promise.

The editors wish to express their deep appreciation to the participants in the conference whose work constitutes this book, and to those who for various reasons ultimately chose not to include their contributions in this volume: Professors Bernard Cohen, Julian Feldman, James G. March and Marion Vanfossen, and Messrs. Morris Berkowitz and Jack Jaffe. Most helpful were recorders William Gellermann and John Martinson.

Warm thanks are extended to the UCLA Western Management Science Institute (James Jackson, Director), under whose sponsorship the conference was held, to the Institute of Industrial Relations (Benjamin Aaron, Director), to the Graduate School of Business Administration (Dean Neil H. Jacoby and Associate Dean George W. Robbins), and to the School's Division of Research (George A. Steiner, Director); all of these provided direct and indirect assistance and support without which neither conference nor book would have been possible.

As usual, valiantly under the pressure of time, the index was prepared by my skilled and uniquely helpful associates, Mrs. Joann Dierlam and Miss Barbara Rood. My personal thanks go to Miss Mary McMurray and to Mrs. Doris (Isolini) Nelson, who carried much of the brunt of the conference, especially in the organizing stages and follow up. Mrs. Anne P. Cook is fondly remembered for her editorial help, which she completed just a few days before her sudden passing.

We gladly acknowledge the cooperation of the several publishers and journals: the Macmillan Company, Free Press, Springer, Knopf, Stanford University Press, the Russell Sage Foundation, Prentice-Hall, *Behavioral Science*, *The Review of Economic Studies* and *Libri*, who permitted reproduction of chapters or briefer excerpts from other publications.

Many of us who shared the experience of the conference reflect with deep personal pleasure and intellectual satisfaction on the face-to-face interchange, significant stimulation and friendship that came about by our being together at Cambria Pines. It's a happy memory for me.

F.M.

Magic, Models, Man, and the Cultures of Mathematics *

2

FRED MASSARIK †

IN 1648, at the Brasen Serpent in Paul's Churchyard in London, Sir John Wilkins, the renowned teacher of Christopher Wren, published a slim volume entitled *Mathematicall Magick*. Sir John was no social scientist. His concern was with "the wonders that may be performed by mechanicall geometry," mainly with the—to us—commonplace devices of pulleys, wedges, levers and wheels, but also with such sophisticated inventions as submarines, the art of flying and—let us note well—"the divers kinds of automata"! Wilkins was both realist and scholar. In an age that favored abstract philosophy over applied technology, he saw to the efficacy of his literary public relations: in addressing himself to the practitioner, as well as to the academician, he was much aware that the combination of "mathematicall" and "magick" would carry persuasive appeal.[1] But the belief or concept that there is something magical in mathematics continues to this day with a curiously contemporary ring, particularly in certain social and behavioral science specializations.

The "magic of mathematics"—whatever it may be—like other ventures in sorcery, attracts energetic adherents and resolute adversaries. To those comfortable in quests for intuitive meaning, the intrusion of a new mode of thinking inevitably proves discomfiting, at least at the outset. At the same time, the discovery of powerful methods, adequately implemented by a versatile technology, calls forth in others an enthusiasm, and impatience,

---

* This paper, although not delivered at the Cambria Pines Conference on Mathematical Models, was prepared specifically for this volume. I wish to express my thanks to the Institute of Industrial Relations, to the Western Management Science Institute, and to the Division of Research of the Graduate School of Business Administration, University of California, Los Angeles, for making it possible for me to participate in this project, reactivating a long-standing (though, for a period, dormant) interest.

† University of California, Los Angeles.

[1] Wilkins realized that, through the common parlance of the day, the idea of magic would be invoked by many to "explain" exceptional technological advance; see Wilkins' "To the Reader" in the work cited.

that are at odds with leisurely rapprochement and negotiation. And soon, alas, battle lines are drawn; intellectual combat moves to the center of the stage, or, perhaps most dangerously, inarticulate controversy, mutual rejection and eventual silence separate the opponents. We face, then, hazards of an exaggerated bifurcation of viewpoint. Too often we face a split that aligns the "mathematical" behavioral scientists at one bulwark and ensconces the "qualitative," anti-mathematical scholars behind their verbally ornate, reassuring fortifications.[2]

Heroes and Villains: Dichotomies in World View

In real life, as in Western movies, it is extraordinarily convenient to classify the participants as "good guys" and "bad guys." The "game of opposites" always has been popular; the need to dichotomize seems deeply engrained in the human psyche. Perhaps it has its roots in the distinction between the "I" and "Thou," and in the differentiation of the personal "self" from "the rest of the world."

Theologically, there are angels and devils, heavens and hell. Intellectually, there are the separatist, logical operations of exclusive Aristotelian categories, and the theses and antitheses of the Hegelian dialectic. In turn, science "versus" some other mode of dealing with the world (theology, or the humanities, for example) has been a frequent focal point in these dichotomous confrontations. In Sir Wilkins' day it was the rise of "mechanicks" ("applied science") that came to be regarded as the force in opposition to the liberal philosophy. Widespread concern for the humanities, in contradistinction to the sciences, repeats the theme in our own day with endless variations.

The near-equating of science with mathematical reasoning as one pole in this persistent bi-polar exercise was dramatically supported by the Newtonian Revolution and by the development of the calculus. The differentiation of philosophy into *Naturphilosophie* and *Sozialphilosophie* further widened the gap. The former readily linked itself with quantitative approaches, while the latter became identified with qualitative, historical, non-mathematical methods of inquiry. As Harrison White has noted, even Auguste Comte, from his positivist vantage point, argued *ultimately*

---

[2] The "pro-mathematical" position, broadly defined, is effectively stated, in Kenneth J. Arrow, "Mathematical Models in the Social Sciences," in D. Lerner and H. D. Lasswell (eds.) *The Policy Sciences* (Stanford, Calif.: Stanford University Press, 1952), pp. 129–54.

Perhaps the most widely quoted anti-mathematical behavioral scientists are identified with academic sociology. See especially Pitirim A. Sorokin, *Fads and Foibles in Modern Sociology* (Chicago: Henry Regnery Co., 1956), and C. Wright Mills' views on "abstracted empiricism" in *The Sociological Imagination* (New York: Oxford University Press, 1959). For brevity and convenience, we shall cite primarily sociological literature as illustrations of viewpoint, although, of course, examples can also be readily found in psychology, cultural anthropology, and related fields.

for "the eminent logical superiority of the sociological over the mathematical point of view." [3]

The continuing thrust of social positivism, of course, embraced the concept of mathematics with unbridled enthusiasm, following Comte's well-known assertion that mathematics is "the most powerful instrument that the human mind can employ in the investigation of the laws of natural phenomena.[4] The classical view of mathematics, aligned with the humanities, as a prime example of leisurely, "rational" thought had faded. Instead, mathematics had come to be regarded as the tool par excellence —and for many the *only* tool—of any science that was worth its salt. Echoing Quetelet's dictum that "We may . . . judge of the degree of perfection to which a science has arrived by the facility with which it may be submitted to calculation," one or another kind of "social physics" persistently loomed on the horizon, a mirage of eventual scientific salvation.

However unsuccessfully these ventures in "social physics" may have turned out, we have now surely passed the point at which one need bother with the categorical question: Is mathematics applicable to social and behavioral data? It is evident that now, more than ever before, behavioral scientists *are* making use of mathematical modes of thought and data handling in the study of people.

The operational definition, "science is what scientists do," may not be entirely satisfactory—almost reeking with the vapor of tautology—but neither is it totally devoid of merit. Instead of attempting a formal evaluation of the productiveness of behavioral mathematical models, and recognizing that there is not much point in sheer repetition of argument concerning the alleged universal superiority of one method of inquiry over another, this paper focuses on the current practices and values of the researchers themselves. We shall consider the subcultures of mathematics in the behavioral sciences, noting their typical ways of doing things and their ethnocentric leanings. Our excursion will take us to cultures extinct, or on the verge of extinction, to atavistic cultures that somehow manage to persevere, and to viable, new culture forms that seem to be shaping current and future mathematical approaches to knowledge of the human condition.

Some Mathematical (and Anti-Mathematical) Subcultures in the Behavioral Sciences

1. The Shadow Tribe: Form without Substance. Members of the Shadow Tribe are characterized by their symbolic systems—that *look* mathematical

[3] Harrison White, "Uses of Mathematics in Sociology," *Mathematics and the Social Sciences* (J. C. Charlesworth [ed.]) (Philadelphia: American Academy of Political and Social Science, 1963), p. 101.

[4] Auguste Comte, *The Positive Philosophy* (Harriet Martineau [trans.]) (London: John Chapman, 1853), p. 32.

but are not. Perhaps the outstanding example of this cultural mode is Stuart C. Dodd's *Dimensions of Society* (1942).[5] At a stage when computers had not yet found their way into behavioral science research, Dodd spoke with verve and conviction of the need for a mathematical sociology. Now, some 20 years later, many of Dodd's assertions still seem reasonable. The difficulty can be traced to the employment of shadowy systems of notation that lacked proper mathematical significance.

In its own way, this was a happy and optimistic culture. Its values were urgently scientific; rigor, neatness, logic, and order were sought above all. Mathematical applications in the physical sciences, in ever increasing measure, had demonstrated their power. This practice of reaching toward the older natural sciences for stimulation and guidance had, of course, often been the touchstone of better things to come in the social sciences. Now it glowed with renewed promise. A broadening base of statistical sophistication, blended with a positivist faith in the uniformity of natural law, seemed to lend substance to the hopes.

But it turned out that this was not a culture free of self-delusion. The symbols seemed so mathematical! It even appeared possible to engage them in conventional mathematical operations. Soon, however, it became clear that this culture's children were doomed to be stillborn. The symbols, notations, and exhortations imbued old concepts of largely descriptive heritage with little new power. Alas, what emerged has been characterized, somewhat uncharitably, as a complex filing system. Evidently, the Shadow Tribe's culture failed to diffuse; presently it faded, even in its own local bailiwick. It adherents turned to other endeavors, some more genuinely mathematical than others.

In his *Foundations of Sociology* (1939), George Lundberg's view was that:

> The great contribution of Dodd's formulations is that they frame the hypotheses (research problems) in rigorously defined generalized terms, so that results of different investigations would be cumulative with respect to the particular question under investigation and would also be a contribution to a system. That is, researches would not be isolated rocks in a pile, variously shaped and possibly of great individual excellence, but bricks in a gradually growing wall in which the gaps as well as the congruity and usefulness of the whole structure would be constantly observed.[6]

As one examines the sociological literature, and that of related behavioral sciences of the sixties, it is apparent that matters did not come

---

[5] See Stuart C. Dodd, *Dimensions of Society* (New York: The Macmillan Co., 1942). Dodd's aspiration is well stated in the book's subtitle: "A Quantitative Systematics for the Social Sciences."

[6] George A. Lundberg, *Foundations of Sociology* (New York: The Macmillan Co., 1939), p. 112. This volume is viewed by the respective authors as a companion volume to Dodd's *Dimensions of Society*.

to pass as Lundberg had expected;[7] there are few references to the *Dimensions of Society* or to its contents, and surely there has been no large-scale attempt to use Dodd's schema to order social knowledge. In this sense, then, this culture appears to be something of a fossil, in Toynbee's sense of the term. Yet, as one rereads Dodd's and Lundberg's work, one may wonder whether, as basis for a system of data retrieval and as an approach for categorizing data, some renaissance still may be in order? Be that as it may, for the moment, the Shadow Tribe slumbers, encapsulated in mathematical form without substance, isolated and inert.

A subspecies of this culture pattern may be designated as the *Culture of Searchers for Simplicistic Laws.* In some respect, these theorizers conceive social reality as governed by one (or a very few) relatively neat, lawful relationships.[8] One good example of this persuasion is the work of George Kingsley Zipf and his principle of "least effort," [9] often cited but also often criticized. Inevitably, two questions remain: Is the search for a very few behavioral regularities likely to be rewarding? Or, as in the quest for the "divine" proportions or the music of the spheres, does something other than the pot of gold of true knowledge loom at the rainbow's end?

Still, it should be noted that the searchers for these simple relationships were not content with sheer abstract assertion—as was typical of the main Shadow Tribe. Rather, though the data sources often were limited and selective, empirical tests of the basic hypotheses were actually undertaken. To the extent that this was so, members of this species of investigators may be regarded as precursors of more productive culture types (to be considered later). Further, more sophisticated treatments of relationships, that at the outset seemed extremely simple, ultimately may yield useful systematic consistencies, as indicated in this volume by the related work of Catton and Mandelbrot.

[7] In "The Natural Science Trend in Sociology," *American Journal of Sociology,* Vol. LXI, No. 3, November, 1955, pp. 191–202. Lundberg cites another author (N. F. Timasheff, in "Sociological Theory Today," *American Catholic Sociological Review,* March, 1950) as asserting that "The school dominating present day sociology, at least in America, is the neopositivist one. . . . It is best represented by . . . [among other works] S. C. Dodd's *Dimensions of Society.*" Philosophically, Timasheff may have been correct, but, in terms of empirical applications or direct use, he probably misjudged the impact of the Dodd-Lundberg positivism even for the period he wished to characterize.

[8] Comte, incidentally, had no illusions in this respect; he expected no reductionism to one or a few laws. See Comte, *op. cit.,* p. 16: "Because it is proposed to consolidate the whole of our acquired knowledge into one body of homogeneous doctrine, it must not be supposed that we are going to study this vast variety as proceeding from a single principle, and as subjected to a single law. There is something so chimerical in attempts at universal explanation by a single law, that it may be as well to secure this work at once from any imputation of the kind, though its development will show how undeserved such an imputation would be. Our intellectual resources are too narrow, and the universe is too complex, to leave any hope that it will ever be within our power to carry scientific perfection to its last degree of simplicity."

[9] See, George Kingsley Zipf, *Human Behavior and the Principle of Least Effort* (Cambridge, Mass.: Addison-Wesley Press, 1949).

2. The Bland Statistician: The Culture of the Formula User. This is an old culture that probably will remain forever new. It is a culture whose lifeblood is the flow of data and whose status symbols are the performance of mathematical manipulations. Let us be clear: there is nothing necessarily "bad" about status symbols. When appropriate to the task at hand—when genuine, rather than artificially grafted onto the surface of an inferior approach—they may in fact engender substantial new worlds of status.

A high proportion of papers presented at the meetings of the American Psychological and the American Sociological associations make relatively standard use of statistical techniques. To these statistics users, or formula consumers, neither abstract model nor mathematical methodology is an end in itself. Normally, their interests are substantive; they are concerned with the evaluation of a therapeutic technique, with the analysis of a new clinical test, with the description of differential characteristics of minority groups, with attitudes, or social perception, and so on.

As mathematical statisticians and methodologists create new procedures, the culture of the formula user is subject to vogues, to the ascendancy—and disappearance—of fads. Various techniques tend to have their day of popularity, for instance, analysis of variance, multiple correlation, factor analysis these are examples of techniques that, while persistently useful for particular problems, were also used to excess at certain stages in the history of the behavioral sciences because they seemed to be "the thing to do."

The advent of the computer has created new opportunities and problems for the formula consumer. First of all, the computer itself has become the symbol par excellence of being "hep." Its computational power seems to lend significance even to the trivial, and credibility to the doubtful. This, of course, is not the computer's fault. Rather, it is a characteristic of the user culture, particularly as it is expressed (more often sub rosa than overtly) by differentially favorable status ascriptions to the heavily mathematical (and computer sophisticated), as contrasted with the clearly descriptive and simply comparative.

In certain respects, the formula-consumer culture, particularly in its computer applications, tends to be anxiety-ridden. Depending on the basic statistical training of the particular scholar, there exists a frequent need for him to leave his substantive "home," whatever it may be, to initiate ventures in culture contact, journeying into territory that (for him) is often poorly charted and potentially hostile. In their travels across departmental or disciplinary lines, these scholars may encounter no cyclops, but quite often they may run into the trap of the statistician, methodologically sophisticated and detached from substantive behavioral science areas, whose typical comment is "but you can't do it this way." The statistician may well be right: certain crucial assumptions may not have been justified, and certain methods may be inapplicable to the problem at hand. Yet it is also possible that the statistician wishes to impose a rigor or restraint on the anxious researcher's problem (which his data do not deserve), or that an easier and cruder short-cut method may provide heuristically adequate solutions.

Perhaps two of the more disillusioning experiences to which the formula user culture falls heir are the following. First, there are the inevitable *frustrations of the computer program "de-bugging" process.* These are particularly serious when the formula user is deeply immersed in the "sense" of his data and in the exploratory research process, and when each day of delay in "de-bugging" geometrically heightens his frustration. Especially when the formula user must view the computer as a complex, simultaneously beneficent but befuddling "black box," his attitude may be rather like that of the average petitioner in the waiting line of a huge, powerful bureaucracy: a blend of hope, awe, and helpless dependency.

Second, there is the matter of the *overwhelming output.* By the time all the corollary hypotheses and supplemental ideas which turned out to be interesting and testable have been programmed, problems that began as simple and clear-cut often generate computer outputs of truly monumental proportions. The *human* capacity for meaningfully interpreting these avalanches of raw results is limited. Thus the behavioral scientist often finds himself in a dilemma of time and resource allocation. How much of these data can he really "wade" through, and at what point should he cease his labors? Of course, one may argue that the originally formulated hypotheses, and the researcher's serendipity, provide the necessary guides. However, inductive alternatives, too, confront the researcher, and in practical experience it turns out that the computer is often responsible for a beguiling but confusing surfeit of data.

It is worthy of note that the behavioral scientist's anxiety about his mathematical inadequacy persists—indeed is heightened—by advanced mathematical training. For example, in Elbridge Sibley's *The Education of Sociologists in the United States* (1963) it is shown that "deficiencies in mathematical training are more than twice as frequently cited [compared to any other deficiency] by graduates of prestigious (sociology) departments"—even though the proportion of students obtaining their degrees in these departments, and having advanced mathematical training, was higher than that for students in other sociology departments.[10] It would appear, therefore, that formal mathematical course work, in the context of behavioral science education, is no antidote for a sense of inadequacy. Perhaps even fairly enthusiastic nibbling at the edges of the mathematical pie fails to satiate the hunger or to still self-doubt.

Apparently there is basis for the concern, and Sibley suggests that:

---

[10] See Elbridge Sibley, *The Education of Sociologists in the United States* (New York: Russell Sage Foundation, 1963), pp. 134–67, but especially pp. 165–66.

[Although] the percentage of Ph.D.'s who have taken mathematics courses has risen somewhat, it is evident from conversations with faculty members and graduate students that a great majority of the latter are quite unprepared to make effective use of mathematical analysis. One gets the impression, indeed, that a majority of graduate students of sociology who lack mathematical competence find self-justifying reasons for considering it unnecessary.[11]

Thus we emerge with an image of behavioral scientists either pulling away from mathematical applications and "joining" non-mathematical (or perhaps anti-mathematical) cultures, or learning to live somehow in the shadow of statistical methodology and computer technology. In response to this situation, new culture forms have emerged. First, there is the "consultant" who makes his home in the computer culture but who serves as liaison between the computer and the formula user. Neatly attired in white shirt, tie and suit, he epitomizes the "IBM image"; helpfully he listens to the user's requirements, aiding in the transmutation of complex hunch and voluminous raw data into computer-elegant output. When effective, by manner and mien, he serves to reduce—at least in some degree —the formula user's sense of deficiency and concern.

In turn, and with purpose and forethought, efforts have been under way in recent years to "acculturate" the formula user to the computer world. Under the aegis of the Ford Foundation and under various local auspices, computer-oriented courses, institutes, and training programs have sought to disseminate sufficient knowledge and "feel" for the computer culture so as to make the transition to it from other specialization areas more comfortable and productive.

In many ways the "interface" between behavioral scientists and the computer culture provides a fascinating arena for the study of culture contact. In terms of accumulated culture base, the traditional behavioral science disciplines, of course, occupy a dominant and certainly senior position. Yet, as is evident, the computer culture holds the record for rapid growth and for the exceptionally dynamic and rapid accumulation of a vast storehouse of resources, ingeniously created and prestigiously regarded.

Under these circumstances, it is small wonder that the traditional behavioral scientist is largely on the defensive. He must strive either for a meaningful synthesis of his accustomed viewpoints with those so dramatically spawned by the "upstart" computer, or he must more or less gracefully retreat. In some instances, however, he simply may hold to his established and reasoned position—a position which, by its very nature and philosophic base, chooses to regard the computer as irrelevant to its central problem of concern. Certain humanist and clinical viewpoints, and some spokesmen for a *verstehende* social science, may fall in this category.

---

[11] *Ibid.*, p. 164.

Unfortunately, criticism of other positions is too readily regarded as vindication of one's own stand, and the line between rationale and rationalization often is difficult to define.

Our primary concern is with the cultures of mathematics. To see these in perspective, however, let us briefly consider some types of non-mathematical and explicitly anti-mathematical cultures in the behavioral sciences today.

3. The Worlds of Anti-Mathematics. Travellers to foreign social environments have been known to suffer "culture shock." The culture of anti-mathematics may include, among others, those in a transitory state of shock—those who are, for some period of time, simply at a loss in how to come to grips in their work with the complexities of the appropriate mathematical models and with the mechanics of computer use. But this condition often is overcome as the initially exotic clime becomes more familiar.

Beyond an evanescent state of "mathematophobia," however, some rather explicitly and militantly anti-mathematical points of view have grown (or come to be revitalized) in recent years.[12] One rather interesting anti-mathematical subculture has developed as a direct opposition movement to the large-scale application of computer methods to activities affecting large numbers of people. Illustrative of these have been the data processing procedures of many banks (and the numbering of checking accounts, saver identification numbers, etc.) and the telephone company's all-digit dialing system. The fundamental value structure of the emerging protest subculture may be stated by the syllogism: Numbers dehumanize; dehumanization is bad; therefore, numbers are bad. "I don't want to be a number; I am a human being!" has been the culture's battle cry. In behavioral science, the adherents of this viewpoint have argued (much as prior generations of anti-mathematical scholars had done before them) that the essence of human behavior is too subtle, too variable, too complex —and too important—to be reduced to allegedly misleading, simple numerical terms.

At levels more personally adaptive, if somewhat less philosophical, are those scholars who, individually or collectively, have reacted to the infusion of mathematical modes by explicit or implicit withdrawal. There are those who say with comforting personal congruence: "You can't teach an old dog new tricks!" Within the range of their interests and skills, they continue to make relevant and significant contributions to social knowledge. Indeed, in some important respects, their work stimulates and underpins much mathematical model building. (Surely, no one

---

[12] Julius Gould, in "Fashions among the Sociologists" (*20th Century* Vol. 172, No. 1018, Summer, 1963), speaks of the epithet "quantophrenia" which has been applied to the "quantitative" approach by its more hostile critics.

wishes to argue these days that mathematics is an "open sesame" to all hidden recesses of behavioral science).

Finally, there are those whose attitude may be characterized by the German homily: "Hier bleiben will ich nicht, weg gehen mag ich nicht." ("I don't want to stay here, but I don't want to go away.") Theirs is a sense of ambivalence which may lead them, variously, astray into inappropriate mathematical applications (typically mediated by the ever-present computer) or toward vociferous denunciations of all things mathematical. And then there are those who argue that intuition and feel for a problem is *universally* superior to measurement and systematic data manipulation. Here, anti-mathematical ethnocentrism has its day.

It is apparent that the various anti-mathematical (and validly non-mathematical) cultures shade into one another; and in this respect they do not differ from cultural entities and the gradients of culture areas found elsewhere in the world. After all, one man's assertive "sound principle" that qualitative insight is all is another man's "pig-headed refusal" to learn a new mathematics.

In our quest for taxonomy, we must now turn to the newly-evolving and devotedly pro-mathematical cultures on the rise.

4. The Model Builder's Culture: A World in Ascent.   Once upon a time, the phrase was "the Young Turks." Whatever the label, there has grown and come to flourish within the last ten or fifteen years a highly specialized, articulate, and often scintillating group of scholars who have been weened on COBOL and SOAP and raised on the IBM 650 and 7090. These are the model builders. Many of them moved directly and with clear purpose into the heart of a highly mathematical culture area. Others spent often brief apprenticeships in one or another discipline, soon developing intense mathematical specializations. They varied in their substantive interests, but among their special concerns have been the learning of theory, small group behavior, mass behavior, game theory, artificial intelligence and organization theory. Others, having plunged primarily into a mathematical world, found it so intellectually and personally satisfying, as an end in itself, that deeper substantive concerns faded into relative insignificance.

It has turned out that dangers lurk along this road. This kind of model builder subculture has proved to be potentially (and in some instances actually) dysfunctional—at least dysfunctional if the goal is understanding of *significant human behavior*. We come now to a phenomenon that we might call "the seductiveness of mathematics."

The very power of mathematical methods, as expressed by complex systems of symbol manipulation, gives rise to a set of difficulties in the application of these methods to human phenomena. This is not a matter of the old saw that human experience is too complex for mathematical treatment, or that the very concept of the process of human life may be destroyed by abstract, quantitative treatment. Rather, the difficulty unfolds in the following way:

There are some reasonable and appropriate assumptions about human behavior that at the outset guide the development of a given mathematical model. The basic propositions are stated abstractly, and from them a number of consequences quickly follow. These, too, are amenable to succinct and precise notation. Soon a network of rigorous propositions is derived and mathematically manipulated. However, as the tower of derived propositions is built higher and higher, the danger increases that knowledge (or assumptions empirically based) about human behavior is left further and further behind. The model itself becomes a soul-satisfying, plausible, and conceptually elegant end product. It may prove *logically* sound—or it may be attacked on *logical* grounds. But the temperament of the model builder may be such that he is more comfortable with the abstraction than with the hard, somewhat "dirty" data, especially whole-system, gestaltist data, naturalistically derived. The model itself has become an "autonomous motive"; and now its empirical test appears less urgent, a digression from the exciting schematic "mainstream."

Of course, the model builder is not likely to deny the relevance of the empirical test. Highly restricted, experimental data may be generated. But the subculture tends to value the model itself, perhaps more than its presumably "routine" confrontation with behavioral reality. Perhaps this is an unintended, implicit carry-over from the days when the searcher (or researcher) in the world of experience was called "a *mere* empirick," approaching his tasks with potentially faulty sensory equipment and distinguished from a "higher," apparently detached quest for ideal propositions.

For many "Young Turks" of the abstract model school—perhaps moreso than for their more seasoned colleagues—the model becomes the thing, the *only* thing. The computer readily encourages this sometimes single-minded absorption. In its own way, it provides further elaborate transformations as follow from the original set of propositions and instructions. And this, too, is fun. The computer positively reinforces behavior in the intellectual game of generating vast abstract paradigms. These become intrinsically pleasurable and subculturally esteemed.

Certain species of models are intended to be normative rather than descriptive of empirical behavioral reality. These constructions are designed to tell people how they *ought* to behave under certain conditions, as contrasted with how they actually behave. But, presumably, the normative model requires an empirical baseline too. The question must be asked (and, in some recent research, increasingly *is* asked) of how far peoples' actual behavior indeed deviates from the ideally prescribed behavior? In this sense, therefore, there would ultimately seem to be no escape from an empirical confrontation of the abstract model and the social and behavioral world.

The scholar who views life from a humanist standpoint is especially likely to feel extreme frustration when, probably more by accident than through design, he finds himself in contact with the model builders' subculture. What he finds is anything but what he seeks.[13] He wants to look at the total human being, fully engaged in the process of living; instead he finds part-functions of the human being, abstracted to the extreme and treated in isolation from the rest of the total person. Neither his temperament nor his training is likely to have equipped him for a journey along the neatly laid out, bare corridors of the mathematical model. And were he to find his way, he still would feel that the trip has not been worth taking; he would learn something highly specific perhaps, but something strangely foreign to the richness of the total behavioral context that he regards as the principal concern of a human science. Yet the roads to a synthesis of mathematics and humanism are open.

Toward a Culture of Mathematical Humanism: The Road Ahead

It is *not* a contradiction in terms to speak of mathematics and humanism in the same breath. Indeed, we may be in the midst of the evolution of a cultural form which seeks to apply the approach of mathematics—models, computers, and all—to the study of the total human being. In doing so, this culture will view its central value increasingly as the deeply meaningful understanding of human existence *as* human existence, shunning the isolative, segmental abstractionism much in vogue in the mathematical models subculture. It will cease to be concerned solely with those behaviors which find it convenient to consider the human agent in the model as though he (or it?) were a "relatively inexpensive servomechanism." [14]

The base from which mathematical humanism may grow has been well-laid. One foundation is the work of those behavioral scientists (psychologists and sociologists plus a few anthropologists, political scientists, and others) who have looked at the social and individual world as a complicated living process, and who have found it desirable to examine some wholistic relationships by way of ingenious mathematical approaches. Naming names may be risky; however, we venture that some of the works of

---

[13] For a statement of basic humanist postulates relevant to behavioral science, see J. F. T. Bugental, "The Third Force in Psychology," *Journal of Humanistic Psychology*, Vol. IV, No. 1, Spring, 1964, and especially pp. 23–24. These postulates include the following: (1) Man, as man, supersedes the sum of his parts; (2) Man has his being in a human context; (3) Man is aware; (4) Man has a choice; and (5) Man is intentional.

[14] See review of Joan H. Criswell, Herbert Solomon and Patrick Suppes, *Mathematical Methods in Small Group Processes* (Stanford, Calif.: Stanford University Press, 1962), by Harrison White in *American Journal of Sociology*, Vol. LXIX, No. 3, November, 1963, pp. 304–6.

Stouffer, Lazarsfeld, Simon, Guetzkow, Heider, Coleman and Cronbach constitute important progress in this direction.[15]

On the other hand, there are some very good reasons why the advent of the computer and the accelerated concern with mathematical approaches should indeed further the cause of a *human* study of man. First, the very bugaboo of the human condition's complexity, (referred to in passing in this essay, and well-known in this context to the point of cliché) increasingly becomes an anachronism.

Now the models of human behavior can dare to be ever more complex—if indeed reality is complex—and even if we must deal with numerous simultaneously interacting factors, the remarkable capacity of ever-improving computers holds ample potential for providing meaningful solutions. Clearly, we are now in a better position than ever to leave behind naive oversimplification and unrealistic search for "one cause-one outcome" relationships.

As our substantive knowledge grows, *ceteris paribus* will cease to be a convenient shorthand for ignorance. Multiple causation and the richness of interplay among many forces will more and more be handled appropriately without doing fatal violence to the apparently limitless variety of human relationships. As a generation of mathematical humanists grows, there will be less need for the present fragmentation of human functions (often necessitated by vain longing for simplicity), and there will be more empirically based insights into whole human phenomena which reflect the essential conditions of human totalities.

Also, the availability of computer technology will have profound significance for the nature of the actual tasks to be performed by the mathematical humanist. The amount of mechanical research labor in testing paradigms and in data analysis will be greatly reduced. Yesteryear's research assistant, or professional research scientist—who ran a Friden calculator for hours at a time—will be nearly extinct. This kind of researcher is rare, of course, even today. The onerous tasks of doing routine statistics long have been delegated to the hinterlands of graduate student culture ("It's good for them; *I* used to have to do it by hand!") or to other relatively inexpensive research neophytes.

The mathematical humanist will not be afraid, of course, to become involved in the collection of data and in idea-generating "playing with"

---

[15] There is no intent here to provide an exhaustive bibliographic summary of relevant work. Almost by way of free association, the following come to mind as apt illustrations: Stouffer's leadership in the monumental *American Soldier* series; Lazarsfeld's versatile efforts, ranging from his studies of the unemployed in a small Austrian town to his inquiries into the Academic Mind; Simon's work (especially that conducted jointly with March) on organizations; Heider's theorizing on interpersonal relations; Cronbach's approach to testing; Coleman's various analytic and substantive contributions; and Guetzkow's efforts in the study of group and inter-nation behavior. Clearly, the list of others who may be appropriately noted here includes a number of additional contributors to this volume, and any number of other scholars.

data. Clearly, however, neither he nor his graduate assistants (who probably should be learning something besides how to run a hand calculator anyway) will need to spend untold hours in sheer mechanical and computational activities. There will be more time for thought and subtle experimentation, and more opportunity for the more intellectually demanding research tasks of behavioral science. There will be increased ease of access directly to the computer, and more readiness to treat "him" as a friend and willing colleague, a colleague, furthermore, who really will be "glad" to do what he is asked!

All this means that the mathematical humanist, as one species inhabiting the evolving culture of behavioral science, will be able to engage precisely in those activities in which he, as a human being studying his own kind, is best suited to engage. Unlike the all-too-frequently encountered denizen of the models subculture, the mathematical humanist will know something about the infinite variety of the human scene. It will not be necessary for him to make brief and often embarrassingly defensive journeys to the offices of his colleagues in psychology or sociology, asking them questions like "Tell me, what theory of human motivation should I use in this model that I am trying to develop?" Or "To how many groups does the average person really belong?" (I have been asked both of these questions, and I admit that I was not capable of giving that single, simple answer that was expected of me.) Instead of the mechanical "plugging in" of human factors within models concerned with one or another kind of psychological or social phenomena, the mathematical humanist will be as at home in the substantive fullness of his subject matter as in the mathematical realm that, for him, is designed to explicate the human condition.

By way of research strategies, the mathematical humanist will *not* need to reject the abstract part-functions studied to date. He will be able to bridge from them to the totality of human behavior, building increased subtlety into his more complex models and recognizing that it is not mechanical collection of these part-functions but a Gestalt-type integrative synthesis that holds promise for scientific progress.

If the task confronting the mathematical humanist seems all-too-huge, or indeed overwhelming, let us note two conditions.

First, this is perhaps the time to dream that we are in a stage in the development of the behavioral sciences in which increasing numbers of intellectually well-endowed scholars are moving into the field. They have available a research technology unequalled in the history of these sciences. Clearly, the mathematical humanist will not be part of a "mass movement." Yet, within the unfolding scientific landscape, there would seem to be enough of the necessary ingredients to bring forth a significant number of scholars with a viewpoint reflecting a coalescing of concern with understanding the human condition and with the use of mathematical approaches to this end.

Second, it is not necessary to assume that the mathematical humanist will know *all* there is to know, either about mathematics or about the intricacies of the human subject matter. Yes, he will require a thorough grasp of important content; but, perhaps more significantly, he will hold a viewpoint that does not focus on the abstract for its own sake nor on a paradigm solely because of its elegance. Instead, he will forge a link between the abstract and the mathematically elegant, and the meaningful empirical realities of human life.

As we look back on our brief multi-cultural journey, we may reflect that the days of the Shadow Tribe are far behind us, in concept if not in years, and that the era of the formula user, within its useful confines, will continue. With the extreme anti-mathematician perhaps, at best, a state of mutually benign co-existence may evolve; but others, though non-mathematical in their interests, may find themselves increasingly in working harmony with the intent of a mathematical humanism. The question remains however: Will we, as mathematical explorations in behavioral science proceed, in fact witness a transition from abstract, isolative quantitative model building to an integrative mathematical humanism?

The model builder's readiness to broaden his vision, encompassing the full sweep of human life, may hold the key.

3   *Some Themes in This Volume*

THE growing tendency toward mathematical formalism in the behavioral sciences is a complex matter and is nourished by roots that are psychological and sociological as well as aesthetic and scientific.

Certainly, it is evident that a mathematical model usually increases precision, but, as has been observed, it is evident that some uses of mathematical models are motivated by the desire to share some of the prestige mathematics has bestowed on the physical sciences. A more serious harm that applied mathematics can do is to encourage the focusing of attention on problems that can be investigated by mathematical techniques at hand; as a consequence trivial problems may be studied with sophisticated techniques and important issues ignored.

Both the positive and negative aspects of the development of mathematical techniques can be seen in the enormous growth of operations research since 1945. Very powerful and elegant tools have been designed for solving problems faced by large, complex organizations. At the same time those factors not readily amenable to mathematical investigation—"soft" psychological and sociological variables—often have fared less well in mathematical treatment than other, "hard" variables.

It is easier to be critical of mathematical applications in behavioral science than to list solid successes. Yet the evidence presented in this volume shows that the influence of mathematical thinking in behavioral science has been both wide and deep—ever in flux, but ever growing. The following are some discernible themes in the mathematics of behavioral science, prevailing in the field as such, and revealed in the papers that follow.

Mathematics as Methodology

In his proposal of a World Information Center for the social sciences, C. West Churchman (Chapter 4) is concerned with the enormous recent growth of scientific knowledge. The methodological implication of his proposal is that it suggests a profound change in how an experiment would be viewed. In what has come to be regarded as a properly designed experiment, "one must decide beforehand what shall be observed, and one must make sure that the methods of assigning objects to categories remain fixed throughout the experiment." In the "elusive experiment," on the other hand, the classification of data and the treatment of results are decided at the conclusion of the research at the same time as attempts are made at clarification of concepts employed. Ordinary experimentation could be viewed as "elusive," in Churchman's sense, if we regard a sequence of experiments as a unit.

One of Churchman's examples is a treatment to cure patients. One may not know until the conclusion of treatment what the treatment consisted of, or what the definition of *cure* was. That this is the case in psychotherapy will be recognized immediately by psychotherapists.

Another example is of interest. Suppose we are given a generator of decimal digits and are told that it is a random number generator, producing digits distributed rectangularly. We want to test whether this is in fact the case. Now any set of criteria we set up can be satisfied by a series clearly nonrandomly produced. (Trivially, any finite sequence can be regarded as the decimal expansion of a rational between zero and one.) For example, in the first 100 digits it may be observed that the function specifying the positions of the 7s is remarkably simple; hence, the sequence which satisfies our criteria of, say, nearly equal numbers of the digits 0 through 9, equal numbers of second order sequences 00,01, . . ., 99 , and so on, is clearly not produced by a random generator. But, having looked over an initial sequence, we can then test whether a subsequent sequence behaves in the same way, e.g., produces 7s in the same manner. Of course, there exists a function that will specify the position of the 7s in the first 200 digits, but if this function is more complicated than the first one, we are more likely to accept the generator as random. Therefore, the only feasible test of a finite sequence is an elusive one. It is interesting to note that both the tables of Fisher and Yates and those of the RAND Corporation were "adjusted" after they were produced by what was presumed to be a random generator.

The Methodology of Models

What is involved in the transition from a verbal to a mathematical model? For one thing, the mathematical model requires that the assumptions of the theoretical ideas be made explicit. But this is both true and false. The assumptions of the mathematical model may well be explicit. The model that is applied to data, however, is *not quite* this mathematical model. Indeed, anyone who points out that some data cannot be fitted *precisely* by a model might be accused of quibbling. Thus, the assumptions of the fitting and of the testing of the goodness of fit are often vague.

By using a Bayesian approach that requires some estimate of a priori probabilities, Earl B. Hunt (Chapter 5) suggests a procedure for comparing credibilities of several models of the same set of data. David Harrah (Chapter 6) offers a model for the evaluation of information. Methodological contributions of this sort are unfortunately all too rare.

Thomas J. Scheff (Chapter 7) reverses the procedure. By studying medical diagnoses he attempts to infer information about the models used implicitly by diagnosticians.

The Theory of Games

The theory of games is a recent development in mathematics. Although the first papers on the topic were published by Borel in 1927 and by von Neumann in 1928, very little was done in the subject until von Neumann and Morgenstern's monumental *Theory of Games and Economic Behavior* appeared in 1944. Since then, the number of papers published on the topic has been vast.

The relationship of this branch of mathematics to the behavioral sciences is not simple. First, the theory of games, like any other part of mathematics, does not describe reality; it does not tell us what people *do* in conflict situations. It describes the behavior of Economic Man, whose utilities are assumed to be known. In this sense it can no more be tested by studies of choice and decision behavior than the theory of probability can be tested by observing the tosses of real dice.

Nevertheless, the theory of games has profoundly influenced the behavioral sciences in spite of the fact that it answers no questions in this domain. Its influence consists in having stimulated a large body of experimental research in conflict, and in forcing the behavioral scientist to reorient his thinking about conflict situations.

Bernhardt Lieberman's chapter (Chapter 11) is an example of experimental work stimulated directly by the theory of games. His study describes behavior in two- and three-person, zero-sum games in normal form. That subjects do not in general behave in ways defined as rational by the theory of games is of interest to the behavioral scientist but not necessarily to the mathematician.

Otomar Bartos (in Chapter 12) examines the consequences in models of negotiation of taking into account each participant's subjective probabilities of choices of the others.

Harold Guetzkow, in a simulation model (Chapter 13), attempts to mirror some of the reality of international relations by making a number of assumptions of a political nature. These kinds of assumptions are precisely those that are missing from game-theoretical models.

Stochastic Models

The papers using stochastic models can be readily contrasted. Herbert Solomon (Chapter 14) applies a probabilistic model of a very simple type to a study of group learning. Kenneth Colby (Chapter 10) discusses the difficulties of employing stochastic models to describe free association, which clearly ought to be describable in terms of stochastic processes.

James Coleman (Chapter 15) shows why ordinary diffusion models fail to predict accurately and how they have to be modified when the social group is structured into parts.

The discussion by Richard Meier (Chapter 16) of how organizations respond to overload is an example of an empirically oriented work dealing with events to which stochastic models are applicable, but one would guess that the richness of the results might have been largely lost had the writer attempted to formulate his results in explicit mathematical terms.

Finally, Benoit Mandelbrot (Chapter 20), in considering the distribution of sizes of cities, discusses why stochastic models are so successful. We try to explain large effects in terms of some functional relationship, while we attribute small effects to random fluctuation. Mandelbrot suggests that the same laws obtain throughout the range of size, but their operation is impossible to trace in the small.

From the themes, briefly illustrated above by comments on selected chapters, we turn now to the contributions themselves.

P.R.

PART II

Explorations in
Philosophy and Method

How sharp the blade
To trim the tree of chance?
How rich the castle where
    computers prance?

Philosopher, hand me your stone,
A tool with which the blade to hone.
Centers? Choices small in error?
    Chaotic gods . . retreat in
        terror!

Models Bayesian? Parallel?
How much like man?
    The streams of data
    And of time,
    Must tell.

F.M.

4 Toward a Mathematics of Social Science *

C. West Churchman †

IN THIS PAPER I want to make a proposal—which seems to be quite reasonable—and then to discuss its inherent difficulties. I think that, whether or not the proposal could be adopted, it is worthwhile, in terms of understanding social science, to ascertain its chief defects. Furthermore, I think that a consideration of the proposal may suggest a reason for working toward a mathematics of the social sciences.

A WORLD INFORMATION CENTER

The proposal is that the social sciences establish a "World Information Center." Every significant research document would contain a set of results written in a suitable language. These results would be forwarded to the Center. By means of a computer, the Center would identify all previous research results that are relevant. It would then gauge whether the result was consistent with all relevant findings. Finally, it would publish its conclusions about the result in such forms as:

1. The result is redundant;
2. The result is not properly derived from the evidence;
3. The result is inconsistent with previous findings;
4. The result adds confirmation to these n theses and disconfirmation to these m theses.

I am less concerned here with the exact technology of the Center's publications, and more with the purpose it would try to serve: to maximize the relevance of specific pieces of social science research effort. Of course, the Center could be consulted prior to the final design of a research project, and it would be used by screening committees to decide upon the importance of a research proposal.

* Working Paper No. 38, Center for Research in Management Science, University of California, Berkeley, 1961.
† University of California, Berkeley.

Advantages

Before examining the defects of this proposal, we can make explicit its potential advantages, although these may seem obvious on common sense grounds. The central advantage, of course, is research economy: to the extent that research findings can be used as evidence for or against other findings, the total effort required to increase confirmation, precision, stability and other measurement desiderata is thereby diminished.

The increasing size of the social science literature makes it more and more difficult to ascertain what is relevant to a specific research program. The proposed Center would, in part, help to solve this problem.

Some of the by-products of a successful plan come readily to mind:

a) The social sciences tend to be highly fragmented into such areas as economics, econometrics, political science, sociology, psychology, social psychology, psychoanalysis, organization theory, etc. Almost as soon as an area becomes established, a tendency to segment the research sets in. For example, in the last decade management science has come to be recognized as a legitimate social science; but it is already showing signs of splitting into mathematical management science, behavioral management science, computer management science, and management-management science, the last being conceived as an effort to make management science more realistic.

The creation of an Information Center would hopefully reduce this tendency toward fragmentation.

b) Next, a systematic examination of relevance would reveal quite clearly the serious gaps in social science research and might even suggest how the needed research should be designed; or why it can't be designed.

c) Finally, such a center might get social science out of the horrible rut into which statistical methods have forced it. The theories of hypothesis testing and estimation, elegant as these may be logically, have provided many researchers with the opportunity of terminating their thought processes at the end of the research project. Thus, we run into the absurd statements that "A showed that X is true," because the final test was "significant"; and "B showed that X wasn't true," because the final test wasn't "significant."

Hypothesis testing tends to make scientists forget that their purpose in life is not to prove things but to assist their science in making somewhat more warranted assertions. There is no such thing as a "terminated" research project. I'm afraid that often the models of mathematical statistics have misled the scientist into overlooking this obvious point. A successful Center would free the individual scientist of the need for running a test on his findings alone, and would permit various hypotheses and theories to be gauged in terms of their long-run relevance and warrantableness.

Difficulties

Now let us turn to some of the rather obvious difficulties of the proposal. In considering proposals that may eventually lead to decisions, the natural tendency is to ask for a formulation of the problem: a display of the objectives and alternative courses of action. But in many cases the wisest plan is to ask whether any change could feasibly occur, no matter how reasonable the proposal. That is, one first asks how any implementation at all would be possible. This research strategy often seems the most desirable for urban and national planning—and I suppose it is also a good beginning question for the social sciences.

Even if the proposal were adopted, would any social scientists use the Center? First of all, we should recognize that the proposal, to be successful, must impose a drastically new kind of research methodology on the individual scientist. He can no longer consider his piece of research as a unit, since the usual methods of hypothesis testing, estimation and inference would be minor steps in the research design.

Indeed, the Center, if it were successful, might constitute a real threat to the freedom and individual style of the scientist. We all know one reason why fragmentation occurs in the social sciences: It enables each man to develop his own research interests as he sees fit and to establish himself as one of the few experts in a given area. It is easy to predict, therefore, that the Center's output might be largely ignored, except by a select number, and that the Center itself would become the nucleus of a new fragment.

It is not my intent here to solve the difficulties of the proposal, but simply to display them. This difficulty seems to me to fall under the general heading of decentralization of effort in an organization. Perhaps it is true that most groups will naturally tend to decentralize if there is an opportunity to do so, and in many instances this pattern of behavior seems to be appropriate. The solution of this difficulty would seem to depend on a technique of establishing the integration of communication and plan without threatening the freedom of imagination. I'm not sure this can be done, even within one individual.

Design Issues

Assuming that the problems of acceptance could be partially solved, we can turn to some of the central issues of design. The first issue that comes to mind is definition. What are the "social sciences"? Or what *aren't* the "social sciences"? Social science has been made to include such strange bedfellows as comparative anthropologists and "rat" psychologists, ethicists and production engineers, political scientists and psychometricians. The plethora of languages, interests, frameworks and metaphysics makes any suggestion of a unifying information center seem naive indeed.

Nevertheless, the task may not be as difficult as it sounds, at least for the first level of approximation. A number of years ago Ackoff and I tried our hand at constructing a language within which many diverse social science concepts could be adequately expressed. Essentially, we used a language rich enough to include probability assertions about the consequences of a state (where "states" included individuals and certain kinds of properties). We felt we could translate the intent of a wide variety of models and concepts (e.g., sensation, consciousness, power and introversion) within this framework. Others have attempted the same thing, to a less broad degree (e.g., in decision and game theory).

Recent work in deterministic models (e.g., linear programming) and stochastic models (e.g., Markov processes) might permit a much richer basic language structure than has previously been considered feasible. Nevertheless, it would be foolish not to recognize the extreme difficulties of finding a language that even a significant proportion of social scientists would accept. This is especially true because the accepted language would have to be fairly rich in syntactical rules that permit derivations; otherwise, the use of the language for establishing relevance would be greatly impaired.

What all this amounts to is a language designed to accomplish several *opposing* objectives. Suppose we say that (roughly speaking) the semantic *size* of a language depends on the number of qualitatively distinct phenomena that the language can be used to report. The *simplicity* of a language depends on the computational time (or cost) required to establish relationships between the sentences of the language. The *richness* of a language depends on the variety of relationships between the sentences that can be expressed in the language (e.g., purely deductive, statistical aggregations; mutual confirmations, etc.). What we want is a language of a decent size, that is simple and rich. In general, the greater the size of a language, the less simple it is; and the greater its richness, the less simple it is.

To date, there has been little attempt to try to define size; some work on trying to define formal simplicity and computational simplicity; few try to define richness. I'm not sure, therefore, that we are even ready to formulate the problem of a language for the social sciences, and perhaps the proper formulation could only be attained after the proposed center was well under way.

"Results" and the Indexing Dilemma

Next, it is essential to recognize that much social research does not end in a series of distinct "results." In formal disciplines, one can usually recognize quite clearly what has been accomplished, and the accomplishment is usually a theorem of some sort. But the social sciences produce papers and books in which the author describes certain types of behavior, or counts certain features of a social group. There are case histories of sick people, of healthy businesses, of past political and social events; there are census data, economic data, demographic data. How could all these be "reduced" to results that could meaningfully be fed into a computer's memory? Even the quantitative data alone would probably exceed the capacity of any reasonably priced memory we have today. But the task of indexing and storing a description of, say, the events of the Civil War seems to be well beyond any techniques available to us now.

Indexing is, of course, a type of classification, and, like most classification schemes, tries to do two opposite things at one time: to keep the number of classes small and to preserve essential distinctions. A successful indexing system for the social sciences must be based on a taxonomy of social behavior, something that we're very far from having accomplished. If one could single out the weakest social science, with respect to classification, it would undoubtedly be history. Apparently the only languages in which historical events can be expressed are the so-called ordinary languages. These languages are in terms of the dimensions of language introduced above, complicated and of enormous size, but "poor." That is, the relationships between sentences is very difficult to establish simply and explicitly.

Nevertheless, there is no clear evidence that the situation cannot be improved. Much physical and biological history can be written in a language richer and simpler than English. Even large portions of legal history can be indexed economically and relevance criteria established. The question, then, is whether a better language for social and political history is possible. I'd be inclined to start with the history of ideas, where a number of suggestions and beginnings have already been made.

Mathematics and Elusiveness

The proposers of a World Information Center for Social Sciences would next consider the problem of elusiveness. Anyone who has followed the development of the mathematics of the social sciences cannot have failed to observe the intellectual impasse that resulted—and results. Those on the "side" of mathematics feel that their colleagues are simply against clarity because they are intellectually inept, possibly on account of improper training. Those on the other side keep pointing out that the human psyche, in its many manifestations, is essentially elusive: The more precise one becomes about its characteristic the less one really captures its real content.

The young disciples of mathematical social science tend to regard their opponents as diehards, who will in time disappear as the social sciences become more and more adept in mathematical expression. And the problem is especially acute these days in organization theory. On the one hand, can one understand the nature of a human organization without resorting to a precise model? On the other hand, can one express anything very significant about an organization in a mathematical or computer language?

I can't help feeling that the mathematical side has not fairly faced the problems of elusiveness. Briefly put, as soon as a property is ascribed to a human personality, one must immediately recognize that the opposite property holds as well. English, like most ordinary languages, is especially adapted to take care of the elusive: One can describe and counter-describe in the same expression. The mathematically minded will tend to regard this activity as no more than the conjoining of sets, or else as the display of a characteristic over time. The non-mathematically minded will assert that the individual is never captured by the conjunction of a set of properties or by a dynamic model.

The point is that acceptance of one type of mathematics may indeed so narrow our methods and perspective that we cannot capture what is essential about the human being. But perhaps it is too much to ask for a logic in which "p and not-p" is a valid statement.

A better example is the elusive experiment. The more precise and elegant among us tell our students that in a "properly" designed experiment one must decide beforehand what shall be observed, and one must make sure that the methods of assigning objects to categories remain fixed throughout the experiment. We say, in effect, that if one is going to test whether a treatment cures patients, one must decide at the outset what constitutes a sick patient, what constitutes a healthy one, and what constitutes a treatment.

Now in the elusive experiment, none of these conditions apply; it is not until the experiment is over that one can decide what constituted the real illness of the patient, what constitutes his healthy state, and what the treatment really was. The experiment not only tests the efficacy of treatments, it also defines what a treatment means.

I believe that a large part of social science research is conducted by means of elusive experimentation. If the mathematical side objects that this method "confounds" the variables, then the other side can reply that it does so only because the mathematician invented confounding. Real insight, it says, tells the researcher what is happening, even though he can't make his insight precise in the mathematician's sense. In a way, the non-mathematician is right, because, after reflection, one must admit that we have insisted that only a very narrow range of alternatives constitutes "proper" experimentation. Even within a precise framework, one *could* design an experiment in which classification was being learned and an hypothesis was being tested.

Thus, none of the questions about elusiveness could be answered until mathematicians take the need for elusive concepts and methods seriously, and (of course) until those on the other side take the need for a mathematics seriously.

Measuring Confirmation

Finally, a whole set of problems as to the measures of relevance and confirmation must be considered. Here a basic issue has not yet been settled satisfactorily. Some, like Carnap, believe that the degree of confirmation of an hypothesis can be expressed independently of the use to which the hypothesis is to be put. For them, the degree of confirmation expresses a relationship between a set of observation sentences and an hypothesis. Others, like Wald (and like many statistical decision theorists), believe that a weight function, which helps define the seriousness of a mistake, is essential.

Still others, myself included, are convinced that the problem of empirical inference is much more complicated than either the logical formulation of Carnap or the statistical formulation of Wald indicates. Carnap's and Wald's formulations both assume—for one thing—that the raw data are of equal quality. This is clearly not the case, and although one can adjust the system so that the data are weighted, it is not at all clear what weighting procedure ought to be used. How shall we express the suspicion that certain results are not quite correct? More seriously, how shall we establish relevance relationships between the findings of the social sciences?

I suspect that this last task would require quite a long learning process. Or, possibly, experience may yield a far more satisfactory theory of theory testing than any we now have.

Science or Sciences: Singular or Plural?

Whether or not the proposal of this paper were ever to be adopted, there is much to be learned about the social sciences merely through considering the proposal's problems. When The Institute of Management Sciences was formed, the founders insisted upon the plural because research efforts in this area were not sufficiently unified to warrant the singular form. But the journal was called *Management Science*, as an expression of faith in the eventual unification.

Certainly, we do not have *a* social science today: the differences in fundamental method and motive of anthropologists, psychoanalysts and experimental psychologists are much too great to permit us to define a single discipline that includes them all. Trying to design an Information Center that would do more than merely collect and index data—one that would analyze and relate results as well—we begin to discern, in greater detail, the "pluralness" of the social sciences. Perhaps deeper concentration on the topic will tell us whether the plural form is desirable.

Defining Mathematics

Finally, we have "mathematics." This century has adopted a definition of mathematics which is quite different from that in previous centuries. With the advent of meta-mathematics, we can now say some very precise things about the structure of certain formal systems. This has tempted many of us to define mathematics as the discipline that studies these structures. But this definition is really quite unfortunate, for it drastically limits the purpose of mathematics.

The dispute about elusiveness I referred to earlier seems to arise from too narrow a concept of the mathematician's function. For if we define mathematics in terms of certain formal structures, then we have to show that these structures are useful in the study of reality—and not "precisely trivial" as the opponents of mathematical models say. I know we'd be giving up an elegant definition for a less elegant one, but I'd prefer to take a hint from the original root of the word (*máthēma = learning*) and to define mathematics as the study of the manner in which learning systems can operate effectively. So defined, the study of a World Information Center for Social Sciences would be a part of the mathematics of the social sciences.

EDITORS' NOTE:

An approach to the topic treated in this chapter by C. West Churchman is proposed by Alfred de Grazia in devising a "Universal Reference System," described in some detail in *The American Behavioral Scientist*, Vol. VIII, No. 8, April, 1965, p. 3 ff. To quote De Grazia: "The *Universal Reference System* is a computerized documentation and information retrieval system employing citations of material above a modest level of quality, appearing in all social and behavioral sciences, annotated and indexed by author." As to the system's theoretic underpinnings, de Grazia notes: "The theory behind the URS Classification System is operational: '*Who says, Who does what with whom, where and when, by what means, why,*' and *how does he know so?*.'"

In the same issue of *The American Behavioral Scientist*, see Charles L. Ruttenberg's "Report on Data Archives in the Social Sciences" (p. 33 ff.), commenting on The Second Conference on Data Archives in the Social Sciences, held in Paris, September, 1964. He observes that three censuses of survey outputs showed that in 1963, 245 research centers in the U.S.A. and Europe produced some eight million interviews, and that even a sub-sample of ten percent of these interviews would overtax available storage capacities.

It will be interesting to follow the evolution of behavioral science indexing, storage and data retrieval—and most importantly—how data retrieved are used by behavioral scientists, as computer technology and computer convenience continue to grow.

F.M.

5   The Evaluation of Somewhat Parallel Models *

EARL B. HUNT [†]

SUPPOSE several theories have been proposed to explain a particular aspect of behavior: how do we decide which theory is best? The traditional procedure has been to study a specific situation in which the proposed theories predict markedly different behavior. An experiment is then conducted to determine what actually happens. Seldom, if ever, is a theory completely and utterly rejected. Since the level of observation in the behavioral sciences is gross, support of a hypothesis is almost always probabilistic. Different theories provide the "best explanation" of different experiments. Probably more important, there are few testable situations in which the central theorems of two theoretical systems are directly contradictory. Far more common are those cases in which different models generate slightly different probability distributions over the space of possible observations and under a given experimental procedure. By analogy with geometry, the relevant theorems can be said to be "somewhat" parallel, rather than opposed.

An alternative approach to the search for opposed theorems is to ask not "Which model is supported?" but "Is model X good enough?" "Good enough" is usually interpreted as meaning that model X generates a probability distribution which is not demonstrably different from that inferred from experimental data. This is the well-known "goodness of fit" procedure. Although it provides a broad test of a single model's ability to predict the data, it suffers from two major faults. If the sample size can be manipulated, any reasonable model can be accepted or rejected at any desired level of confidence. Without some statement concerning the practical significance of discrepancies, the considerations which determine the required power of a test of fit are not clear. Besides, knowing that model

* This paper was prepared while the author was on the staff of the Western Management Science Institute, Graduate School of Business, U.C.L.A. Dr. James Mac-Queen made many valuable suggestions.
† University of California, Los Angeles (on leave, University of Sydney, Australia).

X is supported tells us nothing about the relative predictive power of model Y. A truly adequate test would compare the two.

The need for such a test is evidenced by the literature. Bush and Estes (1959)[1] reported several comparisons of the ability of two or more learning models to explain the data from different experiments. Graphs and tables were used to summarize their conclusions. Suppes and Atkinson (1960)[2] tested other learning models as predictors of behavior in a two person "game-like" situation. They also justified and summarized their conclusions by graphs and tables. (My own work has been concerned with the evaluation of different Monte Carlo simulations of experiments on human memory.) None fit the data perfectly, but all models fit some experiments. Each of the three disparate research efforts requires a statistical method for evaluation of several models when:

a) There is no single observation which clearly supports one model over all others, and

b) Some observations may be available which indicate that no model under consideration is an adequate theoretical account of the phenomenon being studied.

Such a method will be proposed in this paper. The approach advocated uses an amplification of Bayesian induction, originally developed by Watanabe (1960).[3] Lindley (1956)[4] and DeGroot (in an unpublished paper)[5] have dealt with the related problem of parameter estimation. Many of their results are applicable here. Shuford (1961)[6] has proposed a similar approach to the evaluation problem.

Any procedure based upon Bayes' theorem requires a statement of *a priori* probabilities. In empirical scientific research both the interpretation and accuracy of such statements may be questioned. In this paper *a priori* probabilities will be interpreted as estimates of the *a posteriori* probabilities that would be obtained if a hypothetical infinite sequence of experiments could be performed. The term *credibility* will be used to refer to the probability statement of a particular model. This definition is consistent with Carnap's (1960)[7] description of a rational process of induction. The

---

[1] R. Bush and W. K. Estes (eds.), *Studies in Mathematical Learning Theory* (Stanford, Calif.: Stanford University Press, 1959).

[2] P. Suppes and R. C. Atkinson, *Markov Learning Models for Multiperson Interaction* (Stanford, Calif.: Stanford University Press, 1960).

[3] S. Watanabe, "Information and Theoretic Aspects of Inductive and Deductive Reasoning," *IBM Journal of Research and Development*, Vol. 4, 1960, pp. 208–31.

[4] D. V. Lindley, "On a Measure of the Information Provided by an Experiment," *Annals of Mathematical Statistics*, Vol. 27, 1956, pp. 986–1005.

[5] M. DeGroot, "Uncertainty, Information, and Sequential Experiments," Carnegie Institute of Technology, Mathematics Department, Pittsburgh (Dittoed paper).

[6] Emir Shuford, "Applications of Bayesian Procedures Based on Discrete Prior Distributions," *Psychometric Laboratory Report*, No. 31, University of North Carolina (Chapel Hill), 1961.

[7] R. Carnap, "The Aim of Inductive Logic," *Procedures of the International Congress for Logic and Methodology of Science* (Stanford, Calif.: Stanford University Press, 1960).

method to be used to make the estimate of *a posteriori* credibility from one series of experiments, thus obtaining the *a priori* values for another, is a technique for obtaining approximations to a metric scale from nonmetric information. The nonmetric information represents "guesses" about the characteristics of the hypothetical *a posteriori* credibilities. The particular technique used to make the estimate was developed by Abelson and Tukey (1959).[8]

Definitions

1. An *experiment* is an observation, under specified conditions, of some aspect of the behavior of interest. The conceivable outcomes of the experiment form a finite set, determined solely by the observational techniques used and not by the state of nature or by the models to be evaluated.

2. A *sequence of experiments* (or, for brevity, a *sequence*) is a series of k specified experiments. It will be assumed that all experiments occur an equal number of times within a sequence. (The assertions to be made will generalize quite readily to the case of an unequal number of occurrences of different experiments within a sequence.) *Extending a sequence* will mean the repetition of all experiments within it. Extending the sequence an *infinite* number of times refers to a hypothetical infinite continuation of experiments.

3. Nature is assumed to be probabilistic. This means that there is associated with each experimental procedure the probability distribution:

$$G_j = \{g_{ij}\}, \tag{1}$$

where the g_{ij} specify the probability of observing any possible (ith) outcome using the jth experimental procedure. The observed data is assumed to be sampled from a space (nature) described by the distribution G_j.

4. From the above, it follows that the most accurate model of nature is the collection of probability distributions G_j, as j varies from 1 to k:

$$G = (\text{collection of the } G_j). \tag{2}$$

By definition, and for all i, j:

$$0 \leq g_{ij}, \tag{3}$$
$$\sum_i g_{ij} = 1,$$
$$\sum_j \sum_i g_{ij} = k.$$

Equation (2) may be written:

$$G = \{g_{11}, g_{21}, \ldots g_{m1}, g_{12}, \ldots g_{ij}, \ldots, g_{mk}\}. \tag{4}$$

[8] R. P. Abelson and J. W. Tukey, "Efficient Conversion of Non-Metric into Metric Information," *Proceedings of the American Statistical Association, Social Statistics Section*, 1959, pp. 226–30.

When no confusion would be introduced, the combinations of possible values of i and j in (4) can be represented by a number v, $v = 1, \ldots N$. Thus (4) could be written:

$$G = \{g_v\}. \tag{5}$$

This will considerably simplify the notation.

5. All experiments and evaluations are to be recorded from time $t = 0$ (before experimentation begins) to time $t = \infty$. Time is considered to be discrete, so that t will always be an integer, and the superscript t will be used to indicate the time relation. For instance, $g^{(t)}$ is to be interpreted as the true probability of the event which was observed at time t.

6. All members of a set of models:

$$B = \{b_r\}, \tag{6}$$

are to be evaluated by observing the result of sequences of experiments. Associated with every model, b_r, is a set of probability distributions for each experimental procedure. This will be represented by:

$$P_r = \{p_{ij}(b_r)\}. \tag{7}$$

The members of this set are to be interpreted as statements of the probability that outcome i will be observed under experimental procedure j according to model b_r. If this model is a completely accurate representation of the true state of nature, then:

$$P_r = G \tag{8}$$

For simplicity of notation, it will often be convenient to replace the combination ij with v, where v is defined for P_r as it was defined for G in equation (5).

The set P_r represents the predictions associated with a model, b_r. Also associated with the model is a set of verbal statements, the *rationale* of the model. A statistical procedure can evaluate P_r. In sections 5, 6, and 7 some discussion will be given to the evaluation of the rationale of a model.

Consistent with the above definitions,

$$p_{ij}(b_r) \geq 0. \tag{9}$$
$$\sum_i [p_{ij}(b_r)] = 1 \text{ for all } j, r,$$
$$\sum_j \sum_i [p_{ij}(b_r)] = k \text{ for all } r.$$

7. At any time t (including $t = 0$) there is a number, $q^{(t)}(b_r)$, associated with each model, b_r. The set of these numbers has the properties of a probability distribution.

The symbol $p^{(t)}(b_r)$ will be used to refer to the probability that the event occurring at time t would occur if model b_r were true:

$$0 \leq q^{(t)} (b_r); \tag{10}$$
$$\sum_r q^{(t)} (b_r) = 1.00.$$

The symbol $q^{(t)} (b_r)$ will be referred to as the credibility of b_r at time t.

The Application of Bayes' Theorem to Model Evaluation

Credibility is defined recursively as:

$$q^{(t)} (b_r) = \frac{[q^{(t-1)} (b_r)] \cdot [p^{(t)} (b_r)]}{\sum\limits_{b_{r'} \epsilon B} [q^{(t-1)} (b_{r'})] \cdot [p^{(t)} (b_{r'})]} . \tag{11}$$

Watanabe (1960)[9] has shown that $q^{(t)} (b_r)$ approaches a limit as t increases without limit. (This is equivalent to an infinite extension of the experimental sequence.) The limit is zero unless the following restrictions are met: there is no conceivable observation, v, such that:

$$p_v (b_r) = 0, \text{ and } g_v \neq 0; \text{ and} \tag{12}$$

there is no r', different from r, such that:

$$\sum_v^n g_v [\log_2 p_v (b_r)] < \sum_v^n g_v [\log_2 p_v (b_{r'})]. \tag{13}$$

If restriction (12) is met, at least one model will meet restriction (13). The first restriction is straightforward. By extending the experimental sequence, the probability may be made so arbitrarily small that any conceivable or possible observation (g_v not zero) will be made. If a particular model exists which states that this event is impossible, then the model will be refuted by a counterexample when this observation is made. By the definition of (11), $q^{(t)} (b_r)$ will become zero whenever such an event occurs.

The second restriction is more interesting. Given several models, none of which is logically refutable, the Bayes procedure will eventually assign non-zero credibility only to those models which are associated with a postulated probability distribution that maximizes the likelihood of obtaining the data observed from an infinite sequence of experiments. Since, by definition, the likelihood of the obtained data is the same for each of these models, discrimination between them must be based upon extra-experimental considerations. Such knowledge should have been utilized in specifying the credibilities at $t = 0$. The Bayes procedure will allow for this type of discrimination. For all models in the set B^* (B^* is a subset of

---

[9] *Loc. cit.*

B) of models r, which never satisfy the inequality of (13), the limit of the credibilities, at $t = \infty$, is:

$$q^{(\infty)}(b_r) = \frac{q^{(0)}(b_r)}{\sum\limits_{b_{r'} \in B^*} q^{(0)}(b_{r'})}.\tag{14}$$

In practice, it would be rather unusual to find more than one model in B^*. The data from a finite sequence of experiments will seldom be exactly as likely if either of two models is correct. On the other hand, the smaller the amount of data, the more difficult it will be to distinguish between two models for which (13) is nearly an equality, except on the basis of their *a priori* credibilities.

Thus the Bayes procedure overcomes one of the disadvantages of the goodness-of-fit technique: instead of penalizing the researcher for taking a large sample, it rewards him. Ultimately (when (12) and (13) are the controlling factors in determining credibilities), the selection of models with non-zero credibility is independent of the initial assignment of credibilities.

Granted that, in the limit, Bayesian induction selects a model, will it select a *correct* model? To decide this, it is necessary to define "correct." Since Bayes' theorem is simply a rearrangement of the definition of conditional probability, it is bound to select a model which is correct in the sense of equation (8), if such a model exists in B. If no such model exists, then the recursive induction defined by (11) will result in non-zero credibilities for those models which approximately minimize a measure analogous to chi-square. The term "analogous" is used because what is minimized is the chi-square distance measure which would be observed between the true distribution, G, and a selected model, if the true probabilities were known. Bayesian induction minimizes the quantity $\frac{\Sigma(observed-expected)^2}{observed}$,

instead of the more familiar $\frac{\Sigma(observed-expected)^2}{expected}$.

This is a reasonable measure to minimize in model evaluation. The data is fixed, but the models may be varied. As might be expected by the analogy to chi-square, the approximation breaks down for rare events (when g_v is very small). The proof of these assertions follows.[10]

Maximization of (13) is equivalent to maximizing:

$$X = \sum_v g_v[\log_2 p_v(b_r)] - \sum_v g_v[\log_2 g_v]\tag{15}$$
$$= \sum_v g_v[\log_2 (p_v(b_r) / g_v)].$$

---

[10] This proof was suggested by Professor Leo Breiman.

From the definition of logarithms, maximization of (15) also maximizes:

$$X' = - \sum_{v-1} \sum_{k-1}^{\infty} \left[\frac{(g_v - p_v\,(b_r))^k}{k(g_v{}^{k-1})} \right].$$ (16)

And, by the definitions of G and P_r in section 2:

$$\sum_{v-1}^{N} p_v\,(b_r) = \sum_{v-1}^{N} g_v;$$ (17)

so the term for $k = 1$ in (16) disappears. The sum of the higher order terms of (17) converges to zero, doing so rapidly if g_v is not small. Therefore, maximization of (17) is approximately equivalent to minimizing:

$$X'' = \sum_{v} \left[\frac{(g_v - p_v\,(b_r))^2}{g_v} \right].$$ (18)

Since the observed frequency of events converges to g_v, (18) is "analogous" to chi-square. Because the approximation of (16) by (18) is not accurate if g_v is small, the union of rare events (i.e., infrequently observed outcomes) ought to be treated as a single event. As a tentative suggestion, .05 is recommended as the minimum value of the observed frequency of a single event. It seems more defensible to place this restriction upon g_{ij} rather than upon g_v, since we should aggregate infrequent events within a given experimental procedure (j fixed), and not across procedures.

If a logical refutation occurs, the recursive induction procedure should be used with caution. A model which can be logically refuted by a rare event may still be an excellent predictor of the obtained observations. If the sole purpose of having a model is to make such predictions, the Bayes procedure may be inappropriate.

The Auxiliary Measure $U^{(t)}$

The numerical values assigned to the credibilities establish *semantic* information. They tell us the degree of belief we should have that any particular model is closest to the actual state of nature. Watanabe (and others) have pointed out that we may also require a single indicator of overall uncertainty. A frequently proposed measure is:

$$U^{(t)} = - \sum [q^{(t)}\,(b_r)]\,[\log_2 q^{(t)}\,(b_r)].$$ (19)

As an indicator of overall uncertainty this measure has the following desirable characteristics:

1. It is at a maximum when no distinctions between models can be made, and at a minimum (zero) when a single model has been selected as the closest approximation to the true state of nature.

2. Over an arbitrarily long extension of an experimental sequence, there is some finite t' such that, for all t greater than t', the relation between the expectations of $U^{(t)}$ and $U^{(t')}$ is:

$$E(U^{(t)}) \leq E(U^{(t')}), \quad t > t'. \tag{20}$$

A proof of (20) can be found in Watanabe's (1960) article. Note that a monotonic fall of $U^{(t)}$ is not always to be expected. If the *a priori* credibilities are inversely correlated with the distance between the different models and the true state of nature, the expectation of $U^{(t)}$ will first rise, and then fall.

3. Watanabe has also shown that the expected fluctuation of $U^{(t)}$ about its expected value will fall as t increases.

Property 1 is a straightforward extension of the definition of $U^{(t)}$. Its principal usefulness is to suggest that the value of $U^{(t)}$ could be used as one of the arguments of a decision rule that would determine when to stop experimentation. An alternate criterion, based upon Property 2, is to stop experimentation when the first differences:

$$|\Delta U^{(t)}| = |U^{(t)} - U^{(t-1)}|, \tag{21}$$

are empirically observed to be below a certain prespecified minimum value. Such an observation indicates that the credibilities are approaching their limits, and there is little point in continuing experimentation without altering the sequence of experiments.

Property 2 also suggests a crude "bootstrapping" technique for model evaluation. The purpose of this technique is to avoid situations in which extensive experimentation would be needed to overcome the effect of poorly chosen *a priori* credibilities. Such situations may be indicative of a misunderstanding of the phenomenon being investigated. They will often require a theoretical reorientation rather than further experimental attack.

Define as suspect any situation in which the *a priori* credibilities at time t' (including $t' = 0$) are such that (20) is not satisfied. Let ∂ be the probability of observing a positive value for $\Delta U^{(t)}$ in the interval $t' < t < t''$. If the situation at t' is not suspect, then the inequality:

$$\partial \leq .50, \tag{22}$$

should hold. This hypothesis can be tested against the observed sequence of first differences.

Such a test is particularly appropriate if it is suspected that the state of nature has changed at time t', thus invalidating previous inductions. It can also be used to evaluate the *a priori* credibilities at $t = 0$, where credibility assignment was based entirely on extra-experimental considerations. Of course, (22) can always be satisfied at $t = 0$ by assigning equal credibility to all models (thus maximizing $U^{(t)}$). In the following section it will be argued that this is not an efficient procedure.

Assignment of *A Priori* Credibilities

Credibilities must be assigned at $t = 0$. Since no experimental evidence is available at this point, subtle philosophical questions could be raised. This is especially true if the researcher considers himself to be in complete ignorance before obtaining data.

The philosophical problems can be avoided by defining the goal of *a priori* credibility assignment to be the maximization of the correlation between the set of numbers, $\{q^{(0)}(b_r)\}$, and the set, $\{q^{(\infty)}(b_r)\}$, which the researcher *thinks* he would obtain at the end of an infinite experimental sequence. To do this, the researcher must make explicit assumptions concerning ultimate credibility values. These assumptions will seldom take the strong form of assigning numerical values to the final credibilities. (If such values were known, there would be little point to experimentation.) On the other hand, there will be many situations in which a "semi-metric" ordering of the expected final credibilities can be obtained. For instance, a researcher might be willing to state which models he thinks are better than others. Using this sort of data, an initial ordering of the set $q^{(0)}(b_r)$ could be made. A typical example is:

$$q^{(0)}(b_1) > q^{(0)}(b_2) > q^{(0)}(b_3) \geq q^{(0)}(b_4); \qquad (23)$$

possibly amplified by an ordering of the distance between credibilities:

$$|q^{(0)}(b_1) - q^{(0)}(b_2)| \geq |q^{(0)}(b_2) - q^{(0)}(b_3)| \geq |q^{(0)}(b_3) - q^{(0)}(b_4)|. \qquad (24)$$

Such restrictions can be used to establish a set of allowable initial credibility assignments. The numerical values should be such that the initial credibilities are within this set and, on the average, as close as possible to the final credibilities. Abelson and Tukey (1959),[11] attacking a mathematically identical problem in a different context (the assignment of contrast weights in the analysis of variance), regarded the assignment problem as a game against nature. As an appropriate strategy, they suggested maximizing the minimum correlation between a chosen set of weights and any set which satisfied the initial constraints. The chosen set would, of course, also have to satisfy these constraints. Abelson and Tukey solved their version of the assignment problem and gave some useful heuristics for finding approximate solutions. They also provided exact solutions for certain simple constraints (e.g., rank ordering) which appear to cover most of the relevant situations in the recent literature in experimental psychology.

Maximization of the minimum correlation between the initial and the *assumed* allowable final credibilities is a heuristic device designed to reduce the amount of experimentation that will be required before $U^{(t)}$ reaches

---

[11] *Op. cit.*

an acceptable level. If the assumptions about allowable final results are incorrect, the "maximin" procedure may not produce a nearly optimal set of initial credibilities. On the other hand, if the assumptions are correct, $U^{(0)}$ may be very close to the limiting value, $U^{(\infty)}$. In general, experimentation will be discontinued more rapidly than it would have been had all models been treated as equally likely. Alternately, "suspect" situations will be defined quickly.

Examples of Evaluation by Inductive Inference

This section contains two examples of the application of the above techniques to actual data. The examples have been chosen to indicate the advantages and pitfalls inherent in the inductive inference procedure. In both cases, it is believed that the application of the inference procedure resulted in a more concise evaluation of the relative ability of different models to handle obtained data than was available before the procedure was applied. On the other hand, the inductive inference procedure ignores certain features of the models. As will be shown, these features may be quite important.

None of the examples purport to be a complete analysis of the data or models in question. Example 1 is taken from chapter 3 of Suppes' and Atkinson's (1960) monograph [12] on the application of learning models to two-person game situations. They proposed other models, in addition to the four considered, and evaluated the four discussed here (using data that will not be discussed). In principle, the Bayes technique could be applied to all models and data in the original report. In practice this would entail more computation than was practical for the current purpose.[13]

Example 2 uses data from an unpublished Monte Carlo simulation by the author and Dr. Douwe Yntema of Lincoln Laboratories, M.I.T. Again, not all available data and not all models are included in the discussion. This example is offered to show how statistical induction is being used to guide a current, unfinished research project.

Example 1. Suppes and Atkinson proposed four learning models. The first two were stimulus sampling models, the remaining two were more general linear operator models (Restle, 1959).[14] Model M1 contained the postulate that the effective stimulus universe consists of exactly one ele-

---

[12] *Op. cit.*

[13] Suppes and Atkinson point out, correctly, that analysis of their models, using traditional mathematical methods, would be difficult. Whether they considered the possibility of Monte Carlo simulation is not known.

[14] F. Restle, "A Survey and Classification of Learning Models," *Studies in Mathematical Learning Theory* (R. Bush and W. Estes [eds.]) (Stanford, Calif.: Stanford University Press, 1959).

ment. In model M2 the universe was assumed to contain two elements.

In the first generalized conditioning model, C1, the learning rate parameter at trial n depended upon the combination of response made and reward experienced by the subject on that trial. In the second generalized conditioning model, C2, the learning parameters were functions of the response and reward conditions on trial n and the previous pattern of responses and rewards. Thus, in an asymmetric game situation, model C1 would apply the same learning parameters to both players (although with different frequency), while model C2 would apply different parameters, since the overall response and reward experience of each player would be different.[15]

To the present author, models M1 and M2 appeared to be fairly drastic oversimplifications, while model C2 seemed to be somewhat too complicated. Therefore, before reading Suppes' and Atkinson's report of their experiments, an appropriate *a priori* ordering of initial credibilities would have been:

$$q^{(0)}(C_1) > q^{(0)}(C_2) > q^{(0)}(M_2) > q^{(0)}(M_1), \qquad (25)$$

amplified by an ordering of the distance betwen credibilities:

$$|q^{(0)}(C_2) - q^{(0)}(M_2)| > |q^{(0)}(C_1) - q^{(0)}(C_2)| > |q^{(0)}(M_2) - q^{(0)}(M_1)| \quad (26)$$

These orderings were used to assign credibility measures to each model, as shown in Figure 1.

In chapter 3, Suppes and Atkinson report the ability of the four learning models to describe behavior in gamelike situations. Two subjects at a time participated in the experiment. Each subject (A or B) could make either of two responses (R1 or R2). Subjects responded independently and simultaneously. At the end of each trial, each subject was, or was not, rewarded with a fixed probability (which might be different for each subject) that depended upon which joint response pair (A–R1, B–R2, etc.) had occurred.

This situation can be represented as a game, a fact which was not stressed to the participants. Three different "gamelike situations" were considered: one in which each player could maximize his rewards by a mixed strategy (assign fixed, non-zero probabilities of choice to either response); one in which each player could maximize his rewards by the pure strategy of always making response R1; and one in which each player had a "sure thing" alternative (Savage, 1954)[16] such that, no matter what response the other player made, R1 should always be preferred to R2.

The progress of this game from trial n to trial $n + 1$ can be represented as a series of transitions from state to state within the set of four

---

[15] The notation used here is different from that used in Suppes' and Atkinson's report.

[16] R. Savage, *Foundations of Statistics* (New York: John Wiley & Sons, Inc., 1954).

TABLE 1

PROBABILITY OF AS GREAT OR GREATER DISCREPANCY BETWEEN
OBTAINED AND MODEL RESULTS (SUPPES AND ATKINSON DATA)

| MODEL | EXPERIMENT | | |
	Mixed	Pure	Sure
C1	.50	.005	.005
C2	.34	.10	.25
M2	.005	.005	.005
M1	0	0	0 *

* Model M1 postulates that certain events, which were observed, are impossible.

states defined by the joint occurrence of responses by subjects A and B. All four learning models yield predictions concerning the frequency of each possible transition at asymptote. The probability that a transition matrix, randomly drawn from a universe of transition matrices actually generated by each model, would yield as great or greater discrepancies from the expected values as did the observed transition matrix, can be calculated. The result of this calculation is summarized in Table 1.[17] In

FIGURE 1

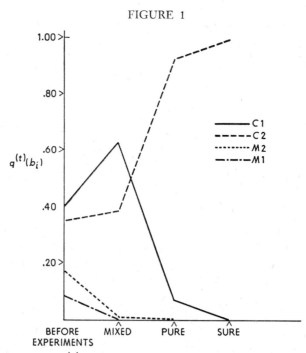

$q^{(t)}(b_i)$ VS. EXPERIMENTAL DATA FOR SUPPES
AND ATKINSON'S LEARNING MODELS

FIGURE 2

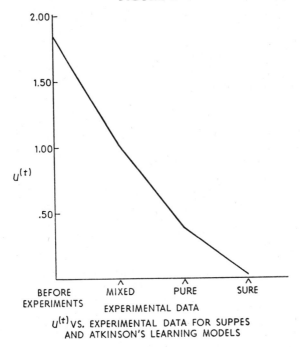

$U^{(t)}$ VS. EXPERIMENTAL DATA FOR SUPPES
AND ATKINSON'S LEARNING MODELS

Figures 1 and 2 the graphs for the set $\{q^{(t)}\ (b_r)\}$ and $U^{(t)}$ are presented, following the convention that the mixed group is examined at $t = 1$, the pure group at $t = 2$, and the "sure thing" group at $t = 3$.

Given this data, it is clear that model C2 is the closest of the four to the hypothetically "true" state of nature. Examination of the other experimental data provided by Suppes and Atkinson confirms this conclusion (although unquestioning acceptance of this model would lead to some difficulties of interpretation). Also, it is clear from Table 1 (as well as from Figure 1) that we should be absolutely certain that model M1 is not correct. This is because M1 predicts that certain transitions between states will never occur over a one-trial interval. These transitions, however, occur. Furthermore, they occur often enough in the experimental data so that they cannot be treated as rare events.

In spite of this, Suppes and Atkinson devote most of their discussion after chapter 3 to an evaluation of the predictive power of Model M1. One cannot maintain that they acted irrationally. This model is a good predictor of some aspects of the data other than asymptotic transition frequency. For

---

[17] Probability values have been substituted for the chi-square values reported by Suppes and Atkinson. Linear interpotation was used when required. Strictly speaking, the Bayes procedure ought to be applied to exact probabilities. The approximations reported here were necessary to reduce computational effort.

instance, the asymptotic frequency of R1 responses can be predicted with considerable accuracy.

A second feature of model M1 which impressed Suppes and Atkinson was that it can be represented as a simple Markov chain, making it possible to generate a great many predictions without an undue amount of computation. This is a legitimately desirable feature of a scientific model. The more accurate model M2, although it can be conceptualized as a Markov chain, does not lead to such tractable mathematics. Model C2 does not describe a learning process that can be represented by a conceptually simple analogue.

Example 2. Yntema and Meuser (1960)[18] gathered data on the ability of human subjects to keep track of several variables at the same time. Their subjects received messages about the *state* of a *variable*. A variable, in turn, was defined as the *attribute* of an *object*. For instance, a message might read "The animal [attribute] of object A [object] is now do [state]." Aperiodically, subjects received questions; for example, " What is the state of the animal of A?"

The basic datum is the percentage of questions which a subject could answer correctly. In the experiment of interest, the structure of the variables was manipulated. In one condition there were six attributes of one object, in another condition three attributes of two objects, then two attributes of three objects, and finally one attribute of six objects. These will be referred to as the experiments (6 x 1), (3 x 2), etc., and this manipulation proved to be an important determinant of subjects' performance.

Several models of the information processing task have been constructed. All the models envisage a two-stage process: data storage and retrieval. In the storage phase a message is broken down into its component parts and, with some cross-referencing, is stored piece by piece in different, randomly selected storage bins. Previously stored information may be lost if a piece of information is placed in an occupied bin.

In the retrieval phase an attempt is made to reconstruct the last message about the variable in question, given the present contents of memory. Several heuristic processes may be tried, each with an increasing probability of being carried to completion regardless of the contents of memory, and each with an increasing probability of producing an incorrect answer. A model may be changed by changing the size of the storage area or by changing the storage and retrieval procedure. Normally the latter change will result in greater modification of the model's behavior.

The resulting models are too complicated for analysis. Therefore each model was tested by comparing obtained data with the results of a Monte

[18] D. B. Yntema and G. Meuser, "Remembering the Present States of a Number of Variables; III: Why It Is Difficult to Keep Trace of Several Variables with the Same Set of States," *Technical Report 589–0013*, Lincoln Laboratories, Cambridge, Mass.

Carlo simulation (using the IBM 7090 of Lincoln Laboratories, M.I.T.). After completing the simulation, but before a detailed analysis was made (so that the argument is somewhat *post hoc*) the current author reasoned that models M1 and M2 were crude approximations, differing only in parameters; that models M3 and M4 represented a more plausible approach (again, differing between themselves only in parameters); and that model M5 introduced some necessary heuristic features that did not become obvious until after experience with models M1 through M4 had been obtained.

In keeping with this reasoning, the following constraints were placed upon *a priori* credibilities:

$$q^{(0)}(M_5) > q^{(0)}(M_4) > q^{(0)}(M_3) > q^{(0)}(M_2) > q^{(0)}(M_1), \tag{27}$$

amplified by the ordering of distances:

$$|q^{(0)}(M_5) - q^{(0)}(M_4)| > |q^{(0)}(M_3) - q^{(0)}(M_2)| \geq |q^{(0)}(M_4) - q^{(0)}(M_3)|,$$

or:

$$|q^{(0)}(M_2) - q^{(0)}(M_1)|. \tag{28}$$

In Table 2 the results of a calculation of the probability of obtaining as great or greater difference between the observed and the simulated data are presented for each condition of the experiment and for each model. Using conventional statistics, we should reject all models on the basis of the 6 x 1 condition alone. On the other hand, optimization of parameters could force any model to match the obtained data for any one condition.

TABLE 2

PROBABILITY OF OBTAINING AS GREAT OR GREATER DISCREPANCY
BETWEEN MODEL SIMULATIONS AND OBSERVED RESULTS FOR THE
SIMULATION OF MEMORY EXPERIMENTS

MODEL	EXPERIMENT			
	6 x 1	3 x 2	2 x 3	1 x 6
M1	.001	.001	.001	.001
M2	.001	.001	.002	.002
M3	.001	.001	.001	.001
M4	.001	.010	.320	.250
M5	.001	.250	.460	.140

We could have used the data from one condition to determine parameters, and then compared each model to the data obtained from the other conditions. There are two reasons why this was not done. The characters of the models themselves suggests that the poor fit is not going to be significantly improved by parameter optimization. Furthermore, this process would simply be too expensive. Each simulation required approximately one hour of machine time in one of the largest and fastest computers available. While it is always possible that more efficient programming would have helped solve this problem, it did not seem likely that sufficient reduction in cost of simulation could be achieved. Sheer economics dictated the use of a test, before parameter optimization was begun, to determine which model was most likely to "pay off."

Figures 3 and 4 summarize the result of applying the Bayes induction procedure to this data. Credibilities at $t = 0$ were established by the Abelson and Tukey method, with *a priori* restraints established by (27) and (28). The results indicate that M5 is, indeed, the closest approximation to the data. Also—a fact which is obvious when Table 2 is examined—any discrimination between models M4 and M5 depends almost entirely upon the results of condition 3 x 2. In such a case, where conclusions rest largely upon the outcome of one experiment in the sequence, the question should be raised as to whether the particular experiment is somehow atypical of the others in the sequence. Here the answer appears to be that it is not. However it might be wise to review the experimental or simulation results obtained in condition 3 x 2.

This example has shown how the application of Bayesian induction can suggest research priorities that might not have occurred if the data had been subjected to a less formal review. As such, the formal review is a heuristic device which may keep the researcher from overlooking some

FIGURE 3

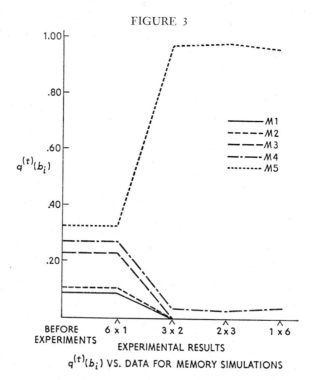

$q^{(t)}(b_i)$ VS. DATA FOR MEMORY SIMULATIONS

FIGURE 4

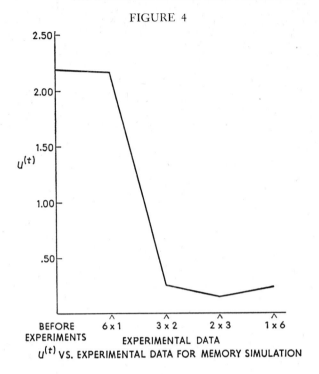

$u^{(t)}$ VS. EXPERIMENTAL DATA FOR MEMORY SIMULATION

aspect of his data. It is certainly not suggested as a replacement for close examination of individual results, but it may provide a valuable supplement.

We do not know whether these examples are, or are not, typical of the problems of model evaluation in experimental psychology. As an interesting conjecture, consider the proposal that in those fields in which there are no clearly discriminating experiments, there also exists a great deal of data which could be used in evaluating models.

Discussion

Given its assumptions, the logic of Bayesian induction speaks for itself. The relevant question is whether or not a technique as broad as an overall evaluation of theories can be useful in the behavioral sciences. Since the aim of the induction procedure is so broad, its advantages, liabilities, and assumptions should be evaluated carefully.

One of the arguments against Bayesian induction is that it does not make a rapid adjustment to new evidence, especially if *a priori* credibilities are poorly chosen. Watanabe estimated that a reasonable "Bayesian" man would require 70 tosses before he admitted that a grocer had given him a two-headed coin! But are such experimental results likely to occur in practice? A cursory examination of the literature indicates that they are not. Either the experimental evidence is sufficiently discriminating, or the estimates based on the Abelson-Tukey method are sufficiently general, to result in a rapid reduction of $U^{(t)}$.

As an example, one can reverse the rank ordering of (27), reduce (28) to equalities, and still not appreciably affect the final evaluation of the Yntema and Meuser results. (The ordering of *a posteriori* credibilities will remain the same, although the absolute value of $U^{(t)}$ is greater for all values of t.) The technique of observing sequences of first differences of $U^{(t)}$ provides an additional check against unusually poor choices of *a priori* credibilities.

Bayesian induction treats each experiment as equally valid. This is a convenient mathematical assumption; we ignore all evaluation of the experiment except the statistical statement of the probability of obtaining the results from a given model. But it is a drastic assumption, which should be accepted only after careful evaluation. All experiments in a given sequence should be comparable in some sense. This is admittedly a vague criterion, but the question is such that a "cookbook answer" is unlikely. Good judgment will have to prevail.

If the discriminative power of an experimental sequence is concentrated upon one or two experiments, the researcher ought to examine these experiments carefully. He should ask what unique factors were present in these experiments and not in the others; and whether the greater discrimination is due to valid or to spurious reasons. As an example of valid concentration of discrimination, we refer to Example 2 of the previous section, the Yntema and Meuser results. While all discrimination is based upon one condition in that sequence, the particular condition is one that is logically demanded by the design of the experiment.

Some of the arguments for Bayesian induction refer to the limiting behavior of variables after an infinite experimental sequence. In the examples given, and in most behavioral science research, only a few experiments are performed in a given sequence. Equally serious, experiments are seldom repeated. Although these limitations do not invalidate the argument, they raise the question of how far the results obtained from a single sequence will be from the limiting values. The decision to (or not to) repeat an experiment is a related topic. In an earlier section, decision rules were suggested as a guide in such matters, but their validity will have to be established in future research.

It is practically axiomatic that any curve-fitting technique will reject a theory if the test is made sufficiently powerful. The Bayesian induction procedure, since it operates on a competitive basis, does not do this. More powerful tests of fit simply make finer discriminations between models possible. However, the extreme Bayes procedure position, which ignores the absolute fit of the model, is certainly not correct. Some attention should be paid to the question of whether or not the best available model provides an adequate fit. It would seem that this question has relevance only when a nonstatistical criterion for significance of discrepancies is available.

As has been pointed out, the Bayes procedure will not necessarily select the best predictor of data. Grant (1962)[19] has suggested an alternative model for prediction evaluation. Also, in company with all statistical tests, the Bayes procedure evaluates only the probability distribution associated with a particular mode. The utility of the model, in terms of theoretical simplicity or relation to a broader theoretical approach, may exert some influence on its selection, apart from its relation to a particular set of data.

The Bayes procedure refines credibility recursively, as the estimate of our relative preference for a model, rather than as our belief that it is an exact replica of the state of nature. Carnap (1960)[20] has presented a description of rational decision making in which credibility is defined in a similar manner. His arguments can be used to defend the approach of this paper.

Finally, some may argue that, for a variety of reasons (rational and otherwise [Barber, 1961][21]), models and theories are not really evaluated statistically. There is, indeed, a need for the analytic induction method. A completely rational decision rule can be thought of as a feature that should be built into an intelligent automaton. There is great interest in the development of such automata (Hovland, 1960,[22] and Minsky, 1961[23]).

Some artificial intelligence systems try to adjust to their environment by making "guesses" about the state of nature. Such devices should concentrate their resources on the evaluation of those "guesses" which have the greatest promise of being correct. This is particularly a problem in the design of concept learners that proceed by hypothesis evaluation. One such device (Hunt and Hovland, 1961)[24] places an arbitrary limit upon the amount of computing that will be performed during the evaluation of a single hypothesis. Another (Kochen, 1960)[25] uses a crude "best fit" selection procedure. A more elegant procedure, based upon Bayesian induction, could be used to monitor hypothesis constructing devices.

---

[19] D. A. Grant, "Testing the Null Hypothesis and the Strategy and Tactics of Investigating Theoretical Models," *Psychological Revue*, Vol. 69, 1962, pp. 54–61.

[20] *Op. cit.*

[21] B. Barber, "Resistance of Scientists to Scientific Discovery," *Science*, Vol. 134, 1961, pp. 596–602.

[22] C. I. Hovland, "The Computer Simulation of Thinking," *The American Psychologist*, Vol. 15, 1960, pp. 687–93.

[23] M. Minsky, "Steps Toward Artificial Intelligence," *Proceedings of the Institute of Radio Engineers*, Vol. 45, 1961, pp. 8–30.

[24] E. B. Hunt and C. I. Hovland, "Programming a Model of Human Concept Formulation," *Proceedings of the Western Joint Computer Conference*, 1961, pp. 145–55.

[25] M. Kochen, "Experimental Study of Hypothesis Formulation by Computer," *Proceedings of the 1960 London Symposium on Information Theory.*

A Model of

6   *Semantic Information*

and Message Evaluation

David Harrah [*]

HOW does a human receiver measure the informativeness of messages? How does he evaluate the performance of a supplier of information? Under what conditions does he prefer one supplier to another? These questions are concerned with semantic information, as distinct from statistical or selective information.[1] As a step toward answering them we offer here a model of how a rational receiver behaves in certain communication situations.[2]

In this model the receiver, R, evaluates informativeness by means of two devices: a semantic information function, I, and a set of questions, Q. The crucial property of I is that, if one sentence implies another, the I values of the two sentences are connected in a certain way (see below). Because of this, we must specify our assumptions concerning R's language and its relation of implication.

We assume that R uses a language, L, having individual constants (which we refer to by a, b, c, d), individual variables (u, v, w, x), and predicates (F, G, H) of individuals, the usual truth-functional logic of sentences (F, G, H), and the usual logic of first-order predicates, quantifiers, and identity. In addition, we allow L to have a *non-logical* part; that is, L might contain some "meaning postulates" in the sense of Carnap,[3] some mathematical axioms, and so on.

We assume that L is consistent. We shall use & to express conjunction, — negation, v disjunction, → the material conditional, ←→ material equivalence, and (x) and (Ex) universal and existential generalization. By statement we shall mean "declarative sentence" or "well-formed formula without free variables." "F is L-true" will mean that F is a statement and

---

[*] University of California, Riverside.

[1] For a discussion of the differences between these types of information, see George A. Miller, "Communication," *Annual Review of Psychology*, Vol. 5, pp. 408f.

[2] This model resembles, but is not identical with, the model presented in David Harrah's *Communication: A Logical Model* (Cambridge, Mass.: The M.I.T. Press, 1963).

[3] See Rudolf Carnap and Yehoshua Bar-Hillel, "An Outline of a Theory of Semantic Information," Report 247, M.I.T. Research Laboratory of Electronics, Cambridge, Mass., October 27, 1952; and Rudolf Carnap, "Meaning Postulates," *Philosophical Studies*, Vol. 3, 1952, pp. 65–73.

F is a theorem of L. "F L-implies G" will mean that $(F \rightarrow G)$ is a theorem of L; similarly for "F and G are L-equivalent" and "F is L-false." "F is consistent" will mean that F is not L-false.

It will become evident later that we are in effect assuming that R is a perfect logician, in this sense: By spending some time and effort R can determine, for any given formula F, whether or not F is L-true or L-false; in particular, given any formulas F and G, R can determine whether or not $(F \ \& \ G)$ is consistent, and whether or not F L-implies G. As a general assumption about human language behavior, this is, of course, unrealistic; the justification for incorporating this assumption in our model will be discussed later.

Next we characterize I via the following assumptions. We assume that R uses a semantic information function, I, which assigns real numbers to statements of L in such a way that:

1. $0 \leqslant I(F) \leqq \infty$.
2. $I(F) = 0$ if, and only if, F is L-true.
3. $I(F) = \infty$ if, and only if, F is an L-false statement.
4. If FL-implies G, then $I(F) \geqslant I(G)$.
5. The information of F relative to G is defined by
$$I(F|G) = I(F \ \& \ G) - I(G).$$

From these assumptions we can derive the following theorems:

Theorem 1. If F and G are L-equivalent, then $I(F) = I(G)$.
Theorem 2. If FL-implies G, then $I(F \ \& \ G) = I(F)$.
Theorem 3. $I(F \ \& \ G) \geqslant I(F) \geqslant I(F \ v \ G)$.
Theorem 4. $I(F|G) \geqslant 0$.
Theorem 5. If FL-implies G, then $I(G|F) = 0$.
Theorem 6. If FL-implies G, then $I(F|H) \geqslant I(G|H)$.
Theorem 7. $I[(F \ \& \ G)|(G \ \& \ H)] = I[F|(G \ \& \ H)]$.[4]

We allow R to change his information function at any time; in the development below we shall use I_i to refer to the information function which R uses in the communication event E_i.

Treating Semantic Information

Our treatment of I differs in several respects from the usual treatment of semantic information.[5] In the usual treatment, the amount of semantic in-

---

[4] For proofs of these theorems see Harrah, *op. cit.*, section 11. For the remaining theorems of this paper, proofs can be constructed parallel to proofs in theorems in Harrah as follows: Theorem 8 here corresponds to theorem 14-1 there; 9 here to 14-6 there; 10 here to 14-2 there; and 11 here to 16-9 there.

[5] We take the usual treatment to be that of Carnap (*op. cit.*) and John G. Kemeny ("A Logical Measure Function," *The Journal of Symbolic Logic*, Vol. 18, 1953, pp. 289–308). Since the birth of information theory, only a few applications—all normative—have been suggested for semantic information functions. In the social sciences these functions seem to have aroused little interest, perhaps because no behavioral model has been developed within which these functions can be applied in a fruitful way. One objective of this paper is to stimulate interest in the theory of semantic information and the construction of such models.

formation of a statement is intended to represent the logical strength of the statement; semantic information is defined (roughly) in terms of the number of atomic statements implied by the statement.

In the model presented here, there is no commitment to an explicit definition of I. R might base his I-values on logical or empirical probability, or on subjective estimates based on considerations of both probability and utility. Because of Theorem 1, however, I is not a subjective information function in the sense of Wells.[6] Also, $I(F)$ cannot be interpreted as representing the utility of F (or the state of affairs signified by F) in the sense required for decision theory. The reason for this is Assumption 4. If we let F be "You will win 10 dollars and your right hand will be cut off," and let G be "You will win 10 dollars," then $I(F) \geqslant I(G)$, and thus (we assume) I does not represent the desirability to R of securing that F or G is the case.

But suppose F signifies a state of affairs over which R has no control—in particular, a state of affairs which has already occurred but which R does not know has occurred. In general, R prefers knowing that an occurred event has occurred to not knowing that it has occurred, so perhaps $I(F)$ can represent the relative desirability of knowing that F is indeed the case. Tentatively, at least, we shall think of $I(F)$ as resulting from two evaluations:

1. An evaluation of the amount of factuality in F, and
2. An evaluation of the utility of being told that F.

The second device which we assume R uses for evaluating messages is a set, Q, of questions. The central idea of the development below is that R evaluates messages according to how they answer questions which express R's interests. In the first 12 definitions below we shall make precise the notion of question, at least for two types of question; and later in the paper we shall clarify the sense in which Q is a device of evaluation.

The basic idea in our analysis of questions is that certain types of question can be identified with certain types of statement. Here we shall analyze "whether" questions and "which" questions; other types of question can be analyzed along roughly the same lines but require a more complicated formalism. It should always be kept in mind here that questions and answers are statements, and thus can have information values. This allows us to interpret the question-and-answer process as an information-matching game, and it might also lead to interesting investigations beyond the immediate concerns of this paper.

Definition 1. Suppose we have a finite sequence $G_1, \ldots, G_n$ of *wffs*, where $n > 1$. Then for each i (such that $1 \leqslant i \leqslant n$), $G_i{}^*$ denotes:

$$((\cdots((((\cdots(-G_1 \,\&\, -G_2) \,\&\, \cdots) \,\&\, -G_{i-1}) \,\&\, G_i) \,\&\, -G_{i+1}) \,\&\, \cdots) \,\&\, -G_n)$$

---

[6] Rulon Wells, "A Measure of Subjective Information," *American Mathematical Society Proceedings of Symposia in Applied Mathematics*, Vol. 12, 1961, pp. 237–44.

Definition 2. F is a *prime disjunction* in a sequence $G_1, \ldots, G_n$ of *wff*s if, and only if, $n > 1$ and F is the disjunction:

$$(((\cdots((G_1{}^* \text{ v } G_2{}^*) \text{ v } G_3{}^*) \text{ v } \cdots) \text{ v } G_{n-1}{}^*) \text{ v } G_n{}^*).$$

Definition 3. F is a *disjunctive question* (i.e., a "whether" question) if, and only if, F is a prime disjunction in some sequence of *wff*s.

Definition 4. A *direct answer to a disjunctive question*, q, is a disjunct of q.

Definition 5. A *which* question is a statement $(Ex_1) \ldots (Ex_n)Fx_1 \ldots x_n$, where $x_1, \ldots, x_n$ are distinct variables occurring free in F, $n > 0$, and F is not $(Ev)G$.

Definition 6. H is a *direct answer to a which question*, q, if, and only if, q is $(Ex_1) \ldots (Ex_n)Fx_1 \ldots x_n$, where F is not $(Ev)G$, and H is a statement: $(x_1)\cdots(x_n)[Fx_1\cdots x_n \longleftrightarrow [(x_1 = a_1 \ \& \cdots \& \ x_n = a_n) \text{ v} \cdots \text{v } (x_1 = b_1 \ \& \cdots \& \ x_n = b_n)]]$.

Roughly, a which question is an assertion that some things have the property F, and a direct answer gives a complete list of things which have the property F.

Definition 7. q is a *question* if, and only if, q is either a disjunctive question or a which question.

Definition 8. d is a *direct answer* if, and only if, d is a direct answer to a question.

Definition 9. F is a *partial answer* to a question, q, if, and only if, F is a statement and there is some consistent direct answer, d, to q, such that d L-implies F.

Definition 10. A *question set* is a finite, non-empty set of questions.

Definition 11. A *direct answer combination*, *DA*, of a question set, Q, is a conjunction whose conjuncts include exactly one direct answer to each question in Q, and nothing else.

Analyzing Communication Events

Now we are ready to analyze communication events. We want our definitions here to be general enough to allow for the situation where the receiver, during the course of a sequence of communication events, changes his mind in various ways. We shall assume, however, that he does not change his language.

Definition 12. A *communication event for R at time t* is an ordered sextuple, $<m, L, k, Q, I, i>$, such that

1. L and I are a language and information function (as specified above);
2. m is a statement of L;
3. k is a consistent statement of L, which R at t believes to be true;
4. Q is a question set; and
5. i is a positive integer.

Definition 13. The *message* in a communication event, E, for R at t, is the first member of E.

In Definition 12, k is R's background knowledge. As will become evident below, i is an index number which serves to make each communication event unique. When discussing a sequence of communication events, we shall use m_i, L_i, etc., to refer to the first, second, etc., members of the communication event E_i.

Definition 14. A *communication sequence for R* is a sequence $E_1,...,E_n$, where $n > 0$, of communication events for R, such that:

1. If $1 \leqslant i \leqslant j \leqslant n$, then the sixth member of $E_i = i$, and if E_j is a communication event for R at t_g, and E_i is a communication event for R at t_f, and t_g is later than t_f, then $j > i$; and
2. If $1 < i \leqslant n$, then $L_i = L_{i-1}$.

Definition 15. The *sender, S, in* a communication sequence, $E_1,...,E_n$, for R is the sequence $m_1 , ... , m_n$.

Though S is thus defined as an abstract entity, we shall continue to speak informally of S in "flesh-and-blood" terms.

Next, we provide R with a procedure by which he can reject messages which produce inconsistencies. Our basic idea, embodied in the next definition, is that if R has to choose between earlier and later messages, he rejects the earlier and retains the later.

This policy is justified by its effects: If one of S's messages, m, is more important than the others, S wants R to receive, "register," and study m, so S places m near the beginning of the message sequence. But if S also wants to send messages which conflict with m he must place the conflicting messages earlier in the sequence, so that if any messages are rejected it will be they and not m. Thus S is forced to place all of his defective messages (if there are any) relatively early in the message sequence.

Definition 16. The *usable message total*, umt$_i$, of E_i in a communication sequence, $E_1 , ... ,E_n$, is the statement formed in the following way:

To $(p \text{ v } -p)$ is conjoined m_h, where h is the greatest number less than or equal to i, such that $(m_h \& k_i)$ is consistent, and to the conjunction thus formed, m_g is conjoined, where g is the greatest number less than h, such that $(m_h \& m_g \& k_i)$ is consistent, and so on, back to the beginning of the message sequence.

We use $(p \text{ v} -p)$ here to indicate some arbitrarily chosen L-truth.

Definition 17. The *final usable message total*, fumt$_{i,j}$, of E_i, *with respect to* E_j *in* a communication sequence $E_1 , \ldots ,E_i , \ldots ,E_j , \ldots ,E_n$, where $1 \leqslant i \leqslant j \leqslant n$, is the alphabetically first conjunction whose conjuncts are $(p \text{ v} -p)$ and just those conjuncts common to both umt$_i$ and umt$_j$.

Definition 18. fumt$_1$* is $(p \text{ v} -p)$. If $i > 1$, the fumt$_i$* is (fumt$_{1,n}$ & fumt$_{2,n}$ &. . .& fumt$_{i-1,n}$).

Definition 19. We shall use $Q_{i,j}$ to refer to the set intersection of Q_i and Q_j; and $k_{i,j}$ to refer to $(k_i \text{ v } k_j)$.

The importance of $Q_{i,n}$ is that it represents what R was interested in at E_i and is still interested in at E_n. The importance of $k_{i,n}$ is that it is what R believed to be true in E_i and still believes to be true in E_n.

Definition 20. A *news-value datum for* E_i in a communication sequence, $E_1, \ldots , E_n$, is a value of $I_i[p \mid (k_{i,n} \ \& \ \text{fumt}_i*)]$ where:

1. p is a conjunction, each of whose conjuncts either is L-true or is a direct or partial answer, r, to a question in $Q_{i,n}$, such that r is L-implied by $(k_{i,n} \ \& \ \text{fumt}_{i,n})$; and
2. If p is not L-true, then p is L-implied by DA, where:
    a) DA is a direct answer combination of some non-empty subset of $Q_{i,n}$, and
    b) $(DA \ \& \ k_n \ \& \ \text{umt}_n)$ is consistent.

Theorem 8. The set of news-value data for E_i in a communication sequence $E_1, \ldots , E_n$ is non-empty and has an upper bound, namely: $I_i [\text{fumt}_{i,n} \mid (k_{i,n} \ \& \ \text{fumt}_i*)]$.

Definition 21. The *news-value of* E_i in a communication sequence $E_1, \ldots , E_n$ is the least upper bound of the set of news-value data for E_i in $E_1, \ldots , E_n$.

Face-Value Information

According to these definitions, R evaluates m_i at E_n via I_i. It might be that $I_i (F) = -\log P(F)$, where $P(F)$ is the probability that F is true, this probability being calculated before S tells R that F is the case. Such an I is a "face-value" function; it represents the ostensible amount of information in F, and the amount of information one would get from F if F were true.

R can use a face-value I—in connection with Definition 21—to analyze S's communicative style; he can use it to pay cash to S for m_i at E_n if he can verify m_i between the time of E_i and the time of E_n. In some situations, R cannot verify m_i by the time of E_n, and thus he wants to pay cash for m_i by a more subtle system. The obvious method is to use an I*, where $I*(F)$

is calculated on the basis of two factors: the ostensible informativeness and a discounting device.

For example, R might let $I^*(F)$ be the log of the ratio of $P_1(F)$ to $P_2(F)$, where $P_2(F)$ is the probability that F is true, calculated after k_i has been specified but before m_i is analyzed; and $P_1(F)$ is the probability that F is true, calculated after E_n has occurred (that is, after the components of E_n have been specified and after the content of m_i has been analyzed). We shall not attempt here to relate this double-probability payment system to our face-value system based on I_i.

Using Definition 21, R can compute the news-value of a communication sequence, $E_1, \ldots, E_n$, as the sum of the news-values of $E_1, \ldots, E_n \ldots E_1,$ $\ldots, E_n$. This system of evaluation is justified formally by such theorems as the following.

Theorem 9. Let $E_1, \ldots, E_n$ be a communication sequence where, for every i such that $1 < i \leqslant n$, $I_i(F \mid G) \geqslant I_{i-1}(F \mid G)$, and $I_i(\mathrm{fumt}_i^* \;\&\; k_{i,n})$ $\geqslant I_i(\mathrm{fumt}_i^* \;\&\; k_{i-1,n} \;\&\; k_{1,n})$; then:

$$I_n[(\mathrm{umt}_n \;\&\; k_n) \mid k_{1,n}] \geqslant \sum_{i=1}^{n} I_i[(k_{i,n} \;\&\; \mathrm{fumt}_{i,n}) \mid (k_{i,n} \;\&\; \mathrm{fumt}_i^*)].$$

This theorem says that in a communication sequence where R's usable knowledge keeps growing and his information values suffer no deflation, the news-value which R will have to pay for does not exceed the amount of information which is added to the usable part of his initial knowledge by the usable messages and his final knowledge. Note that R's knowledge is required to grow merely in a quantitative sense; there is no requirement on the logical relations between k_i and k_{i-1}.

Theorem 10. In a communication sequence $E_1, \ldots, E_n$, the news-value of $E_i = 0$ if:

1. $Q_{i,n}$ is empty;
2. $Q_{i,n}$ has no consistent direct answer combinations; or
3. $(k_{i,n} \;\&\; \mathrm{fumt}_i^*)$ L-implies $(k_{i,n} \;\&\; \mathrm{fumt}_{i,n})$.

The next few definitions present an analysis of one type of message adequacy.

Definition 22. $Q_{i,n}^*$ is the set formed from $Q_{i,n}$ by omitting all questions which have no true direct answers.

Definition 23. A *datum for the cumulative q-adequacy* of a communication sequence $E_1, \ldots, E_n$ at E_i is z if, and only if, $Q_{i,n}^*$ is non-empty and has no L-true direct answer combinations, and z is a value of:

$$\frac{I_i(p)}{I_i(DA)},$$

where DA is a true direct answer combination of $Q_{i,n}{}^*$ and p is a conjunction, each of whose conjuncts either is L-true or is a direct or partial answer, r, to a question in $Q_{i,n}{}^*$, such that r is L-implied by both DA and ($k_{i,n}$ & $\text{fumt}_{i,n}$).

Definition 24. Let $E_1, \ldots, E_n$ be a communication sequence. Then:

1. If $Q_{i,n}{}^*$ is non-empty, and has L-true DA's, then the *cumulative q-adequacy of* $E_1, \ldots, E_n$ *at* $E_i = 1$.
2. In all other cases, the *cumulative q-adequacy of* $E_1, \ldots, E_n$ *at* E_i is the least upper bound of the set consisting of zero and all the data for the cumulative q-adequacy of $E_1, \ldots, E_n$ at E_i.

Communicative Rapport

Roughly, the cumulative q-adequacy is the ratio of what R has actually obtained to what he would have obtained from a true answer to all his questions. The cumulative q-adequacy of a communication sequence $E_1, \ldots, E_n$ at E_n can be regarded as the adequacy of the sender S in $E_1, \ldots, E_n$, and hence the notion of cumulative q-adequacy might be of some use in the study of communicative rapport. The next theorem compares two situations: (a) the one in which S distributes his news into a sequence of messages, and (b) the one in which S puts all the news into a single complex message.

Theorem 11. Let $E_1, \ldots, E_n$ and E_s be two communication sequences, such that $L_i = L_s$, $k_{i,n}$ is L-equivalent to k_s, $Q_{i,n} = Q_s$, $I_i = I_s$, and $\text{fumt}_{i,n}$ is L-equivalent to m_s. Then the news-value of E_i in $E_1, \ldots, E_n$ might not be equal to the news-value of E_s in E_s, but the cumulative q-adequacy of $E_1, \ldots, E_n$ at E_i is equal to the cumulative q-adequacy of E_s at E_s.

Cumulative q-adequacy can never exceed 1.0, and it has this value when Q_n is non-empty and all the questions in Q_n have been answered truly. Thus Q, via its set of direct answer combinations, serves as a "cutoff" device in the evaluation of message adequacy, and in this sense Q serves as an evaluation function.

The sense in which Q serves as an evaluation device in connection with news-value is more complicated. "Which" questions have infinitely many direct answers, so if $Q_{i,n}$ includes "which" questions it might be that $Q_{i,n}$ has no one DA which stands as an upper bound, so to speak, on all its other DAs. But there are cases in which $Q_{i,n}$ has a DA which actually functions as a kind of upper bound on news-value. This could be the case, for example, where:

1. $Q_{i,n}$ contains only disjunctive questions (so that, in effect, the subsets of $Q_{i,n}$ have only a finite number of DAs), and
2. $Q_{i,n}$ has at least one DA which is consistent with (k_n & umt_n).

We can argue, citing theorems such as those presented above, that our evaluation system is rational, and that our model can be regarded as a model of how R ought to behave. What are the possibilities that this model will prove to be a good empirical model? Toward answering this question, all we have to offer here is the following discussion.[7]

Three Nested Models

Let us note first that we can regard the model as comprising three nested models:

a) The question model, which is the theory of L, k, Q, and I;
b) The message-processing model, which is the question model together with the theory of message processing embodied in Definitions 16 and 17;
c) The news-evaluation model, which is the model as a whole.

We conjecture that it will prove fruitful and convenient to divide our empirical investigations into three phases, corresponding to (a), (b) and (c).

Concerning (a). Our question model can be tested via the information properties of questions and answers. The theory predicts, for example, that a direct answer to q L-implies q, and thus is at least as informative as q; that some questions convey no information; that some questions have positive information values; and that some questions are more informative than others.

Predictions like these can presumably be tested by standard interview or questionnaire methods. They might also be tested in a task situation in which the subject needs to ask questions but must pay for both his questions and answers (different amounts for direct and partial answers). The point of such an experiment would be to see whether the subject is willing to pay various prices put on the questions and answers by the experimenter.

Concerning (b). The message-processing model is testable via its prediction about R's policy of message rejection, that R will reject earlier messages in order to retain later ones. This might be tested in a task situation where the subject must secure information from the experimenter, or from a competitor, and pay for it; and the point of the experiment would be to analyze R's reaction to a message which produces inconsistencies. In all experiments on (b), the factor of memory must be controlled, and R must be allowed sufficient memory resources so that any "primacy" or "recency" effect will not represent the influence of a strategy of memorization.

Concerning All of (a) through (c). It might seem that none of these models is empirically sound because all of them embody the assumption that R is a perfect logician. We conjecture, nevertheless, that there is a class of situations for which this assumption is realistic; and these are economic

---

[7] I am indebted to Professors C. West Churchman, Julian Feldman, Harold Guetzkow, and Earl Hunt for valuable suggestions in connection with this discussion.

situations in which both R and S are highly motivated, well equipped, and well organized. Our underlying assumption here is that competition motivates people to be efficient, and resources of the appropriate kind enable them to be efficient. Perhaps there are situations of this sort outside the narrowly commercial sphere; for example, where R is a research team and S is a library or news service or news analyst.

Probably the easiest way to begin experimenting on (c) is to study a task-oriented subject, R. R will win money if he succeeds in the task, but to succeed he must buy information from other subjects, S, whose role is to compete with each other as suppliers of information, and who earn money by selling information. But it costs them money to send the information, and the information might be rejected.

Periodically, R dips into his "information fund" to pay the Ss, and he pays them according to their respective contributions. They are free to answer his questions or not, and he is free to do as much or as little business with each of them as he chooses. The point of this experiment would be to determine how R handles his money: that is, how the Ss react and how their reaction forces R to alter his money handling.

In all experiments on (c) it would be important to analyze relatively long runs of behavior—runs which are long enough to allow for reaction and adjustment effects to take place—for it is in the context of long-run interactions that many of our otherwise doubtful assumptions might be justified. For example, our implicit assumption that every question set has a non-empty subset with true or consistent DAs might prove realistic for a long run, because, if R's questions are offensive to S, S will penalize R in some way.

Likewise for our choice of a face-value evaluation system. In actual practice, a news service is forced to acquire a reputation for honesty and accuracy; if it sends a message, therefore, the message must either be true as it stands, or it must be prefaced with an intentional operator such as "It was reported that . . ."

Since the above was written I have developed another model, closely resembling the one presented here but differing slightly in the definition of *news-value* (see "A Model for Applying Information and Utility Functions," *Philosophy of Science*, Vol. 30, 1963, pp. 267-73). Between the two models there are clear formal differences, chiefly in the derivation of upper bound theorems. Whether there are any discernible empirical differences remains to be seen.

7   *Decision Rules, Types of Error,*
and Their Consequences
in Medical Diagnosis *

Thomas J. Scheff [†]

MEMBERS of professions such as law and medicine frequently are confronted with uncertainty in the course of their routine duties. In these circumstances, informal norms have developed for handling uncertainty so that paralyzing hesitation is avoided. These norms are based upon assumptions that some types of error are more to be avoided than others; assumptions so basic that they are usually taken for granted, are seldom discussed, and are therefore slow to change.

The purpose of this paper is to describe one important norm for handling uncertainty in medical diagnosis, that judging a sick person well is more to be avoided than judging a well person sick, and to suggest some of the consequences of the application of this norm in medical practice. Apparently this norm, like many important cultural norms, "goes without saying" in the subculture of the medical profession; in form, however, it resembles any decision rule for guiding behavior under conditions of uncertainty.

In the discussion that follows, decision rules in law, statistics, and medicine are compared in order to indicate the types of error that are thought to be the more important to avoid and the assumptions underlying this preference. On the basis of recent findings of the widespread distribution of elements of disease and deviance in normal populations, the assumption of a uniform relationship between disease signs and impairment is criticized. Finally, it is suggested that to the extent that physicians are guided by this

* This paper was written with the financial support of the Graduate Research Committee of the University of Wisconsin. Colleagues too numerous to list here made useful suggestions. David Mechanic was particularly helpful. The original version was presented at the Conference on Mathematical Models in the Behavioral and Social Sciences, and a revised version subsequently appeared in *Behavioral Science*, Vol. 8, No. 2, April, 1963.
† University of California, Santa Barbara.

medical decision rule, they too often place patients in the "sick role" who could otherwise have continued in their normal pursuits.

Decision Rules

To the extent that physicians and the public are biased toward treatment, the "creation" of illness, i.e., the production of unnecessary impairment, may go hand in hand with the prevention and treatment of disease in modern medicine. The magnitude of the bias toward treatment in any single case may be quite small, since there are probably other medical decision rules ("When in doubt, delay your decision") which counteract the rule discussed here. Even a small bias, however, if it is relatively constant throughout Western society, can have effects of large magnitude. Since this argument is based largely on fragmentary evidence, it is intended merely to stimulate further discussion and research, rather than to demonstrate the validity of a point of view. The discussion will begin with the consideration of a decision rule in law.

In criminal trials in England and the United States, there is an explicit rule for arriving at decisions in the face of uncertainty: "A man is innocent until proven guilty." The meaning of this rule is made clear by the English common law definition of the phrase "proven guilty," which, according to tradition, is that the judge or jury must find the evidence of guilt compelling *beyond a reasonable doubt*. The basic legal rule for arriving at a decision in the face of uncertainty may be briefly stated: "When in doubt, acquit." That is, the jury or judge must not be equally wary of erroneously convicting or acquitting: the error that is most important to avoid is to erroneously convict. This concept is expressed in the maxim: "Better a thousand guilty men go free than one innocent man be convicted."

The reasons underlying this rule seem clear. It is assumed that, in most cases, a conviction will do irreversible harm to an individual by damaging his reputation in the eyes of his fellows. The individual is seen as weak and defenseless, relative to society, and therefore in no position to sustain the consequences of an erroneous decision. An erroneous acquittal, on the other hand, damages society. If an individual who has actually committed a crime is not punished, he may commit the crime again, or more important, the deterrent effect of punishment for the violation of this crime may be diminished for others. Although these are serious outcomes they are generally thought not to be as serious as the consequences of erroneous conviction for the innocent individual, since society is able to sustain an indefinite number of such errors without serious consequences. For these and perhaps other reasons, the decision rule to assume innocence exerts a powerful influence on legal proceedings.

Type 1 and Type 2 Errors

Deciding on guilt or innocence is a special case of a problem to which statisticians have given considerable attention: the testing of hypotheses. Since most scientific work is done with samples, statisticians have developed techniques to guard against results which are due to chance sampling fluctuations. The problem, however, is that one might reject a finding as due to sampling fluctuations which was actually correct. There are, therefore, two kinds of errors: rejecting a hypothesis which is true, and accepting one which is false. Usually the hypothesis is stated so that the former error (rejecting a hypothesis which is true) is the error that is thought to be the more important to avoid. This type of error is called an "error of the first kind," or a Type 1 error. The latter error (accepting a hypothesis which is false) is the less important error to avoid, and is called an "error of the second kind," or a Type 2 error [Neyman, 1950, pp. 265–66]‡.

To guard against chance fluctuations in sampling, statisticians test the probability that findings could have arisen by chance. At some predetermined probability (called the alpha level), usually .05 or less, the possibility that the findings arose by chance is rejected. This level means that there are five chances in a hundred that one will reject a hypothesis which is true. Although these five chances indicate a real risk of error, it is not common to set the level much lower (say .001) because this raises the probability of making an error of the second kind.

A similar dilemma faces the judge or jury in deciding whether to convict or acquit in the face of uncertainty. Particularly in the adversary system of law, where professional attorneys seek to advance their arguments and refute those of their opponents, there is often considerable uncertainty even as to the facts of the case, let alone intangibles like intent. The maxim, "Better a thousand guilty men go free than one innocent man be convicted," would mean—if taken literally rather than as a rhetorical flourish—that the alpha level for legal decisions is set quite low.

Although the legal decision rule is not expressed in as precise a form as a statistical decision rule, it represents a very similar procedure for dealing with uncertainty. There is one respect, however, in which it is quite different. Statistical decision procedures are recognized by those who use them as mere conveniences, which can be varied according to the circumstances. The legal decision rule, in contrast, is an inflexible and binding moral rule which carries with it the force of long sanction and tradition. The assumption of innocence is a part of the social institution of law in Western society; it is explicitly stated in legal codes, and is accepted as legitimate by jurists and usually by the general populace, with only occa-

---

‡ References in brackets, [ ], are listed under "References" at the end of this chapter.

sional grumbling, for example, a criminal is seen as "getting off" because of "legal technicalities."

Decision Rules in Medicine

Although the analogous rule for decisions in medicine is not as explicitly stated as the rule in law, and probably is considerably less rigid, it would seem that there is such a rule in medicine which is as imperative in its operation as its analogue in law. Do physicians and the general public consider that rejecting the hypothesis of illness when it is true, or accepting it when it is false, is the error that is most important to avoid? It seems fairly clear that the rule in medicine may be stated as: "When in doubt, continue to suspect illness." That is, for a physician to dismiss a patient when he is actually ill is a Type 1 error, and to retain a patient when he is not ill is a Type 2 error.

Most physicians learn early in their training that it is far more culpable to dismiss a sick patient than to retain a well one. This rule is so pervasive and fundamental that it goes unstated in textbooks on diagnosis. It is occasionally mentioned explicitly in other contexts, however. Neyman, for example, in his discussion of X-ray screening for tuberculosis, states:

[If the patient is actually well, but the hypothesis that he is sick is accepted, a Type 2 error] then the patient will suffer some unjustified anxiety and, perhaps, will be put to some unnecessary expense until further studies of his health will establish that any alarm about the state of his chest is unfounded. Also, the unjustified precautions ordered by the clinic may somewhat affect its reputation. On the other hand, should the hypothesis [of sickness] be true and yet the accepted hypothesis be [that he is well, a Type 1 error], then the patient will be in danger of losing the precious opportunity of treating the incipient disease in its beginning stages when the cure is not so difficult. Furthermore, the oversight by the clinic's specialist of the dangerous condition would affect the clinic's reputation even more than the unnecessary alarm. From this point of view, it appears that the error of rejecting the hypothesis [of sickness] when it is true is *far more important* to avoid than the error of accepting the hypothesis [of illness] when it is false [1950, p. 270, italics added].

Although this particular discussion pertains to tuberculosis, it is pertinent to many other diseases also. From casual conversations with physicians, the impression one gains is that this moral lesson is deeply ingrained in the physician's personal code.

It is not only physicians who feel this way, however. This rule is grounded both in legal proceedings and in popular sentiment. Although there is some sentiment against Type 2 errors (unnecessary surgery, for instance), it has nothing like the force and urgency of the sentiment against Type 1 errors. A physician who dismisses a patient who subsequently dies of a disease that should have been detected is not only subject to legal action for negligence and possible loss of license for incompetence, but also to moral condemnation from his colleagues, and from his own conscience for his delinquency. Nothing remotely resembling this amount of moral and legal suasion is brought to bear for committing a Type 2 error. Indeed, this error is sometimes seen as sound clinical practice, indicating a healthily conservative approach to medicine.

The discussion to this point suggests that physicians follow a decision rule which may be stated: "When in doubt, diagnose illness." If physicians are actually influenced by this rule, then studies of the validity of diagnosis should demonstrate the operation of the rule. That is, we should expect that objective studies of diagnostic errors should show that Type 1 and Type 2 errors do not occur with equal frequency, but, in fact, that Type 2 errors far outnumber Type 1 errors. Unfortunately for our purposes, however, there are apparently only a few studies which provide the type of data which would adequately test the hypothesis. Although studies of the reliability of diagnosis abound [Garland, 1959], showing that physicians disagree with each other in their diagnoses of the same patients, these studies do not report the validity of diagnosis, or the types of error which are made, with the following exceptions.

We can infer that Type 2 errors outnumber Type 1 errors from Bakwin's study of physicians' judgments regarding the advisability of tonsillectomy for 1,000 school children.

Of these, some 611 had had their tonsils removed. The remaining 389 were then examined by other physicians, and 174 were selected for tonsillectomy. This left 215 children whose tonsils were apparently normal. Another group of doctors was put to work examining these 215 children, and 99 of them were adjudged in need of tonsillectomy. Still another group of doctors was then employed to examine the remaining children, and nearly one-half were recommended for operation [Bakwin, 1945, p. 693].

Almost half of each group of children was judged to be in need of the operation. Even assuming that a small proportion of children needing tonsillectomy was missed in each examination (Type 1 error), the number of Type 2 errors in this study far exceeded the number of Type 1 errors.

In the field of roentgenology, studies of diagnostic error are apparently more highly developed than in other areas of medicine. Garland [1959, p. 31] summarizes these findings, reporting that, in a study of 14,867 films for tuberculosis signs, there were 1,216 positive readings which turned out to be clinically negative (Type 2 error) and only 24 negative readings which turned out to be clinically active (Type 1 error)! This ratio is apparently a fairly typical finding in roentgenographic studies. Since physicians are well aware of the provisional nature of radiological findings, this great discrepancy between the frequency of the types of error in film screening is not too alarming. On the other hand, it does provide objective evidence of the operation of the decision rule "Better safe than sorry."

Basic Assumptions

The logic of this decision rule rests on two assumptions.

1. Disease is usually a determinate, inevitably unfolding process, which, if undetected and untreated, will grow to a point where it endangers the life or limb of the individual, and, in the case of contagious diseases, the lives of others. This is not to say, of course, that physicians think of all diseases as determinate: witness the concept of the "benign" condition. The point here is that the imagery of disease which the physician uses in attempting to reach a decision—his working hypothesis—is *usually* based on the deterministic model of disease.

2. Medical diagnosis of illness, unlike legal judgment, is not an irreversible act which does untold damage to the status and reputation of the patient. A physician may search for illness for an indefinitely long time, causing inconvenience for the patient, perhaps, but, in the typical case, doing the patient no in-irradicable harm. Obviously, again, physicians do not *always* make this assumption. A physician who suspects epilepsy in a truck driver knows full well that his patient will probably never drive a truck again if the diagnosis is made, and the physician will go to great lengths to avoid a Type 2 error in this situation.

Similarly, if a physician suspects that a particular patient has hypochondriacal trends, the physician will lean in the direction of a Type 1 error in a situation of uncertainty. These and other similar situations are exceptions, however. The physician's *usual* working assumption is that medical observation and diagnosis, in itself, is neutral and innocuous, relative to the dangers resulting from disease.[1]

In the light of these two assumptions, therefore, it is seen as far better for the physician to chance a Type 2 error than a Type 1 error. These two assumptions will be examined and criticized in the remainder of the paper. The assumption that Type 2 errors are relatively harmless will be considered first.

In recent discussions it is increasingly recognized that in one area of medicine, psychiatry, the assumption that medical diagnosis can cause no irreversible harm to the patient's status is dubious. Psychiatric treatment, in many segments of the population and for many occupations, raises a question about the person's social status. It could be argued that in making a medical diagnosis the psychiatrist comes very close to making a legal decision, with its ensuing consequences for the person's reputation. One might argue that the Type 2 error in psychiatry, of judging a well person sick, is at least as much to be avoided as the Type 1 error, of judging the sick person well. Yet the psychiatrist's moral orientation, since he is first and foremost a physician, is guided by the medical—rather than the legal—decision rule.[2] The psychiatrist continues to be more willing to err on the

---

[1] Even though this assumption is widely held, it has been vigorously criticized within the medical profession. See, for example, Darley [1959]. For a witty criticism of both assumptions, see Ratner [1962].

[2] Many authorities believe that psychiatrists seldom turn away a patient without finding an illness. See, for example, the statement about large state mental hospitals in Brown [1961, fn. p. 60], and Mechanic [1962]. For a study demonstrating the presumption of illness in psychiatric examinations, see Scheff [1963].

conservative side, to diagnose as ill when the person is healthy, even though it is no longer clear that this error is any more desirable than its opposite.[3]

There is a more fundamental question about this decision rule, however, which concerns both physical illness and mental disorder. This question primarily concerns the first assumption, that disease is a determinate process. It also implicates the second assumption, that medical treatment does not have irreversible effects.

In recent years physicians and social scientists have reported finding disease signs and deviant behavior prevalent in normal, noninstitutionalized populations. It has been shown, for instance, that deviant acts, some of a serious nature, are widely admitted by persons in random samples of normal populations [Wallerstein and Wyle, 1947; Porterfield, 1946; Kinsey, Pomeroy and Martin, 1948]. There is some evidence which suggests that grossly deviant, "psychotic" behavior has at least temporarily existed in relatively large proportions of a normal population [Clausen and Yarrow, 1955; Plunkett and Gordon, 1961]. Finally, there is a growing body of evidence that many signs of physical disease are distributed quite widely in normal populations. A recent survey of simple high blood pressure indicated that the prevalence ranged from 11.4 to 37.2 per cent in the various subgroups studied [Rautahargu, Karvonen, and Keys, 1961; cf. Stokes and Dawber, 1959; Dunn and Etter, 1962].

It can be argued that physical defects and "psychiatric" deviancy exist in an uncrystallized form in large segments of the population. Lemert [1951, p. 75] calls this type of behavior, which is often transitory, *primary deviation*. Balint [1957, p. 18], in his discussion of the doctor-patient relationship, speaks of similar behavior as the "unorganized phase of illness." Balint seems to take for granted, however, that patients will eventually "settle down" to an "organized" illness. Yet it is possible that other outcomes may occur. A person in this stage might change jobs or wives instead, or merely continue in the primary deviation stage indefinitely, without getting better or worse.

This discussion suggests that in order to know the probability that a person with a disease sign would become incapacitated because of the development of disease, investigations quite unlike existing studies would need to be conducted. These would be longitudinal studies of outcomes in persons having signs of disease in a random sample of a normal population, in which no attempt was made to arrest the disease. It is true that there are a number of longitudinal studies in which the effects of treatment are compared with the effects of nontreatment. These studies, however, have always been conducted with clinical groups, rather than with persons

---

[3] "The sociologist must point out that whenever a psychiatrist makes the clinical diagnosis of an existing need for treatment, society makes the social diagnosis of a changed status for one of its members" [Erickson, 1957, p. 123].

with disease signs who were located in field studies.[4] Even clinical trials appear to offer many difficulties, both from the ethical and scientific points of view [Hill, 1960]. These difficulties would be increased many times in controlled field trials, as would the problems which concern the amount of time and money necessary. Without such studies, nevertheless, the meaning of many common disease signs remains somewhat equivocal.

Given the relatively small amount of knowledge about the distributions and natural outcomes of many diseases, it is possible that our conceptions of the danger of disease are exaggerated. For example, until the late 1940s, histoplasmosis was thought to be a rare tropical disease, with a uniform fatal outcome. Recently, however, it was discovered that it is widely prevalent, and fatal outcome or impairment extremely rare [Schwartz and Baum, 1957]. It is conceivable that other diseases, such as some types of heart disease and mental disorder, may prove to be similar in character. Although no actuarial studies have been made which would yield the true probabilities of impairment, physicians usually set the Type 1 level quite high, because they believe that the probability of impairment from making a Type 2 error is quite low. Let us now examine that assumption.

The "Sick Role"

If, as has been argued here, much illness goes unattended without serious consequences, the assumption that medical diagnosis has no irreversible effects on the patient seems questionable.

The patient's attitude to his illness is usually considerably changed during and by the series of physical examinations. These changes, which may profoundly influence the course of a chronic illness, are not taken seriously by the medical profession, and, though occasionally mentioned, they have never been the subject of a proper scientific investigation [Balint, 1957, p. 43].

There are grounds for believing that persons who avail themselves of professional services are under considerable strain and tension (if the problem could have been easily solved, they would probably have used more informal means of handling it). Social-psychological principles indicate that persons under strain are highly suggestible, particularly to suggestions from a prestigeful source, such as a physician.

It can be argued that the Type 2 error involves the danger of having a person enter the "sick role" [Parsons, 1950] in circumstances where no serious result would ensue if the illness were unattended. Perhaps the combination of a physician determined to find disease *signs*, if they are to be found, and the suggestible patient, searching for subjective *symptoms* among the many amorphous and usually unattended bodily impulses, is

---

[4] The Framingham study is an exception to this statement. Even in this study, however, experimental procedures (random assignment to treatment and nontreatment groups) were not used [Dawber, Moore, and Mann, 1957, p. 5].

often sufficient to unearth a disease which changes the patient's status from that of well to sick, and may also have effects on his familial and occupational status. (In Lemert's terms [1951], the illness would be *secondary deviation* after the person has entered the sick role.)

There is a considerable body of evidence in the medical literature concerning the process in which the physician unnecessarily causes the patient to enter the sick role. Thus, in a discussion of "iatrogenic" (physician-induced) heart disease, this point is made:

> The physician, by calling attention to a murmur or some cardiovascular abnormality, even though functionally insignificant, may precipitate [symptoms of heart disease]. The experience of the work classification units of cardiac-in-industry programs, where patients with cardiovascular disease are evaluated as to work capacity, gives impressive evidence regarding the high incidence of such functional manifestations in persons with the diagnosis of cardiac lesion [Warren and Wolter, 1954, p. 78].

Although there is a tendency in medicine to dismiss this process as due to quirks of particular patients, e.g., as malingering, hypochondriasis, or as "merely functional disease" (that is, functional for the patient), causation probably lies not in the patient but in medical procedures. Most people, perhaps, if they actually have the disease signs, and are told by an authority (the physician) that they are ill, will obligingly come up with appropriate symptoms. A case history will illustrate this process. Under the heading "It may be well to let sleeping dogs lie," a physician recounts the following case:

> Here is a woman, aged 40 years, who is admitted with symptoms of congestive cardiac failure, valvular disease, mitral stenosis and auricular fibrillation. She tells us that she did not know that there was anything wrong with her heart and that she had had no symptoms up to 5 years ago when her chest was x-rayed in the course of a mass radiography examination for tuberculosis. She was not suspected and this was only done in the course of routine at the factory. Her lungs were pronounced clear but she was told that she had an enlarged heart and was advised to go to a hospital for investigation and treatment. From that time she began to suffer from symptoms—breathlessness on exertion—and has been in the hospital 4 or 5 times since. Now she is here with congestive heart failure. She cannot understand why, from the time that her enlarged heart was discovered, she began to get symptoms [Gardiner-Hill, 1958, p. 158].

What makes this kind of "role-taking" extremely important is that it can occur even when the diagnostic label is kept from the patient. By the way he is handled, the patient can usually infer the nature of the diagnosis, since in his uncertainty and anxiety he is extremely sensitive to subtleties in the physician's behavior. An interesting example of this process is found in reports on treatment of battle fatigue. Speaking of psychiatric patients in the Sicilian campaign during World War II, a psychiatrist notes:

Although patients were received at this hospital within 24 to 48 hours after their breakdown, a disappointing number, approximately 15 per cent, were salvaged for combat duty . . . any therapy, including usual interview methods that sought to uncover basic emotional conflicts or attempted to relate current behavior and symptoms with past personality patterns seemingly provided patients with logical reasons for their combat failure. The insights obtained by even such mild depth therapy readily convinced the patient, and often his therapist, that the limit of combat endurance had been reached as proved by vulnerable personality traits. Patients were obligingly cooperative in supplying details of their neurotic childhood, previous emotional difficulties, lack of aggressiveness and other dependency traits [Glass, 1953, p. 288; cf. Kardiner and Spiegel, 1947, ch. 3, 4].

Glass goes on to say that removal of the soldier from his unit for treatment of any kind usually resulted in long-term neurosis. In contrast, if the soldier was given only superficial psychiatric attention and *kept with his unit,* chronic impairment was usually avoided. The implication is that removal from the military unit and psychiatric treatment symbolizes to the soldier—behaviorally rather than with verbal labels—the "fact" that he is a mental case.

The traditional way of interpreting these reactions of the soldiers, and perhaps the civilian cases, is in terms of malingering or feigning illness. The process of taking roles, however, as it is conceived of here, is not completely or even largely voluntary. (For a sophisticated discussion of role-playing, see Goffman [1959, pp. 17–22].) Vaguely defined impulses become "real" to the participants when they are organized under any one of a number of more or less interchangeable social roles. It can be argued that when a person is in a confused and suggestible state, when he organizes his feelings and behavior by using the sick role, and when his choice of roles is validated by a physician and/or others, that he is "hooked," and will proceed on a career of chronic illness.[5]

The diagnosis of "false positives," then, may be as important to avoid as "false negatives." This problem becomes particularly crucial in the screening of populations with low base rates of disease, as in routine chest X-rays, screening of army recruits, and so on. Even assuming a high degree of validity in diagnosis, the large proportion of true negatives tends to magnify the number of false positives. For example, suppose the accuracy of diagnosis for a disease were 0.95, but the disease existed in only 25 out of a thousand in population. In this case, for every thousand patients screened, 24 true positives would be detected, but 49 false positives would also be

---

[5] Some of the findings of the Purdue Farm Cardiac Project support the position taken in this paper. It was found, for example, that "iatrogenics" took more health precautions than "hidden cardiacs," suggesting that entry into the sick role can cause more social incapacity than the actual disease [Eichorn and Andersen, 1962, pp. 11–15].

diagnosed.[6] Since in many diseases the accuracy of diagnosis does not even approach 0.95, these considerations would seem to call into question the wisdom of most routine screening.

Implications for Research

The hypothesis suggested by the preceding discussion is that physicians and the public typically overvalue medical treatment, relative to non-treatment, as a course of action in the face of uncertainty, and that this overvaluation results in the creation as well as the prevention of impairment. This hypothesis, since it is based on scattered observations, is put forward only to point out several areas where systematic research is needed.

From the point of view of assessing the effectiveness of medical practice, this hypothesis is probably too general to be used directly. Needed for such a task are hypotheses concerning the conditions under which error is likely to occur, the type of error that is likely, and the consequences of each type of error. Significant dimensions of the amount and type of error and its consequences would appear to be characteristics of the disease, the physician, the patient, and the organizational setting in which diagnosis takes place. Thus for diseases such as pneumonia, which produce almost certain impairment unless attended and for which a quick and highly effective cure is available, the hypothesis is probably largely irrelevant. On the other hand, the hypothesis may be of considerable importance for diseases which have a less certain outcome, and for which existing treatments are protracted and of uncertain value. Mental disorders and some types of heart diseases are cases in point.

The working philosophy of the physician is probably relevant to the predominant type of errors made. Physicians who generally favor active intervention probably make more Type 2 errors than physicians who view their treatments only as assistance for natural bodily reactions to disease. The physician's perception of the personality of the patient may also be relevant: Type 2 errors are less likely if the physician defines the patient as a "crock," a person overly sensitive to discomfort, rather than as a person who ignores or denies disease.

Finally, the organizational setting is relevant to the extent that it influences the relationship between the doctor and the patient. In some contexts—as in medical practice in organizations such as the military, or in an industrial setting—the physican is not as likely to feel personal responsibility

---

[6] For an application of the idea of base rates to a problem similar to the one discussed here, see Skolnick; for a comprehensive discussion of the interaction of the base rates ("antecedent probability") and diagnostic accuracy, see Meehl and Rosen: J. H. Skolnick, Scientific theory and scientific evidence: an analysis of lie-detection, *Yale Law Journal*, 70, 1961, 694–728; P. E. Meehl and A. Rosen, Antecedent probability and the efficiency of psychometric signs, patterns, or cutting scores, *Psychological Bulletin*, 52, 1955, 194–216.

for the patient as he would in others, such as private practice. This may be due in part to the conditions of financial remuneration and, perhaps equally important, the sheer volume of patients dependent on the doctor's time. Cultural or class differences may also affect the amount of social distance between doctor and patient, and therefore the amount of responsibility which the doctor feels for the patient. Whatever the sources, the more the physician feels personally responsible for the patient, the more likely he is to make a Type 2 error.

To the extent that future research can indicate the conditions which influence the amount, type, and consequences of error, such research can make direct contributions to medical practice. Three types of research seem necessary. First, in order to establish the true risks of impairment associated with common disease signs, controlled field trials of treated and untreated outcomes in a normal population would be needed. Second, perhaps in conjunction with these field trials, experimental studies of the effect of suggestion of illness by physicians and others would be necessary to determine the risks of unnecessary entry into the sick role.

Finally, studies of a mathematical nature seem to be called for. Suppose that physicians were provided with the results of the studies suggested above. How could these findings be introduced into medical practice as a corrective to cultural and professional biases in decision making procedures? One promising approach is the strategy of evaluating the relative utility of alternative courses of action, based upon decision theory or game theory.[7]

Ledley and Lusted [1959] reviewed a number of mathematical techniques which might be applicable to medical decision making, one of these techniques being the use of the "expected value" equation, which is derived from game theory. Although their discussion pertains to the relative value of two treatment procedures, it is also relevant, with only slight changes in wording, to determining the expected values of treatment relative to nontreatment. The expected values of two treatments, they say, may be calculated from a simple expression involving only two kinds of terms: the probability that the diagnosis is correct, and the absolute value of the treatment (at its simplest, the absolute value is the rate of cure for persons known to have the disease).

The "expected value" of a treatment is:

$$E_t = p_s v_s^s + (1 - p_s) v_h^s.$$

(The superscript refers to the way the patient is treated, the subscript refers to his actual condition. s signifies sick, h, healthy.) That is, the expected value of a treatment is the probability, p, that the patient has the disease, multiplied by the value of the treatment for patients who actually have the disease, plus the probability that the patient does not have the disease

---

[7] For an introductory text, see Chernoff and Moses [1959].

$(1 - p)$, multiplied by the value (or "cost") of the treatment for patients who do not have the disease.

Similarly, the expected value of nontreatment is:

$$E_n = p_s v_s^h + (1 - p_s) v_h^h.$$

That is, the expected value of nontreatment is the probability that the patient has the disease, multiplied by the value (or "cost") of treating a person as healthy who is actually sick, plus the probability that the patient does not have the disease, multiplied by the value of not treating a healthy person.

The best course of action is indicated by comparing the magnitude of E_t and E_n. If E_t is larger, treatment is indicated. If E_n is larger, nontreatment is indicated. Evaluating these equations involves estimating the probability of correct diagnosis and constructing a payoff matrix for the values of v_s^s (proportion of patients who actually had the disease who were cured by the treatment), v_h^s (the cost of treating a healthy person as sick: inconvenience, working days lost, surgical risks, unnecessary entry into sick role), v_s^h (cost of treating a sick person as well: a question involving the proportions of persons who spontaneously recover, and the seriousness of results when the disease goes unchecked), and finally, v_h^h (the value of not treating a healthy person: medical expenses saved, working days, etc.).

To illustrate the use of the equation, Ledley and Lusted assign *arbitrary* absolute values in a case, because, as they say, "The decision of value problems frequently involves intangibles such as moral and ethical standards which must, in the last analysis, be left to the physician's judgment" [1959, p. 8]. One might argue, however, that it is better to develop a technique for systematically determining the absolute values of treatment and non-treatment, crude though the technique might be, than to leave the problem to the perhaps refined, but nevertheless obscure, judgment processes of the physician. Particularly in a matter of comparing the value of treatment and nontreatment, the problem is to avoid biases in the physician's judgment due to the kind of moral orientation discussed above.

It is possible, moreover, that the difficulty met by Ledley and Lusted is not that the factors to be evaluated are "intangibles," but that they are expressed in seemingly incommensurate units. How does one weigh the risk of death against the monetary cost of treatment? How does one weigh the risk of physical or social disability against the risk of death? Although these are difficult questions to answer, the idea of leaving them to the physician's judgment is probably not conducive to an understanding of the problem.

Following the lead of the economists in their studies of utility, it may be feasible to reduce the various factors to be weighed to a common unit. How could the benefits, costs, and risks of alternative acts in medical practice be expressed in monetary units? One solution might be to use payment rates in disability and life insurance, which offer a comparative evaluation of the "cost" of death, and permanent and temporary disability of various degrees. Although this approach does not include everything which physicians weigh in reaching decisions (pain and suffering cannot be weighed in this framework), it does include many of the major factors. It therefore would provide the opportunity of constructing a fairly realistic payoff matrix of absolute values, which would then allow for the determination of the relative value of treatment and nontreatment, using the expected value equation.[8]

Gathering data for the payoff matrix might make it possible to explore an otherwise almost inaccessible problem: the sometimes subtle conflicts of interest between the physician and the patient. Although it is fairly clear that medical intervention was unnecessary in particular cases, and that it was probably done for financial gain [Trussel, Ehrlich, and Morehead, 1962], the evaluation of the influence of remuneration on diagnosis and treatment is probably in most cases a fairly intricate matter, requiring precise techniques of investigation. If the payoff were calculated in terms of values to the patient *and* values to the physician, such problems could be explored. Less tangible values, such as convenience and work satisfactions, could be introduced into the matrix. The following statements by psychiatrists were taken from Hollingshead and Redlich's study of social class and mental disorder:

"Seeing him every morning was a chore; I had to put him on my back and carry him for an hour." "He had to get attention in large doses, and this was hard to do." "The patient was not interesting or attractive; I had to repeat, repeat, repeat." "She was a poor unhappy, miserable woman—we were worlds apart" [1958, p. 344].

This study strongly suggests that psychiatric diagnosis and treatment are influenced by the payoff for the psychiatrist as well as for the patient. In any type of medical decision, the use of the expected value equation might show the extent of the conflict of interest between physician and patient, and thereby shed light on the complex process of medical decision making.

[*Also see* Author's Afterthoughts.]

---

[8] It is possible that more sophisticated techniques may be applicable to the problem of constructing medical payoff matrices [Churchman, Ackoff, and Arnoff, 1957, ch. 6, 11]. The possibility of applying these techniques to the present problem was suggested to the author by James G. March. For approaches of this type, see M. S. Blumberg, Evaluating health screening procedures, *Operations Research*, 5 (June, 1957); W. W. Walton, Modern decision theory applied to medical diagnosis, unpublished Ph.D. dissertation, The Johns Hopkins University, 1964; and Charles D. Flagle, A threshold method for utility estimation and resolution of conflict, unpublished paper presented at Operations Research Conference, Cambridge, England, 1964.

REFERENCES

BAKWIN, H.   Pseudocia pediatricia. *New England Journal of Medicine,* 1945, 232, 691–97.

BALINT, M.   *The doctor, his patient, and the illness.* New York: International Universities Press, 1957.

BROWN, ESTHER L.   *Newer dimensions of patient care.* New York: Russell Sage, 1961.

CHERNOFF, H., AND MOSES, L. E.   *Elementary decision theory.* New York: Wiley, 1959.

CLAUSEN, J. A., AND YARROW, M. R.   Paths to the mental hospital. *Journal of Social Issues,* 1955, 11, 25–32.

CHURCHMAN, C. W.; ACKOFF, R. L., AND ARNOFF, E. L.   *Introduction to operations research.* New York: Wiley, 1957.

DARLEY, W.   What is the next step in preventive medicine? *Association of Teachers Preventive Medicine Newsletter,* 1959, 6.

DAWBER, T. R.; MOORE, F. E., AND MANN, G. V.   Coronary heart disease in the Framingham study. *Amer. Journal of Public Health,* 1957, 47, part 2, 4–24.

DUNN, J. P., AND ETTER, L. E.   Inadequacy of the medical history in the diagnosis of duodenal ulcer. *New England Journal of Medicine,* 1962, 266, 68–72.

EICHORN, R. L., AND ANDERSEN, R. M.   Changes in personal adjustment to perceived and medically established heart disease: a panel study. Paper read at American Sociological Association Meeting, Washington, D.C., 1962.

ERICKSON, K. T.   Patient role and social uncertainty—a dilemma of the mentally ill. *Psychiatry,* 1957, 20, 263–74.

GARDINER–HILL, H.   *Clinical involvements.* London: Butterworth, 1958.

GARLAND, L. H.   Studies of the accuracy of diagnostic procedures. *American Journal Roentgenological, Radium Therapy, Nuclear Medicine,* 1959, 82, 25–38.

GLASS, A. J.   Psychotherapy in the combat zone. *Symposium on Stress.* Washington, D.C., Army Medical Service Graduate School, 1953.

GOFFMAN, E.   *The presentation of self in everyday life.* Garden City, N. Y.: Doubleday Anchor, 1959.

HILL, A. B. (ed.).   *Controlled clinical trails.* Springfield, Ill.: Charles C. Thomas, 1960.

HOLLINGSHEAD, A. B., AND REDLICH, F. C.   *Social class and mental illness.* New York: Wiley, 1958.

KARDINER, A., AND SPIEGEL, H.   *War stress and neurotic illness.* New York: Hoeber, 1947.

KINSEY, A. C.; POMEROY, W. B., AND MARTIN, C. E.   *Sexual behavior in the human male.* Philadelphia and London: W. B. Saunders, 1948.

LEDLEY, R. S., AND LUSTED, L. B.   Reasoning foundations of medical diagnosis. *Science,* 1959, 130, 9–21.

LEMERT, E. M.   *Social pathology.* New York: McGraw-Hill, 1951.

MECHANIC, D.   Some factors in identifying and defining mental illness. *Mental Hygiene,* 1962, 46, 66–74.

NEYMAN, J.   *First course in statistics and probability.* New York: Holt, 1950.

PARSONS, T.   Illness and the role of the physician. *American Journal of Orthopsychiatry,* 1950, 21, 452–60.

PLUNKETT, R. J., AND GORDON, J. E.   *Epidemiology and mental illness.* New York: Basic Books, 1961.

PORTERFIELD, A. L.   *Youth in trouble*. Fort Worth, Tex.: Leo Potishman Foundation, 1946.

RATNER, H.   *Interviews on the American character*. Santa Barbara: Center for the Study of Democratic Institutions, 1962.

RAUTAHARGU, P. M.; KARVONEN, M. J., AND KEYS, A.   The frequency of arteriosclerotic and hypertensive heart disease in ostensibly healthy working populations in Finland. *Journal of Chronic Diseases*, 1961, 13, 426–39.

SCHEFF, T. J.   The societal reaction to deviance: ascriptive elements in the psychiatric screening of mental patients in a midwestern state. *Social Problems*, 11 (Spring, 1964), 401–13.

SCHWARTZ, J., AND BAUM, G. L.   The history of histoplasmosis. *New England Journal of Medicine*, 1957, 256, 253–58.

STOKES, J., AND DAWBER, T. R.   The "silent coronary": the frequency and clinical characteristics of unrecognized myocardial infarction in the Framingham study. *Annual of Internal Medicine*, 1959, 50, 1359–69.

TRUSSEL, R. E.; EHRLICH, JUNE, AND MOREHEAD, MILDRED.   *The quantity, quality and costs of medical and hospital care secured by a sample of teamster families in the New York area*. New York: Columbia University School of Public Health and Administrative Medicine, 1962.

WALLERSTEIN, J. S., AND WYLE, C. J.   Our law-abiding law-breakers. *Probation*, 1947, 25, 107–12.

WARREN, J. V., AND WOLTER, JANET.   Symptoms and diseases induced by the physician. *General Practitioner*, 1954, 9, 77–84.

Author's Afterthoughts on This Chapter

This paper concerned preferred errors in medical diagnosis: the relative frequency of types of error, the causes for the preference of one type of error over another, and a discussion of some of the possible consequences of this preference. Although the paper was largely limited to preferred errors in medicine, much of the discussion is probably applicable to many other areas as well. As an example of the broader applicability of the notion of preferred error in organizational decision-making, a recent study of military weapons acquisition will be discussed.

In the review of the accuracy of medical diagnosis by Garland (cited above), a representative study of errors in the screening of X-ray films reported 24 Type 1 errors (diagnosing a sick person as well) and 1,240 Type 2 errors (diagnosing a well person as sick). As was argued above, this study strongly suggests that the Type 2 error is the preferred error, being 50 times as prevalent as the Type 1 error in this study.

In their comparisons of the estimated and actual costs of development of military aircraft and missiles, Marshall and Meckling provide data which can be used to show the extent of error preference in cost estimation by the prime suppliers for Air Force contracts.[9] Although Marshall and Meck-

---

[9] A. W. Marshall and W. H. Meckling, "Predictability of the Costs, Time, and Success of Development," *The Rate and Direction of Inventive Activity: Economic and Social Factors* (National Bureau of Economic Research) (Princeton, N.J.: Princeton University Press, 1962), pp. 461–77. This study was pointed out to me by Stanley M. Besen, University of California, Santa Barbara.

ling consider cost, time of availability, performance, and utility, these remarks will be limited to their data on cost, since it provides the clearest (and most extreme) example of error preference.

Because of rapid technological change, the unpredictability of Russian strategy, and for many other reasons, estimating costs of developing a plane or missile is highly uncertain. Do contractors tend to under- or over-estimate costs in the face of this uncertainty?

By rearranging the Marshall-Meckling adjusted data, it would appear that under-estimation is the preferred error: in the 22 cases there were 16 cases of under-estimation and five cases of over-estimation.[10] (In one case the estimate was accurate.) It would appear, therefore, that there is an error preference in the contractor's decision process, but that it is not as strong as was the case with the screening of the X-ray films, since the ratio of preferred errors to the nonpreferred errors is not as great.

If we look at the magnitude of the errors in each case, however (which was not possible with the X-ray film screening), a different picture emerges. For the 6 cases where the development costs were over-estimated, the mean overage was approximately 5 percent. For the 16 cases where the costs were under-estimated, the mean overage was 345 percent! This is to say that the mean under-estimate is 69 times greater than the mean over-estimate, suggesting a very powerful preference for a particular type of error.

As Meckling and Marshall point out, once the magnitude of this bias has been discovered, many reasons for its existence (some obvious, others not so obvious) can be found. For example, the reward for under-estimation is great (the low bid usually gets the contract) and the penalty relatively small, since most contracts are made on a cost-plus basis with few, if any, penalty clauses. Since the original estimates on many of these contracts were already in the hundreds of millions of dollars, substantial overages of this kind represent a problem of enormous magnitude in the rational allocation of time and resources.

This example from the area of weapons acquisition, when considered together with the discussion of decision rules in law, medicine, and statistics, suggests two avenues for future investigation of decision making in organizations. First, in situations involving considerable uncertainty, and/or where the consequences of an erroneous decision are great, error preference is a very important component in the structure of the organization, perhaps as important as the avowed goals of the organization, or any other central component of organizational structure. Secondly, and more generally, the ways in which organizations protect themselves against the consequences of error preference might provide a fruitful avenue for the exploration of bureaucratic mechanisms. Two examples, one from judicial behavior, the

---

[10] *Ibid.* I have averaged the judgments of the two independent raters, A and B, presented in Table 2, p. 469.

other from weapons acquisition, illustrate the latter point.

In a study of the hospitalization of the mentally ill, the author found that the preferred error of most of the judges in a Midwestern state was to erroneously hospitalize rather than to erroneously release.[11] These judges were quite conscious of this preference, but justified this preference by referring to the recommendation of the court-appointed psychiatrists, which was almost invariably against release. It appeared to us that these judges were using the psychiatric recommendations to "cover" their own decisions, since some of them had very low opinions of the psychiatrists and their recommendations.

An echo of this organizational technique can be heard in the testimony of a missile expert, Werner von Braun, before a congressional investigating committee:

A physics professor may know a lot about the upper atmosphere, but when it comes to making a sound appraisal of a [missile research and development program] he is pretty much at a loss.

. . . .

When confronted with a difficult decision involving several hundred million dollars, and of vital importance to the national defense, many Pentagon executives like to protect themselves. It helps if a man can say, "I have on my advisory committee some Nobel prize winners, or some very famous people that everybody knows." And if these famous people then sign a final recommendation, the executive feels, "Now if something goes wrong, nobody can blame me for not having asked the smartest men in the country what they think about this."[12]

Whether the decision involves medical diagnosis, mental hospitalization, conviction of a crime, estimating a defense contract, or many other issues which are highly uncertain and/or socially important, the existence of preferences for types of error, and the organizational arrangements for guarding these preferences, may constitute an important field for research and analysis.

---

[11] Thomas J. Scheff, Social conditions for rationality: how urban and rural courts deal with the mentally ill, *American Behavioral Scientist*, 7 (March, 1964), 21–24.

[12] U.S. Senate *Hearings* (1958), *Inquiry into the Missile Program*, pp. 589, 590, 591, 592. Quoted in Merton J. Peck and Frederic M. Scherer, *The Weapons Acquisition Process: An Economic Analysis* (Cambridge, Mass.: Harvard University Press, 1962), p. 245.

PART III   *Individual Behavior:*
The Search for Pattern

tiny droplets of behavior
shower our beings.

giant waves, cumulate
inundate our souls.

i must breathe pattern
through the night of waves

see order
at the bottom
of my

See.

F.M.

8 *Some Experiments on the Detection of Repetition in Sequential Simulation**

FRED ATTNEAVE [†]

VIRTUALLY ALL psychological phenomena involve some responsiveness on the part of the organism to lawfulness in the external world. Thus adaptive behavior is in general possible only because of relatively invariant relationships which exist between certain stimulating conditions and the consequences of certain acts. Perceptual processes generally capitalize upon lawful interrelationships among stimulating conditions (i.e., receptor-events). In one aspect these constraints among stimuli constitute *redundancy*, and make possible a drastic simplication of the receptor-input; in another aspect they constitute *coherency*, and increase the reliability of the organism's classifications of external events.

We still have remarkably little detailed knowledge about either the varieties or the degree of lawfulness to which man is sensitive. Wertheimer's 1923 list of perceptual grouping principles, which should have served merely as a preliminary essay into this area, sums up the present state of our knowledge almost as well as anything that has been written subsequently. A direct attack upon the problem of sensitivity to order has apparently never been undertaken.

The ability to detect certain restricted varieties of lawfulness is explored in the present research. The "stimuli" are all sequences of either lights or sounds. In most of the experiments to date, the lawfulness has consisted of simple repetition, or cycling, of random sub-sequences. The method is essentially psychophysical: *O* watches or listens to a complete sequence, and then judges whether it was random or non-random.

* The research summarized in this paper was supported by a grant from the National Science Foundation, and this should perhaps be regarded as one of those not-very-appropriate papers that turn up in every symposium—for the obvious reason that the author's recent research is only loosely related to the subject of the symposium. The experiments discussed here have been chiefly concerned with the "feeling out" of an area rather than with the testing of any well defined models.

† University of Oregon.

Instrumentation

Figure 1 shows a block diagram of the essential apparatus.

FIGURE 1
SCHEME OF APPARATUS

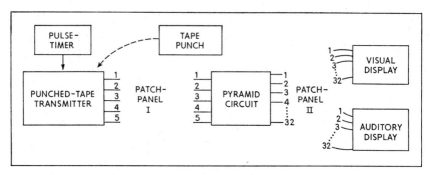

Any desired sequence of characters, each character consisting of five binary elements, may be punched on plastic tape. Elements are represented as electrical potentials at the output of the tape transmitter. The pyramid circuit "fans out" these five binary elements into $2^5 = 32$ alternative stimulus-events, which may be of either a visual or an auditory nature. The visual display is a horizontal array of 32 (or fewer) neon lamps, about one inch apart. The auditory display is essentially a small, resistance-tuned electronic organ, from which any one of 32 tones, varying in pitch on a chromatic scale, may be selected for presentation. The pulse-timer is an electronic (thyratron) device that serves to pace the whole system; that is, controls the rate at which stimulus-events occur. By means of the two patch-panels, the experimenter is completely free to vary the relationship between tape-characters and stimulus-events.

Experiments on the Detection of Repetition

Four studies have been carried out in which the lawfulness consisted of cyclical repetition—without noise or alteration—of blocks of events. For every lawful or repetitive sequence in these experiments, there was a completely random (except as subsequently noted) control sequence of equal length. As in most psychophysical studies, a few practiced observers (4 to 8 per experiment) made repeated judgments over a number of experimental sessions. These Os were always told what kind of regularity to look for; i.e., cyclical repetition.

In most cases O was required to give, in addition to a judgment of + (lawful), or — (random), a *confidence* rating of 1 (least confidence) to 3 (greatest confidence) on his own judgment of each sequence. Responses thus ranged from —3 to +3. The response O (zero) was allowed as an indication of complete indecision.

At the end of an experiment each O's responses were redivided into "lawful" and "random" about that cutting point on the response scale which minimized his errors. For example, if an O said "+1" more often in response to random sequences than in response to lawful sequences, then his +1 was considered a random response. The effect of this re-cutting operation was to eliminate or minimize individual response-biases, or constant error in the psychophysical sense.

Each of the four experiments employed several independent variables in a factorial design. It may save confusion to list all of these variables at once:

1. Modality (visual vs. auditory); Experiments 1, 3, and 4. The interest here was not primarily in determining which modality is superior, but rather in determining whether effects of other variables show intermodal generality.
2. Rate of presentation (1 event per second vs. 5 per second); Experiment 1.
3. Cycle-length, i.e., number of events per cycle; Experiments 1, 2, 3, and 4.
4. Number of cycles per sequence; Experiment 2.
5. Number of equiprobable alternative events; Experiment 2.
6. Run-structure of sequences; Experiment 3.
7. Spacing of stimuli on their respective continua, i.e., distances between lights or intervals between tones; Experiment 3.
8. Collapsing of a variable number of alternatives into a single high-probability alternative (no stimulus); Experiment 4.

Several of these variables may be dismissed with brief comments. In no case have results been dramatically different from one *modality* to the other, though there is some evidence for the superiority of the auditory when the sequences are long. *Rate of presentation,* varied by a factor of 5 in Experiment 1, showed only a minute effect (in favor of the slower rate), again only in the case of longer sequences. Subsequently, the faster rate of 5 events per second was used as a matter of experimental convenience. Varying the *spacing* of stimuli on their continua by a factor of 4 (No. 7 in the list above) was found to make no difference whatever.

In Experiment 1, 4 Os were run for 12 sessions (6 visual, 6 auditory), in the course of which they made a total of 2304 judgments. Number of *alternative* lights or tones was fixed at 32, and *number of cycles* per lawful sequence was fixed at 5. *Length of cycle* was varied, and took the values 6, 8, 10, 20, 30, and 40 events per cycle. Figure 2 shows percentage-correct responses for each of these conditions; and results are graphed separately for lawful sequences and random control sequences of equal length, but are collapsed over modalities and other conditions.

What is striking here is the very high degree of accuracy that is main-

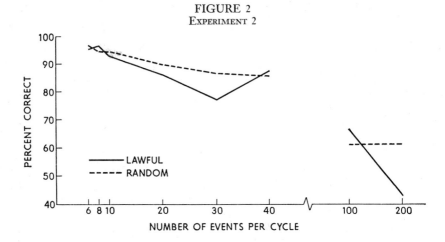

FIGURE 2
EXPERIMENT 2

tained up to 40 events per cycle. Results for the 100 and 200 cycle lengths are not strictly comparable with the others, since they were obtained after the main body of the experiment (and with the faster presentation rate only), in an effort to determine something about the upper limits of the observer's abilities. The auditory modality is better at these lengths: percentages correct (averaged over lawful sequences and random controls) were 75 and 69 for the auditory, and 62 and 38 for the visual sequences that repeated after 100 and 200 events, respectively. These results become somewhat less astonishing when it is clearly realized that O does not need to store all the events in the cycle in order to detect the repetition; instead he may remember some very short sub-sequence, particularly one that happens to have certain distinctive features, and simply wait and see whether it recurs (see Experiment 3, below).

Experiment 2 employed 4 Os in each of two replications which were identical, except for 0s and random differences in stimulus sequences. A total of 7680 judgments was obtained. Only the *visual* display was used, but *cycle length, number of cycles* per sequence, and *number of alternative lights* were all varied factorially. Effects of cycle length are shown in Figure 3.

That the level of accuracy is generally lower than that shown in Figure 2 is due chiefly to the fact that number of cycles per sequence has been reduced, on the average. Note, however, that accuracy on random sequences does *not* decrease with length, as it did in Experiment 1. This discrepancy is not attributable to omission of the auditory modality from the present experiment, since it persists when only the visual data from Experiment 1 are considered.

An explanation is possible in terms of altered betting odds (as a function of total length of sequence) from one experiment to the other. An O in

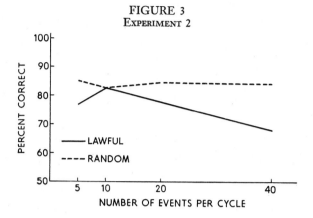

FIGURE 3
EXPERIMENT 2

Experiment 1 may know or believe that repetition is harder to detect the longer the sequence, since total length varies directly with cycle length. Therefore the longer the sequence, the more willing he may be to bet (on the basis of inconclusive evidence) that it is lawful. The result of this tendency would be to distribute his errors over lawful and random stimuli.

In Experiment 2, however, long repetitive sequences are often *easier* than short ones because number of cycles is also a variable; therefore an increasing willingness to accept inconclusive evidence—the longer the sequence—would have no basis, and errors on random sequences should not vary appreciably with their length. In support of this explanation it may be remarked that in Experiments 3 and 4, length and difficulty are related as in Experiment 1, and that, in the present respect, the results of these experiments resemble those of Experiment 1 rather than those of Experiment 2.

The very powerful effect of *number of cycles* may be seen in Figure 4. The increase in accuracy with number of cycles may follow a genotypical compound probability law, but averaging proportions over several hetero-

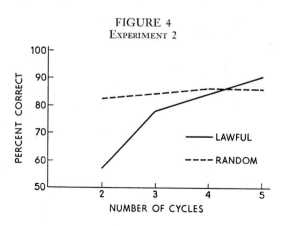

FIGURE 4
EXPERIMENT 2

geneous conditions would result in a somewhat flatter empirical function, as is indeed the case. The horizontal function for random sequences is essentially the same as its counterpart in Figure 3, since the total length is the variable in both cases.

FIGURE 5
EXPERIMENT 2

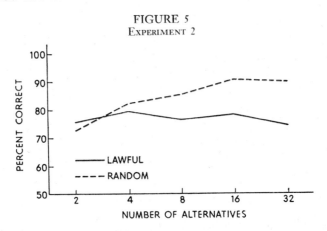

Varying *number of alternative lights* from 2 to 32 made no reliable difference in performance on repetitive sequences, but random sequences were more often identified as such as alternatives increased (Figure 5). A possible reason for the latter effect is that any short sub-sequence is more likely to recur by chance, in a random sequence, the fewer the alternatives, and that observers failed to make due allowance for this likelihood.

It appeared to us, from the comments as well as the behavior of our observers, that what they were typically doing was picking up some relatively short, distinctive sub-sequence to remember, and then waiting to see whether they could match it one or more times later in the sequence.

What "distinctive" might mean in this context is not clear in detail, but a *run* would seem to constitute a particularly obvious example of a distinctive sub-sequence. Therefore it was decided to vary the *run-structure* of sequences in Experiment 3. In sequences of type N, no event was allowed to follow itself, in those of type E events followed themselves with exactly the expected frequency, and in those of type D events followed themselves with double the expected frequency. Nonrepetitive control sequences were now quasi-random, with the same run-structure as corresponding repetitive sequences, and Os were carefully instructed that a + judgment should specifically mean cyclical repetition. As in Experiment 2, 4 Os were used in each of the two replications. Other variables in the factorial design were *modality, spacing* of lights and tones on their respective continua, and *cycle-length* (16, 32, 48, and 64 events). *Number of alternatives* was fixed at 8 and *number of cycles* at 3. These parameters made for a somewhat harder task than was anticipated.

The hypothesis that sequences with more runs would be easier was confirmed, but the effect was a rather weak one. Overall percentage correct was 64 on type N sequences, 69 on type E, and 71 on type D. It seems likely that runs constitute only one basis out of many for distinctiveness of subsequences.

An observer in Experiment 3 (who was outstandingly better than anyone else in her performance, particularly on the lights) was questioned about the techniques or strategies that she might have used. She said that she had simplified the display by concentrating on two or three lights at one end of the array and ignoring all the others. Thus we were led to try an experimental manipulation that had not been considered previously: of objectively "masking off" some variable number of stimulus-alternatives and substituting "blank" intervals for them.

This was done with both lights and tones in Experiment 4. The program tapes of type E from Experiment 3 were used again, but of the 8 possible stimulus-alternatives, either 8, 4, 2, or 1 were actually "exposed." Thus in the condition of 2 exposed stimulus alternatives, for example, only two lights or tones occurred, each with a probability of .125, whereas an interval containing no stimulus occurred with a probability of .75. During a run of "blank" intervals the regular 5-per-second beat of the tape transmitter in an adjacent room was always audible to the Os. Two groups of 4 Os were counterbalanced with respect to the order, over 4 sessions, of the conditions mentioned above. Each session was half visual, half auditory. "Exposed" lights were always adjacent and 1 inch apart; "exposed" notes were the first 1 to 8 tones of a major diatonic scale.

FIGURE 6
Experiment 4

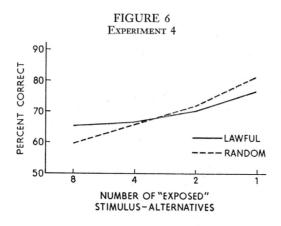

NUMBER OF "EXPOSED"
STIMULUS-ALTERNATIVES

It was our guess that the task might be easiest with either 4 or 2 "exposed" stimulus alternatives. The function obtained (Figure 6) was quite monotonic, however: performance was optimal when all but one of the lights or tones were masked off! The effect is a sizable one; it obtains about equally for the two modalities, and is at least as great for random as for repetitive sequences.

This effect is not the result of merely reducing the number of stimulus-alternatives (or the amount of stimulus-information): compare the very different effect of varying number of equi-probable alternatives, shown in Figure 5. Psychological simplification of the task is achieved, rather, by collapsing or pooling a number of low-probability alternatives into a single high-probability alternative—"no-stimulus," in the present case. We believe, as a result of informal observation, that some such principle has considerable generality. If a repetitive time-series of sufficient complexity is graphed, the recursive nature of the function may be far from obvious at a glance. However, if a mask is placed over the graph so that only a few peaks of the function appear above the top, the repetition is much more easily detectable.

A Statistical Model
9   for the Study
of Conformity

John B. Miner *

IN THE PAST TEN YEARS the concept of conformity has achieved a rather amazing position. It has become a frequent topic of discussion, a major concern of popular writers, and at the same time has generated a sizable amount of significant scientific research. The present paper will be concerned primarily with one approach which has emerged from the research, and with the presentation of data obtained as a result of the application of one particular conformity model. Since this model has been developed in conjunction with the work on the Tomkins-Horn Picture Arrangement Test (1957, 1959), more frequently referred to as the PAT, it will be presented in terms of its application to that particular instrument. It should be understood, however, that the approach is not inherently limited to any one measurement procedure.

The Tomkins-Horn Picture Arrangement Test requires the subject to select that arrangement of a set of three pictures which he feels makes the best sense. There are a total of 25 such arrangements to be made, the specific content of the pictures varying from plate to plate. The picture stimuli have been selected to represent everyday life, with more than half depicting some aspect of the work situation. All 75 individual pictures contain people, and 40 percent of them contain more than one person. Since there are six possible ways in which the three pictures may be arranged, and since the test has been administered to a representative sample of the United States population aged 10 and above (by Gallup Poll interviewers), it is possible to determine what percent of the people in the United States might be expected to choose each of the alternatives on each of the 25 plates. A percentage table may be set up along the following lines:

ARRANGEMENT NUMBERS

	1	2	3	4	5	6
Plate 1	27	28	4	12	23	6
Plate 2	11	4	11	3	10	61

* University of Oregon.

95

There are, of course, 25 plate entries in the actual table employed. The average frequency with which the specific 25 arrangements selected by a given individual are also selected by others in the population may be estimated by totaling the percentage values associated with each arrangement the individual chooses and dividing by 25. This is the average frequency for his responses. It represents an estimate of the extent to which, in his everyday life, the individual selects responses which are frequently, or only rarely, given by others; which are conforming or deviant. High scores, of course, indicate conformity. The average percentage for the U.S. population sample is 33.5, the standard deviation is 5.5.

In addition to this average frequency measure, which gives an overall estimate of the degree to which an individual's behavior may be characterized as conforming, it is also possible to compute an estimate of the extent of adherence to social norms. For this purpose we have arbitrarily defined a social norm as a response (arrangement) which is given by 50 percent or more of the group. Thus for the two plates previously noted, only arrangement 6 on Plate 2 would qualify as a social norm for the United States population. There are nine such norms contained in the Tomkins-Horn Picture Arrangement Test, and the extent of adherence to social norms may be estimated by determining how many of the nine arrangements an individual actually selects. In the United States population sample the mean is 5.9 and the standard deviation 1.7.

These two measures, both of which are derived from a statistical definition of conformity, appear to be highly related. In the 15 different samples, that will be discussed later in this paper, the median correlation was .89, with values ranging from .60 to .97.

A further question concerns the reliability of these measures. The evidence available is somewhat sparse, but it is encouraging. The Tomkins-Horn Picture Arrangement Test was administered twice to a group of 88 Princeton University underclassmen, with three weeks intervening. This group is well above the population average in conformity and the scores are unusually homogeneous. This latter factor, plus the actual and quite valid changes that may be expected to have occurred during the three-week interval, tend to minimize the chances of obtaining very high correlations. Nevertheless, a coefficient of .67 was obtained for average frequency of response and a coefficient of .66 for adherence to social norms. When a correction for restriction of range is applied, the estimate of reliability in the population for the average frequency measure is .87 and for the social norms measure .77. The latter clearly suffers from the fact that only nine social norms appear in the test, thus reducing the number of items for this measure from 25 to 9. Nevertheless, the reliabilities appear to be adequate for purposes of group comparison.

Comparison with Alternative Approaches

The model for conformity which has been employed in developing these measures is, of course, far from new. In *Psychodiagnostik* (1921) Rorschach described the Original response to his test and defined it as a response which occurred less than once in every 100 records. Later, in a posthumous paper published by Oberholzer (1923), Rorschach spoke of the Vulgar responses, those which appear at least once in every three records, as providing a measure of the subject's "share in the common mode of perceiving."

More recent writers have preferred the term Popular to Vulgar, and have employed varying statistical definitions, but this approach to the measurement of conformity remains a major aspect of Rorschach Test interpretation. Our adherence to social norms is conceptually identical with the Rorschach Popular, although based on a somewhat more demanding statistical criterion. The average frequency measure represents an extension of the same approach to all responses given by a subject.

This method of studying conformity should be contrasted with an alternative procedure which has recently achieved widespread acceptance. The major impetus has come from Asch's work (1951). He exposed individual experimental subjects to a series of consistent group judgments which were at variance with perceptual reality. Conformity was said to occur when the individual resolved the resulting conflict in favor of the group and denied reality.

This approach had its roots in Sherif's research (1936) on the autokinetic effect. In this early work the stimulus was ambiguous, a small speck of light in a dark room. Thus the fact that subjects adjusted their reports of perceived movement to the standards established by other members of the group did not seem too surprising. In the Asch situation the stimulus is highly structured, a line of a given length. Here, the finding that subjects will report as equal, lines which clearly differ by sizable amounts provides a very striking demonstration of the power of pressures to conform.

In this social psychological approach to the study of conformity, the standards of the group are explicitly stated and a conflict situation is produced. If this conflict is resolved in favor of the group rather than the individual, the subject has conformed. In the PAT, and in other individually oriented, clinical procedures, the group standards are not stated as such. Rather the subject brings to the test the knowledge of group standards which he has acquired throughout life. In many ways this is more like most *real life* conformity situations, where people characteristically respond in relation to what they believe the group standards to be. Usually the standards are *not* stated explicitly as they are in the Sherif and Asch experiments. People try to avoid behavior which might be expected to result in ridicule or rejection or anger on the part of others. But their expectations in this regard are a function of past learning in interpersonal situations. They develop, through experience, a set of internal standards which they bring forth at appropriate times. These standards influence their behavior in a variety of situations; some of a social nature, and some quite devoid of human interaction.

In the PAT, the conflict between group and individual is also less apparent. This also seems to approximate more closely most *real life* conformity situations. Characteristically, people conform in adult life almost automatically. The period of conscious conflict is most likely to occur during the early phases of the learning process, and thus it tends to predominate in childhood. As adults, we short-circuit many aspects of the original stimulus-response sequence and respond without thinking or experiencing emotion. Perhaps the capacity to do this is what is meant by maturity. The term maturity is certainly often used in a sense which seems primarily to indicate conformity.

In any event, conflict is experienced in such situations only when a person wishes to respond in a manner considered overly aggressive, or self-centered, or bad, or strange. This wish may be experienced as a compulsion or just a vague "What if I . . ." In the PAT, conflict may arise when there is a temptation to select an arrangement which is perceived as rather odd. Then the internalized group norms emerge into consciousness, the expectation of ridicule or criticism by whoever may read or interpret the response is experienced, and the individual frequently selects a more "sensible" arrangement. For PAT sample plates, see Figure 1.

FIGURE 1

SAMPLE INSTRUCTIONS AND PLATES:
THE TOMKINS–HORN PICTURE ARRANGEMENT EXPERIMENT (PAT)*

INSTRUCTIONS

This is an experiment to see how well you can arrange pictures so as to tell a story that makes sense.

Each page contains a set of three pictures. Each of the three pictures has a mark at the bottom of the picture; one is marked △, another is marked ☐, and another is marked ○.

Your job is to put one of these marks on each of the three lines at the bottom of the page in the order which makes the best sense. Following each mark write one sentence which tells the story.

You will have to turn the booklet around to see the different pictures.

---

* Reproduced with permission of Springer Publishing Company and Profs. Silvan Tomkins and Daniel Horn (figures reduced one-half).

FIGURE 1–Continued

Now turn the page and you will find a sample showing just what you are to do.
Study the sample and then turn to the next page with the set of pictures numbered 1. Fold the booklet so that you have just this set of pictures in front
   of you and write down your answer using the three marks and a short sentence
   following each. After you have finished with 1, turn the booklet over and
   go on with the set numbered 2, and so on for the rest of the experiment.
   There are twenty-five sets of pictures in the experiment.
Be sure you understand just what you are to do.

[Now turn the page, and go ahead with the experiment.]

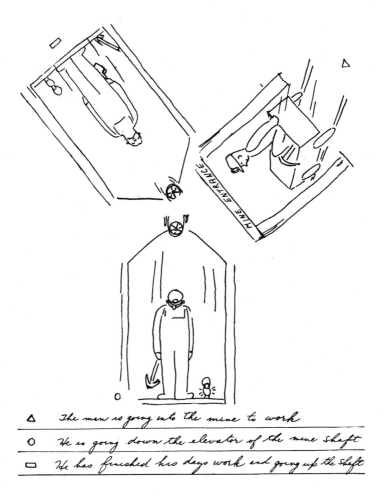

△   The man is going into the mine to work

○   He is going down the elevator of the mine shaft

▢   He has finished his days work and going up the shaft

FIGURE 1—Concluded

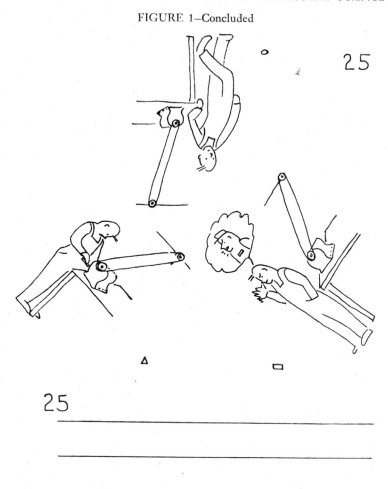

The pressure in such situations is not identical with that of a face-to-face group, but such thoughts as "whoever reads that will think I'm crazy" can be a very real force in determining human behavior. Such overtly experienced conflict between the group and the individual is probably not a common occurrence among normal adults taking tests such as the PAT and Rorschach. The conflicts presumably were experienced and modes of resolution developed many years before.

If this analysis is correct, the approaches taken by researchers such as Sherif and Asch must be considered as partial abstractions from real life. They should have value primarily in providing an understanding of the early stages of conformity learning when group standards are explicitly stated and conflict is overtly experienced. The statistical model proposed here should yield much greater insight into the nature of adult behavior since it incorporates more aspects of the *real life* situations which it attempts to explain. The PAT has been used in applying the model since it provides a series of miniature conformity situations which have particular value because known probabilities can be attached to response alternatives. Such a model should prove a fruitful source of valid hypotheses and should generate measures which effectively predict human behavior. The data which follow are presented in an attempt to show that this is in fact the case.

The Congruence of U.S. and Organizational Norms

Although the discussion so far has centered on data obtained from a representative sample of the United States population, it should be evident that samples drawn from any social grouping may be employed and the frequency with which each response (arrangement) is selected calculated. Thus it is possible to define the norms for any social unit. Adherence to norms and average frequency of response measures can be computed for a member as a function of response tendencies in his particular group. We can thus designate the individual who conforms to his group just as we have designated the individual who is a conformist relative to others in this country.

Although an individual may be a member of a great number of different groups at the same time, he is particularly likely to be associated with both an organizational (or institutional) group and a nation. Thus, the question of the consistency of conformity between these two social units is important. Can a person be a conformist in terms of a specific organization, but a deviant in terms of American culture patterns? This could easily occur, of course, if the group had characteristic response patterns which differed markedly from those of the society overall.

In order to study this question samples were obtained from six different organizational groups. They were selected primarily because it was thought that they might yield frequencies differing from those in the population sample.[1] The samples noted in Table 1 were used to compute group frequencies, and subsequently each member's PAT was scored both on the basis of the U.S. data and the specific group data. The two types of measures were then correlated.

It is evident from the table that U. S. and group response patterns are highly correlated in all six instances. The coefficients are reliably above zero at well beyond the .01 level. The person who is a conformist in any

---
[1] I would like to express appreciation to Charles T. Anderson, Philip H. Margules, Paul Kivisto, and Elsie Fosdick for their assistance in collecting these samples.

TABLE 1

CORRELATIONS BETWEEN CONFORMITY MEASURES BASED
ON U. S. FREQUENCIES AND ON SPECIFIC GROUP FREQUENCIES
FOR VARIOUS ORGANIZATIONAL AND
INSTITUTIONAL GROUPS

Group	N	Conformity Measures Average Frequency of Responses	Adherence to Social Norms
Marketing Department of Large Corporation	110	.84	.70
Underclassmen at Princeton University	148	.84	.64
Female Patients in Locked Ward of State Hospital	57	.86	.85
Patients at State Hospital for Epileptics	66	.96	.83
Inmates of State Hospital for Sex Offenders	47	.98	.93
Inmates of State Prison for Women	59	.96	.90

one of these groups is also likely to be a conformist relative to the U. S. population as a whole. The effort to identify organizations with deviant norms appears to have been unsuccessful.

A few words, however, should be said about the samples:

a) The marketing department employees were drawn from all levels within the sales organization. The sample includes a high proportion of the total number in the group and is believed to be representative. Although the average duration of organization membership is not known, it was almost certainly over five years.

b) The majority of the Princeton underclassmen were sophomores with about a year and a half in residence at the university. They were tested in introductory psychology classes.

c) The locked-ward patients were drawn from a single wing of the hospital, but there was, of course, selection in accordance with testability. Most were diagnosed as suffering from some form of schizophrenia and the mean duration of the present hospitalization was 3.6 years.

d) The epileptics were similarly selected from the patient population of a special state hospital. On the average, they had been there 5.8 years.

e) The sex offenders on the other hand, although committed by the court to this particular hospital, had been in residence for a much shorter period of time when tested. The mean length of stay was just over six months.

f) The female prisoners had been sentenced for a variety of crimes, ranging from petty theft to murder. The duration of imprisonment prior to testing is not known.

These samples do not exhaust the populations studied and are not known definitely to be representative. Nevertheless, there is reason to believe the findings would not change with the selection of additional samples from the same populations. In one instance where this was done, the addition of a new sample, equal in size to the original, resulted in an average change of only 1.2 percent in the frequency data. The largest change was only 6 percent. Changes of this magnitude could not have any sizable effects on the correlation coefficients of Table 1.

The Congruence of U.S. and Various Subgroup Norms

In an effort to locate instances where conformity to group norms was not almost synonymous with conformity to the U. S. culture pattern, additional samples were studied, as indicated in Table 2.[2] The two occupational samples were obtained in response to a mail request and have been

TABLE 2

CORRELATIONS BETWEEN CONFORMITY MEASURES BASED
ON U. S. FREQUENCIES AND ON SPECIFIC GROUP FREQUENCIES
FOR VARIOUS OCCUPATIONAL AND
CULTURAL GROUPS

| | | Conformity Measures | |
| | | Average Frequency | Adherence to |
Group	N	of Responses	Social Norms
Officers of Large Corporations	44	.91	.68
Senior Members of University Faculties	41	.94	.79
Southern Negroes in Representative U.S. Sample	41	.90	.78
Members of Jewish Religion in Representative U.S. Sample	49	.96	.84
Civil Service Applicants in Pakistan	43	.88	.84
High School Seniors in Rome, Italy	42	.92	.69

described in considerable detail elsewhere (1955, 1962). The Negro group is derived from the representative sample for the PAT. It contains all Negroes residing in the Deep South (South Carolina, Georgia, Alabama, Mississippi, Louisiana, and Arkansas). If geographical frequencies for the Deep South (based on whites and Negroes) are substituted for the U. S., and frequencies for the Negro population in the country as a whole for the Southern Negroes, the resulting correlations are .97 and .91, respectively. Clearly, the use of the whole country as the superordinate group is not a necessary condition for obtaining high correlations. If figures for the U. S. Negro population and for the total U. S. are employed, the coefficients are .96 and .87, using the same sample of 41 Southern Negroes.

The Jewish sample contains all those in the representative sample for the

---

[2] Appreciation is expressed to John E. Culver, Randolph C. Sailer, and Franco Ferracuti for their help in gathering these samples.

PAT who indicated a preference for the Jewish religion. The two foreign groups both contain subjects who have been exposed to strong Western influences. The Pakistanis are a very well educated group and are quite conversant with the English language. It therefore seemed appropriate to assume the suitability of U.S. frequencies for experimental purposes. No samples representative of either Pakistan or Italy are available for the PAT.

Our efforts to find large groups with norms differing from those of the United States as a whole have been fruitless to date. No such group has been found. Testing is now under way in certain rural areas of Korea, and this attempt in a non-Western culture may be successful. Nevertheless, the data currently available are striking in the extent to which they emphasize common patterns in human behavior. Past research has tended to point up the differences between groups perhaps because it is in these areas that much socially significant behavior occurs.

The present findings do not imply that such differences are nonexistent; the psychotics, epileptics, sex offenders, and criminals have certain kinds of behaviors in common, which appear considerably less frequently in the population at large. On the other hand, it also seems clear that human beings in our society have many patterns of behavior and thought in common, and that large group membership is not likely to produce extensive deviation from the national pattern. The extent of this cultural conformity has perhaps not been fully recognized previously.

The question remains, however, why do these organizational, institutional, occupational, caste and nationality groups produce so little that is consistently unique among their members? What might serve to explain these findings? One possibility is that, contrary to the assumptions of many writers in the field of organization theory, these various groups have very little impact on their members. They are not a major contributing force in the development of conformity, nor do they select on this basis.

An alternative is that the impact of the groups tends to be isomorphic with society. They produce conformity, but primarily to societal norms, not to their own unique norms. Such a view would be consistent with Selznick's views (1949) regarding the role of societal constraints on organizational decision making.

A third explanation would predicate selection as the basis for the findings. It may be that there is a strong tendency for groups to select members, or for members to select groups, using the presence of national behavior patterns as a guide. This would seem unlikely for the psychotics, epileptics, sex offenders, Southern Negroes, and Jews, but it might hold for the other groups.

It is possible to analyze the data in such a way as to shed some light on this question. The extent of adherence to United States norms (responses with a frequency in the U.S. sample of 50 percent or more) and of adherence to each group's norms (responses with a 50 percent or greater frequency in the specific group) have been computed. A comparison of the two means, obtained through the application of the two sets of norms to the same group, will indicate whether the group exhibits more "norming"; that is, is more homogeneous than the relevant segment of society. This analysis indicates, then, whether a group has added anything above and beyond what might be expected from membership in the society as a whole. The results are presented in Table 3. The maximum possible score, based on the U.S. data, is 9. For the different groups the maxima vary from 18 (Princeton undergraduates) to 4 (state hospital patients).

TABLE 3
MEAN CONFORMITY AS INDICATED BY ADHERENCE TO
SOCIAL NORMS MEASURES BASED ON U.S.
FREQUENCIES AND ON SPECIFIC GROUP FREQUENCIES

Group	Adherence to U. S. Norms	Adherence to Group Norms	t	p
Marketing Department	6.9	10.6	24.67	< .01
Princeton Students	6.4	12.2	41.43	< .01
State Hospital Patients	4.4	2.2	10.48	< .01
Hospitalized Epileptics	5.5	5.2	2.50	< .02
Sex Offenders	5.9	7.6	11.33	< 0.1
Female Prisoners	5.1	4.2	8.18	< .01
Corporate Officers	6.0	9.9	15.60	< .01
University Professors	6.0	7.6	7.27	< .01
Southern Negroes	4.1	2.9	5.00	< .01
Jewish Religion	6.1	8.0	11.76	< .01
Pakistani Civil Service	5.3	5.7	2.50	< .02
Roman High School Students..	5.9	6.8	4.74	< .01

It is clear that, for a number of groups, an increase in homogeneity occurs. These groups—the marketing department, Princeton students, sex offenders, corporate officers, university professors, Jewish religion, Pakistani civil service, and Roman high school students—clearly add something. Either the members are influenced toward conformity to the group and national norms, which are essentially isomorphic, or the members are selected (or select themselves) in accordance with the societal norms. Probably both occur. We have some evidence, derived from repeat testing of college students, that the university as an organization can produce increased conformity to national norms (1963), and presumably other organizations have a similar impact.

In the four remaining groups, the state hospital patients, epileptics, prisoners, and Southern Negroes, there is a striking lack of homogeneity. All score low on conformity to national norms, and even lower on conformity to their group norms. There is a real lack of "groupness." These would seem to be essentially collections of relatively diverse individuals who have been thrown together because of a limited set of responses or characteristics which they have in common. Apparently, findings such as these can be used to operationally define the presence or, in the immediate instance, the absence of a group.

The discussion so far has concentrated on relatively large groups, whose members lack frequent face-to-face interaction. What about small units, such as gangs and work groups and families? Do they develop norms, so that a majority of the members respond in a manner at variance with the culture pattern? Our research in this area is as yet very limited. Analysis of results obtained from one group of tabulating machine operators ($N=$ 15) in a large corporation indicated a sizable amount of homogeneity (mean adherence to own norms 11.1 as against 5.5 for U.S. norms; $t = $ 15.56, $p < .01$), but the same tendency to maintain response patterns similar to the country as a whole. The U.S.-group correlations were .92 for average frequency and .86 for adherence to norms.

In another group of salesmen ($N=17$), all working out of the same regional office under the same management—although having only limited personal contact—there was a similar high level of "groupness" (mean adherence to own norms 10.5 as against 6.1 for U. S. norms; $t = 11.00$, $p < $ .01). But in this instance the high correlations between U. S. and group frequencies failed to emerge. The figure for average frequency of response was .26; for adherence to social norms .31. Neither differs reliably from zero. The group does not have norms which are completely at variance with those of society (as would be indicated by a reliable negative correlation), but neither is there evidence that its norms are consistently those of the U. S. as a whole. The meaning and potential generalizability of this one, disparate finding are not entirely clear at present. Studies of small groups are continuing.

Conformity and Performance

Another test of the statistical model for conformity might be applied in the area of performance prediction. An ideal model should generate measures which will yield sizable correlations with some aspects of human behavior. In view of the evidence that conformity is at a high level among male college graduates in the labor force (1962), many of whom are employed in industrial management, initial efforts to predict behavior have been undertaken within that group. Although the data currently available are rather sparse and further study is clearly needed, it has been possible to obtain some information regarding the extent to which conformity may be related to success at the lower and middle management levels.

The sample to be reported here contains 30 men, all working for the same large corporation, whose salaries ranged from $10,000 to $30,000 a year. Tomkins-Horn Picture Arrangement Test protocols were available for each manager so that average frequency of response and adherence to social norms measures could be computed. Only the United States frequencies could be used since appropriate frequencies for the company's managerial group as a whole were not available. In all instances the writer had had an opportunity to discuss the performance of these men and their potential for advancement with their superiors in the company.

The results of these interviews were subsequently quantified using a 10-point scale for present job performance and a 4-point scale for advancement potential. In most cases the writer had a general idea regarding the man's position on the conformity-deviance dimension (and on a number of other characteristics) at the time the discussions were held. Thus the possibility of contamination cannot be completely ruled out. On the other hand, the interviews were conducted primarily for the purpose of making decisions regarding placement; not to validate the conformity measures. Thus motivation to distort the ratings in accordance with preconceived notions about the nature of the conformity-performance relationship was at a minimum. As compared with findings derived from other pilot studies— and these results must be considered in that category—the correlations which are presented in Table 4 would appear to be relatively free of bias.

TABLE 4
CORRELATIONS BETWEEN CONFORMITY MEASURES
AND PERFORMANCE CRITERIA

	Criterion Measures			
	Performance Ratings		Potential Ratings	
Conformity Measures	*r*	*p*	*r*	*p*
Average frequency of responses	.33	.05 – .10	.55	$< .01$
Adherence to social norms	.32	.05 – .10	.55	$< .01$

These findings suggest that the more conforming manager is more likely to be considered as having a future in the company. The data on present performance are less clear-cut. The linear correlations fall just short of accepted significance levels. When curvilinear coefficients are calculated, they rise considerably (.51 and .48, both with $p < .01$). However, appropriate tests do not definitely establish the existence of a nonlinear relationship, probably because of the small number of cases. The scatter plots suggest, however, that both the deviant and the marked conformist may be rated high on present job performance, even though the former is not seen as likely to be promoted to higher levels.

Conformity and Intelligence

At the time the representative national sample for the PAT was collected, a short, multiple-choice vocabulary test was also administered to all subjects. This test has been subsequently shown to have a high correlation with more comprehensive measures of general intelligence (1961). The analyses relating conformity to intelligence have been based on results obtained with this verbal measure, and with the average frequency of response index of conformity, as derived from the PAT. This latter measure was employed because it appears to be more reliable than adherence to U.S. norms, and thus should be more discriminating.

The correlation in the total sample of 1500 was .32. The relationship is linear and reliable. This finding is entirely consistent with the implications of the prior theoretical discussion. If intelligence is defined as the ability to learn, or as—what appears to be much the same thing—the capacity for complex reasoning,[3] and conformity is in part a function of learned standards, then a positive relationship should exist. The lower the intelligence, the greater the probability that certain standards necessary for conformity have not been internalized, and the greater the probability that deviance will be found irrespective of the extent to which the individual may actually wish to conform. The lack of "groupness" in some of the samples (found to be relatively devoid of norms) may well be partially due to the difficulty many of the members experience in learning common patterns of response.

The more intelligent a person or the members of a group, on the other hand, the greater the *potential* for conformity. With a greater ability to learn, an individual can internalize standards more rapidly and thus acquire a greater number of conforming responses. This does not, of course, guarantee that extensive conformity will result. Many, no doubt, learn the standards only to reject them. But a high level of intelligence offers the possibility of conformity—and, in many cases, apparently—the reality. A low level of intelligence makes conformity much more difficult to attain, although strong motivation may on occasion have a sizable compensating effect. The correlation is, after all, only .32.

Conformity and Age

A similar analysis has been carried out that relates the average frequency of response measure based on U.S. norms to age. In the representative sample of 1500, a correlation of —.21 was obtained. However, this linear coefficient is clearly an underestimate. The scores *rise* with age, up to the late teens, and then remain relatively constant until the mid-thirties, when they begin a steady decline. If the relationship is estimated using only those in the U.S. sample aged 30 and above (N = 947), an age-conformity correlation of —.40 results.

This may, however, be an artifact. When the high conformity group,

---

[3] For an elaboration of this point, see J. B. Miner, *Intelligence in the United States* (New York: Springer Publishing Co., Inc., 1957).

those aged 16 through 34, was compared with those 50 or more years old, a number of differences emerged which might well acount for the conformity differential. The older group (N = 445), with a mean conformity score of 31.6, had a lower level of intelligence, a lower educational level, and more Negroes than the younger group (N = 491), with a mean score of 35.1.

In order to check on the effect of these variables, two matched samples numbering 249 subjects were selected from the larger groups. These were the largest samples that could be constituted and yet maintain perfect matching on intelligence, education, and race. The younger group had a mean age of 26 and a conformity index of 34.9. The older group had an average age of 61 and a mean conformity of 32.4. The conformity measures remain reliably different ($t = 4.94$; $p < .01$). It looks very much as if people become less conforming as they grow older.

There is, however, an alternative explanation. Perhaps the older people, having been born and raised in a different period, developed norms differing from the younger segment of our society. If this were so, they might have maintained a high level of conformity to these norms and still appear as nonconformists when compared with the total U. S. frequencies. In other words, it may be that the older group is highly homogeneous, but nevertheless deviant from the society as a whole.

This hypothesis may be tested by applying the approach previously developed to study the congruence of norms. All individuals aged 65 and over (N = 152) in the representative national sample were scored on their own frequencies. Correlations were computed as in the previous studies. The average frequency of response measures yielded a coefficient of .96, and the adherence to social norms measures a coefficient of .81. The mean adherence to U.S. norms is 4.9, and to group norms 2.6 ($t = 22.20$; $p < .01$). It is clear that the older people in this country do not in any real sense constitute a group and that such "norming" as does occur is highly congruent with that of the younger segment of our society.

The evidence strongly suggests that a sizable proportion of the people in the United States become less conforming as they grow older. One possible explanation is that in the late thirties and early forties the power of the group begins to wane. Less is to be gained by conforming as ambitions are satisfied and status attained, or perhaps as it becomes increasingly clear that the group never will confer that which is desired. If the group is not seen as likely to provide what a person wants, then the necessity for conforming to group norms is considerably reduced.

An Evaluation

The model has proved of considerable value as a source of insights into the nature and extent of the congruence between societal norms and those of various organizational, institutional, occupational, caste, and nationality groups. It has provided a possible operational definition of a group and pointed up the importance of further studies with small social units. It has suggested certain hypotheses about the conformity-intelligence relationship which were borne out by the data. When measures generated by the model were applied, they unearthed considerable evidence regarding the relation of age to conformity. Similar studies suggested that managerial job performance and conformity may be related, although perhaps not in a linear fashion. This is the positive evidence that has been developed to date. But certain deficiencies of the approach have also become increasingly evident as work progressed.

For one thing there is no procedure inherent in the method of measurement which will provide information on whether a given response existed prior to group membership. Thus it is impossible to tell (after the fact) whether an individual joined a group or was selected for membership, and whether he had conforming response tendencies or developed such tendencies after becoming a member. This is a deficiency of all present psychological measurement, but it is nevertheless important. On the other hand, the approach offers the possibility of studying such problems through the measurement of all potential group members and the comparison of scores obtained by subsequent joiners and non-joiners, as well as through repeated measurement of members.

Another problem arises because of the impossibility of differentiating deviance or nonconformity (the two terms are used synonymously) which is attributable to deficiencies in learning from that which represents an active rejection of norms. Although for many purposes the distinction is not a necessary one, there are occasions when it becomes important. Only when an individual remains deviant in spite of high intelligence, adequate sensory capacities for learning, and exposure to a given group or culture over a considerable period of time, can we be sure that learning deficiencies are not a factor. The model would clearly benefit if causal factors could be incorporated as explicit entities. This would seem particularly important in studying the emotionally disturbed.

Finally, there is the problem of content area differences in conformity. It seems highly probable that the ability model, as utilized in the field of intelligence, is appropriate to the analysis of conformity. People must, out of motivation and exposure, develop special sensitivities to certain kinds of norms. Perhaps they conform more when in groups than when alone, when at work than when at home, in heterosexual situations than in homosexual. We have at present no adequate basis for differentiating the important dimensions of conformity, and the statistical model is of little help in pointing the way.

REFERENCES

Asch, S. E.   "Effects of Group Pressure upon the Modification and Distortion of Judgments," in Harold Guetzkow (ed.), *Groups, Leadership and Men* (Carnegie Press, 1951).

Miner, J. B.   *Intelligence in the United States* (New York: Springer Publishing Co., 1957).

———.   "On the Use of a Short Vocabulary Test to Measure General Intelligence," *Journal of Educational Psychology* (1961), Vol. 52, pp. 157–60.

———.   "Conformity among University Professors and Business Executives," *Administrative Science Quarterly*, Vol. 7 (1962), pp. 96–109.

———.   "Evidence Regarding the Value of a Management Course Based on Behavioral Science Subject Matter," *Journal of Business*, Vol. 36 (1963), pp. 325–35.

———.   *Studies in Management Education* (New York: Springer Publishing Co., 1965).

———, and Culver, J. E.   "Some Aspects of the Executive Personality," *Journal of Applied Psychology* (1955), Vol. 39, pp. 348–53.

Rorschach, H.   *Psychodiagnostik* (Bern: Hans Huber, 1921).

———, and Oberholzer, E.   "Zur Auswertung des Formdeutversuchs für die Psychoanalyse," *Zeitschrift für die gesamte Neurologie und Psychiatrie* (1923), Vol. 82, pp. 240–74.

Selznick, P.   *TVA and the Grass Roots* (Berkeley: University of California Press, 1949).

Sherif, M.   *The Psychology of Social Norms* (New York: Harper, 1936).

Tomkins, S. S., and Miner, J. B.   *The Tomkins-Horn Picture Arrangement Test* (New York: Springer Publishing Co., 1957).

———, and ———.   *PAT Interpretation—Scope and Technique* (New York: Springer Publishing Co., 1959).

Applications of Stochastic and Computer Models to the Process of Free Association

10

Kenneth Mark Colby, M. D. *

A CLINICIAN struggles daily with a class of difficult empirical problems. In psychotherapeutic work he tries to understand and modify the behavior and feelings of emotionally suffering persons who present themselves as patients. The clinician soon learns his powers and limitations in influencing persons in psychotherapeutic situations. He looks to basic or clinical psychological research for help in increasing his limited understanding and skills. But research thus far has provided little of practical value for the clinical artisan.

Psychotherapy research at the moment attempts to utilize both naturalistic and experimental methods. Although my own interest lies in an experimental approach, it is not my intention here to go into the details of particular experiments; instead I will briefly describe and compare two sorts of mathematical models applicable to such studies. My purpose is to compare the advantages and limitations of stochastic and computer models in experimental psychotherapy research.

In one type of experiment, a subject lies on a couch and free-associates out loud, continuously. An observer sits behind him out of sight, remaining silent for the most part but occasionally saying something. Spoken output from the subject can be viewed as a time series, a sequence of states with a continuous parameter of time (see Figure 1).

The diagram illustrates a time-series, beginning at $+$ in State 1, remaining in State 1 at $+_2$, jumping to State 3 at $+_3$, etc. The states are equivalent to a random variable X, having a value of 0 or 1, and corresponding to the presence or absence of the state in question. A stochastic process is one in which the transition from one state to another contains a probabilistic random element. The states in this sort of experiment are defined by the information content of the messages output by the subject. His utterances are tape-recorded and then divided into sentences, using the scoring method of Dollard and Auld, to give countable units.

In one experiment, after a suitable antecedent state-sequence, the ex-

* Stanford University.

FIGURE 1

FREE-ASSOCIATION TIME SERIES

+1
+2
+3
+4
+5----
S0
S1
S2
S3
S4
S5

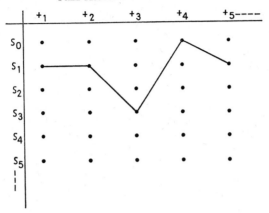

FIGURE 2

TREE DIAGRAM

S1
S1
INPUT
.6
.2
.2
S1
S2
S3

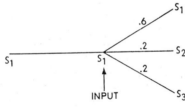

FIGURE 3

MATRIX NOTATION

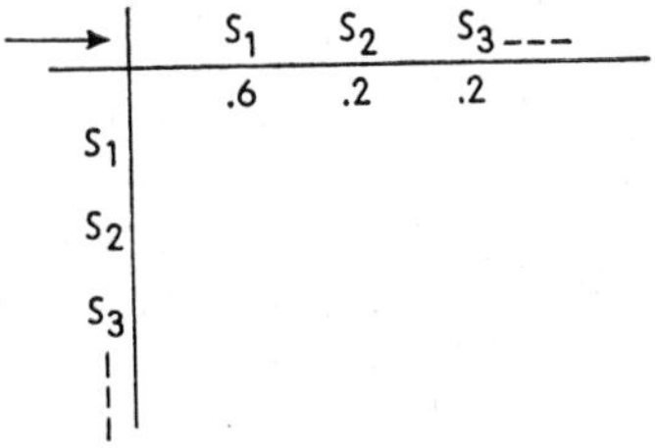

S1
S2
S3---
.6
.2
.2
S1
S2
S3

perimenter made a statement and then remained silent to observe the effect of this spoken input on subsequent free-association. The situation can be represented by a tree diagram (Figure 2) or in matrix notation (Figure 3). Given sufficient repetitions, one can count frequencies and assign probabilities to the state transitions produced by spoken input. Using this model in such an experiment, we would be looking for a probability law such as:

> Given antecedent state S, and making an input I,
> one obtains sequent state S_3 with probability p.

One might want to compare the effect of different inputs on similar antecedent states. For example, in one experiment we compared the effect of asking a question with a causal-correlative statement. It was found that a causal-correlative has a much greater amplifying power than an interrogative, ampilfying power here being defined as extending a response set and increasing the density of the antecedent state within that response set.

There are all sorts of things one might want to try. For example, can a spoken input attenuate an antecedent state as well as amplify it? Or can one make an avoided state appear in free association in a time-enduring way? Or what are the consequences of extending the model from a two-stage to a three-stage transition using two inputs?

The Stochastic Perspective

Now we come to the question of the advantages and disadvantages of using a stochastic perspective. In choosing a mathematical model we like to feel it is appropriate to the subject matter, and that there is some degree of fit between the properties of a mathematical system and the properties of empirical observation. Free association can be appropriately described as a stochastic process; reliable counts of frequencies can be made and probability estimates given. Experienced clinicians are more accepting toward this model than toward one which does not take into account the variability of person-states and patient-states through time. One difficulty with the extensive statistical approach is that, by taking readings at only a single point in time, it fails to provide as definitive a description of "patienthood" as an intensive approach which makes repeated observations at relatively close intervals over stretches of time.

But there are disadvantages to the stochastic model. I should preface this criticism with a few remarks about the dilemma of an empirical investigator in applying a mathematical system. First, we may be using it in such a naive and oversimplified form that we do not gain the advantages of its power and rigor. Second, if we try to apply it in a sophisticated form we cannot find empirical conditions which fit the definitions and assumptions of the mathematical system. Furthermore we lack the mathematical insight to really understand all the steps of development in a formal model.

In applying a stochastic model to the experimental situations described, how many assumptions of the model are violated by the empirical conditions? As you might suspect, a good many, such as the assumption of a stationary source, independence of number of trials, independence of past history, and so forth. One can repair some of this by using special cases, such as multi-order Markovian chains, or, if one wants to get fancy, using Jowett's serial analysis of variance. But a more telling drawback to stochastic models is revealed in the following: Is the research question you are asking one in which a mean probability can yield a useful answer?

Roughly stated, one question we are asking in psychotherapy research is how does one person affect or benefit another person by listening and talking—by communicating with him. If we eventually have dependable knowledge that input I produces the state transition $S_1 \rightarrow S_3$ with mean probability 0.7, we admittedly have learned something we did not know before. But we have not gained on the person-on-person-effect problem as much as we would like because:

a) The structure and mechanisms involved are as mysterious as ever, so we will be limited to predicting only mean probabilities in long runs; and

b) We still have no good hold on the individual case and the individual event.

Statistical generalizations, while yielding some advance in information, represent a weak level of explanation by summary. We are ultimately searching for a good, that is, probable explanation by theory of an event, rather than for an explanation by summary of a probable event.

The Bush-Mosteller learning model assumes that what lies in the box between input-output functions is simply a random wheel. But the brain-mind must be more orderly and organized than this, as evidenced by the failure of the Bush-Mosteller model to account for negative recency in binary choice experiments.

As Chassan has pointed out, one advantage of an intensive stochastic study of individual experimental subjects or patients is that in time we begin to find out some of the conditions under which significant statistical distributions or probabilities appear. When we begin to know these conditions, we begin to move away from purely probabilistic random-wheel notions toward specifying sets of conditions acting as determinants of state-sequence transitions.

The Computer Perspective

This brings me now to that class of quasi-explanatory deterministic models known as computer models or computer simulations. Strictly speaking, they are not formal mathematical models. They involve a conceptual instrument known as a program and a technical instrument, the hardware computer. A program represents an attempt to specify a set of determinants—a set of possible mechanisms inside the black box which can generate the kind of state-sequence output observable empirically. The program may contain random elements if one chooses, hence it may not be strictly deterministic. But it is deterministic, in holistic sense, in that the entire system comes into play with a large number of positive and negative feedbacks regulating individual causal sequences. A program can provide a possible explanation, or a quasi-explanation by theory, through the same type of information processing which goes on in a person when he free-associates in an experimental or clinical psychotherapeutic session.

Besides being interesting, of what use would such a computer model be?

I view it as a new type of experimental "animal," or, in fact as an "experimental person." We are all familiar with the difficulties of experimenting with persons. Strangely enough, they are just not good experimental subjects for the kinds of questions we are asking about persons. Psychological experiments contain all sorts of uncontrolled variables, and we are never quite sure just what independent variables a person is responding to. Persons change slowly in time, and they are irreversible in time. We cannot go back and try alternative inputs under the same initial conditions. Finally, there are good ethical reasons why we cannot say and do anything we please to persons. An ill-chosen spoken input in an experimental context can be very disruptive to someone's psychological health and is not easily erased by an explanation of the deceptive game underlying most experiments.

The hope would be to construct a program on which one might conduct experiments with great control, at least over the initial conditions and the independent variables. This program model would contain processes designated neurotic as well as healthy. Then an effort would be made to influence or modify the program by inputs now used by therapists and by inputs representing innovations in content and method.

The model we are working on now is a complex system of symbols organized into lists and list structures. The symbols represent data and processes vested into one another in such a way as, when running on hardware, to carry out hierarchical steering functions. The particular data are themes taken from a patient who has been studied intensively over a long time. The model is case-descriptive in that the data are idiosyncratic. It is also norm-descriptive in that certain processes are included which are inferred to be general and assumed to hold for a large number of persons. Finally, the model is normative in the sense that some processes represent an idealized way the mind *should* work under certain circumstances.

Thus, this is an "Irish stew model," containing a little bit of a lot of things. We do not worry whether the subsidiary hypotheses and simplifying assumptions are true or not since the logic of this approach is not to discover a law but to test the conjunctions of all these elements and to follow out the consequences of alternative conjunctions.

The program contains knowledge in the form of beliefs, that is, propositions "held" as true. When concerned with the expression in output of a given complex of beliefs, it may run into intense conflict, one process commanding one direction and another counter-commanding. In this situation "anxiety" rises, and an attempt is made by inhibitory and distortive processes to change one of the pair involved in the conflict. If this distorting transformation fails, "anxiety" rises again and more powerful distortions are successively selected until the new belief created can get through the system without conflict.

Output is in the form of simplified English statements expressing the urgent concerns of the program and how it "feels" during processing. In this model of a neurotic process, "anxiety" is reduced at the cost of distorting information and not allowing optimal discharge of excitation.

If we can ever get the conjunction of the processes and subroutines involved in the model to work harmoniously, I think you can sense the advantages it will have as an experimental tool. In areas of ill-defined problems, it is difficult to get consensus on elementary terms. A computer model states very explicitly what a belief is, what conflict is, what anxiety is, or—rather than "is"—how these elements are represented in a language the computer can process. Computer models provide a way of rapidly coming to decisions about alternative organizations of highly complex systems. Finally, they have properties of versatility, subtlety, and evolving growth, which make them appropriate models for mental processes.

We may be overly ambitious and presumptuous in these attempts. Sticking to simpler models or analyzing data statistically from live persons may be the better way to gain reliable information. All psychotherapists sense that we are not making the most of our observations nor of our potential skills. Both basic and clinical research will have to widen the scope of their inquiry if we are to get beyond our present impasse. We will have to try all sorts of novel approaches (and computer models are certainly novel for psychotherapy) in attacking the challenging and non-trivial problem of relieving neurotic suffering through person-to-person communicative processes.

PART IV

Group Behavior:
Interaction and Conflict

Confront! Confront!
The sages cry,
    Head on, head on;
    War is no Träumerei!

Be your plea the classic, James-ian
Or your roots the later, Games-ian,
    War-like equivalents: to action!
    To grasp man in interaction,
To gently quarrel, and be hip
We now must turn to our lesson
    In simulated Gamesman-ship.

                        F.M.

J. Windedahl

11

Experimental Studies of Conflict in Some Two- and Three-Person Games *

Bernhardt Lieberman†

THE THEORY of games of strategy has fascinated workers in a number of intellectual disciplines, including mathematics, economics, psychology, sociology, and political science. If we ask why it has had such a pervasive appeal, one answer would seem to be that it has applied the abstraction, the intellectual depth, the power, and the techniques of genuine mathematics to questions of social import.

It has become obvious to many that "conflicts of interest," even among reasonable individuals, are inevitable. Since social conflicts are often characterized by their complexity, and too often are resolved by destructive and mutually harmful acts, efforts have been made to develop techniques and understanding that will increase the likelihood of nondestructive solutions.

Numerous attempts also have been made to comprehend the essential elements of social conflicts. Game theory is one such attempt; it is a mathematical construction that is designed to analyze social conflicts and then prescribe a resolution of the situation that should be reasonable to the participants. It is an intellectual construction of depth and significance that makes use of the rigor of the mathematical discipline. By a process of simplification, abstraction, and analysis, the theory provides insights into situations of pure conflict, and into situations in which there are elements of both conflict and cooperation.

Game theory deals with situations in which persons [1] are contesting for

* Much of this work was done during my tenure as a Public Health Service Postdoctoral Research Fellow (8534) of the National Institute of Mental Health, in the Department of Social Relations, Harvard University.

I wish to thank Professor R. Duncan Luce for his substantive contributions to these studies. Discussions with Professor Frederick Mosteller and Howard Raiffa were most helpful.

This paper is reprinted from *Mathematical Methods in Small Group Processes*, Joan Criswell, Herbert Solomon, and Patrick Suppes (eds.), (Stanford, Calif.: Stanford University Press, 1962.)

† Harvard University.

[1] In the game theory literature and in this chapter, *person* refers to a *set of interests* rather than to a single individual. Thus, both bridge and a war between two nations are two-person games.

a quantifiable commodity or object of value; that is, situations from which the persons in conflict wish to obtain a maximum amount of this commodity or object. Given these conditions, the theory attempts to present a normative resolution of the conflict; it attempts to prescribe proper or appropriate behavior for one or more persons in such situations.

If a theory is normative, and we discover that persons have, without knowledge of the theory, been behaving as it prescribes, the logical construction has descriptive value. Thus, the prescriptive and descriptive aspects of a primarily normative theory are not unrelated. In an age that has recognized and emphasized the irrational (or nonrational) factors that drive and govern man's behavior, it would be refreshing to discover that in certain situations a sensible resolution of conflicts is the course people normally adopt. We shall see that, to some small extent, this anachronistic notion about behavior is true.

One of the contributions of von Neumann and Morgenstern was to provide an interesting and useful way of classifying and looking at various types of conflict in small groups. Two distinctions of value were made: one between zero-sum and non-zero-sum games, and the second between two-person and n-person games.[2] These two classifications yield four classes of games. They are: the two-person, zero-sum game; the two-person, non-zero-sum game; the n-person, zero-sum game; and, finally, the n-person, non-zero-sum game. In only one of these classes, the two-person, zero-sum game, do we have a situation of pure conflict. In each of the three other classes there is usually some element of joint effort or cooperation among the players.

Only in the simplest situation, the two-person, zero-sum game, where we have a condition of pure conflict, do we have what is generally accepted to be an adequate normative solution of the conflict. Where cooperation is mixed with conflict, where people are opponents and, simultaneously, have to coordinate their interests, we do not have anything that approaches the convincing solution we have for the two-person, zero-sum game.

Conventional game theory requires that payoffs be presented (or be capable of being presented) in explicit matrices. Many interesting social conflicts do not satisfy the rather stringent requirements of game theory. These considerations and others have led many to criticize the limitations of game theory. Some have levelled the criticism that the theory is too abstract and does not include many features that are essential to the understanding of social conflicts.

---

[2] A zero-sum game is one in which, on each play of a game, the sum of the payments is zero. Card games, such as poker, are zero-sum games since whatever one or more players have won, the remaining players have lost. Non-zero-sum games do not have this requirement. It is common to refer to two-person and n-person games. The latter refers to the general game, where n is equal to or greater than three.

For a more complete discussion of these basic terms, see R. D. Luce and H. Raiffa, *Games and Decisions* (New York: John Wiley & Sons, 1957).

Thomas Schelling has suggested an alternative classification of the range of socially interesting games.[3] He suggests that, rather than discuss zero-sum and non-zero-sum games, we consider social conflicts on a scale ranging from those that involve pure conflict to those of pure cooperation. The pure conflict game, the two-person, zero-sum game, is one extreme. The other extreme is the coordination game, where two people receive payoffs only if they coordinate their activity and cooperate. In the coordination game, maximum payment comes to the players simultaneously, and so neither player has any incentive to reduce the rewards to the other players. Between these two types of interactions, there is what Schelling calls the *mixed-motive* game. This is a game that, by conventional classification, would be an *n*-person, zero-sum game, or a two- or *n*-person non-zero-sum game.

The studies to be reported in the rest of this chapter deal with the simplest types of conflicts described by game situations. Three experimental studies will be discussed: the first deals with a two-person, zero-sum game which has a saddle point; the second deals with a two-person, zero-sum game which requires the use of mixed strategies for its solution; the third deals with two variants of the three-person, zero-sum majority game.

The three studies reported here were concerned with the rationality and nonrationality of intelligent human subjects. If one is interested in specifying the situations in which intelligent individuals are rational (in a game theory sense) and those in which they are not rational, it is necessary to study the very simplest situations—where rational solutions exist. These studies were designed to compare the actual behavior of intelligent individuals with the behavior prescribed by zero-sum game models. They are descriptive; and they provide some picture of how groups of intelligent individuals behave in situations of conflict described by zero-sum game models.

STUDY ONE: BEHAVIOR IN A STRICTLY DETERMINED 3 X 3 MATRIX GAME [4]

The first study describes how intelligent individuals behave when playing a strictly determined 3 x 3 zero-sum, matrix game. The two-person, zero-sum game with a saddle point is a model of only a limited number of two-person conflicts. However, we cannot say that such a game is not a model of any important conflicts. Haywood gives an example [5] of a very significant conflict that was resolved by choices of optimal strategies. His

---

[3] T. Schelling, *The Strategy of Conflict* (Cambridge, Mass.: Harvard University Press, 1960).

[4] This study has been described in detail elsewhere; see B. Lieberman, "Human Behavior in a Strictly Determined 3 x 3 Matrix Game," *Behavioral Science* (1960), Vol. 4, pp. 317–22.

[5] In Luce and Raiffa, *Games and Decisions*, p. 64.

analysis of the battle of the Bismarck Sea in World War II indicates that both the Japanese and American Commanders adopted minimax strategies.

The experimental game of Study One is described by the accompanying matrix. In this game the minimax model dictates that both players choose Strategy 3, 100 percent of the time.

Player Red

		1	2	3	*row minima*
	1	+15	0	−2	−2
Player Blue	2	0	−15	−1	−15
	3	+1	+2	0	0
column maxima		+15	+2	0	

Fifteen pairs of subjects played 200 repetitions of the game. Payments were in cents; +15 indicates a 15-cent payment from red to blue and −15 indicates a payment from blue to red. The subjects were given $2.50 at the start of the game and were allowed to keep the amount they had in their possession at the conclusion of the 200 plays.

Approximately half of the subjects, after some experience with the game, adopted the minimax strategy. Even those subjects who did not choose Strategy 3 100 percent of the time were, in the final trials, making the optimal choice 85 percent of the time. On the final 20 trials, 94 percent of the subjects' choices were of the optimal choice, strategy 3.

These data have something to tell us. In situations where subjects can see the essential elements of a game (such as this two-person, zero-sum game with a saddle point), and where the subjects have the intellectual abilities to solve the game, we may expect rational behavior to be the modal behavior.

STUDY TWO: A FAILURE OF GAME THEORY TO PREDICT HUMAN BEHAVIOR

The mixed success of the model as a descriptive theory in Study One led to an investigation of its adequacy when randomized strategies are necessary for the solution of a game. This second study describes how people behave both against a rational opponent and against a nonrational opponent in a two-person, zero-sum game requiring the use of mixed strategies.

Certain probability learning phenomena may be considered analogous to such games. In some two-alternative experiments, subjects' choices of one alternative are rewarded with a probability p, and their choices of the second alternative are rewarded with the probability $(1-p)$. In these studies it is possible to think that the subject is engaged in a matrix game against nature, where nature behaves as if she were playing in accordance with some mixed strategy. It is well known that, in the above experiment, subjects' choices often match the probability of reward. Where subjects receive a unit reward for each correct prediction, and suffer a unit loss (or no loss) for each false prediction, and where $p = 0.50$, matching behavior is optimal in the minimax sense. Where rewards and losses are unit values, and $p \neq 0.50$, subjects should choose the more frequently rewarded side on every trial to maximize the number of rewarded choices.

Edwards studied a number of probability learning situations, which can be thought of as 2 x 2, zero-sum, matrix games.[6] The elements of some of his matrices were varied from unit values, and from the results it appears that his subjects did not behave in conformity with the minimax solution. Siegel and Goldstein studied probability learning situations in which amounts of money could be lost.[7] Again, their subjects did not behave as the minimax model might state they should. In both of the studies, subjects were not playing against a human opponent, who was apparently attempting to win money from them; and thus a critical assumption of game theory was not satisfied. It should be said that neither the Edwards nor the Siegel and Goldstein study was designed to test the adequacy of a game theory model.

In the present study the subjects were faced with an opponent who stated he was attempting to win money from them. One of the two game situations involved was designed to satisfy the assumptions of the theory of games; the second situation yielded information about play against a nonrational opponent.

Method

The Game. A single subject played the following matrix game 300 times against the experimenter. On each play of the game both the experi-

		E	
		1	2
S	1	+3	−1
	2	−9	+3

[6] W. Edwards, "Reward Probability, Amount, and Information as Determiners of Sequential Two-Alternative Decisions," *Journal of Experimental Psychology* (1956), Vol. 52, pp. 177–88.

[7] S. Siegel and P. A. Goldstein, "Decision Making in a Two-Choice Uncertain Outcome Situation," *Journal of Experimental Psychology* (1959), Vol. 57, pp. 37–42.

menter and the subject have a choice of playing a 1 or a 2. If S1–E1 occurred, the subject received 3 cents from the experimenter. If S1–E2 occurred, the experimenter received 1 cent from the subject. The other two payoffs were similarly determined. The minimax solution of this game requires that the subject play S1 with a probability 0.75, and S2 with a probability 0.25. The experimenter should play E1 with a probability 0.25, and E2 with a probability 0.75.

The above game was designed so that the prescription of the minimax model was in contradiction to a matching prediction. If, in this situation, subjects' choices were to match (or tend to match) the probability of reward, they would choose S1 with a probability 0.25, and S2 with a probability 0.75, when the experimenter played rationally. Given the Edwards and the Siegel and Goldstein data cited above, there was little reason to believe that the subjects' choices would match the probability of reward, but such an outcome was considered possible.

Another feature of the game is also of interest. The value of the game is zero; when the experimenter played rationally, the expected outcome of the game was zero, no matter what choices the subjects made. This fact affects the interpretation of the results and will be discussed below.

Subjects. The subjects of the study were 20 men; all undergraduate students of Harvard College and in residence during the academic year 1958–59.

Materials. The materials used consisted of the following: (1) a matrix game board that identified the payoffs; (2) $5.00 in cash for each game; (3) 600 red and 600 blue choice cards; (4) red, white, and blue chips; (5) written instruction sheets; (6) pencils and scrap paper; and (7) screens that hid each player's choice cards from his opponent's view.

Procedure. The subjects were divided randomly into two groups of 10 each. Against the first, group O, the experimenter played in an optimal manner over the entire 300 plays of the game. Against the second, group N, he played optimally for the first 100 repetitions of the game and then changed to a nonoptimal, randomized strategy, choosing E1 and E2 with equal probability, with 0.50 for the final 200 trials.

Both the experimenter and subject had $2.50 at the start of the game. Each exchanged $2.00 in cash for chips, and used these to make payments during the course of play. Both held a number of their colored choice cards in their hands. A play of the game, or a trial in the experiment, consisted in each player's selecting a choice card from his hand with a 1 or 2 on it. Each placed his card face-down in front of him on a table; and, after both choices were made, the cards were turned over, revealing the choices and determining the outcome of the play. Chips were exchanged after each play of the game; and, when the 300 choices were completed, the subject received an amount of money equal to the value of the chips remaining in his possession.

The experimenter's choices were all fixed in advance and were the same for each of the 10 games against the subjects of group O. The first 100 choices against the players of group N were identical to those against group O. The last 200 against the subjects of group N were identical for all members of that group, but, of course, differed from the choices against group O.

An essential assumption of game theory is that a player is in conflict with a *responsive* opponent who is attempting to win money (or some other quantifiable object or good) from him. If the subjects perceived and could state that the experimenter's choices were fixed in advance, and would not change no matter what he (the subject) did, an argument could be made that an essential assumption of game theory was not satisfied and the model could not be disconfirmed as a descriptive theory by the present study.

To avoid this problem, a procedure was adopted that prevented the subjects from seeing how the experimenter selected his choice card for each play of the game. Both the experimenter and the subject had screens in front of them, and from behind which they played. Each player could see the screen and the game board, but neither could see his opponent's choice cards or the cards he held in his hand. The subjects were told that the screens were being used to prevent either player from obtaining any extraneous clues concerning his opponent's choices. In addition, the written instructions to the subjects stated that the experimenter was playing in a way that would reduce the amount of money he could lose and would increase his chances of winning the subjects' money.

Questionnaire. At the completion of the experimental session, each subject completed a questionnaire containing questions about how he played the game and how he believed the experimenter played the game.

Results

Group O. The results presented in Figure 1 indicate quite clearly that the subjects of group O did not play as the minimax model commands. The mean percentages of choices of S1 for the 10 subjects, considered in trial blocks of 25, differed grossly and significantly from the prescription of the minimax model (random fluctuation around 75 percent).[8] The percentage of choices of S1 varied from a high of 52.8 percent to a low of 28.0 percent; S1 was chosen 40.9 percent of the time over the entire 300 plays of the game. From inspection of Figure 1, it appears that the mean curve may have reached a stable level of response at about 40 percent.

In addition, it was not the case that some of the 10 players adopted the minimax strategy while others did not. Inspection of the data of the individual subjects (not presented here) indicates that *not one* of the 10 sub-

---

[8] A t test led to a rejection of the null hypothesis ($\alpha = 0.05$) that the choices of S1 were drawn from a population of responses in which the probability of choice of S1 was 0.75.

FIGURE 1

CHOICES OF S1 WHERE THE EXPERIMENTER PLAYED RATIONALLY ON ALL 300 TRIALS
(Group O)*

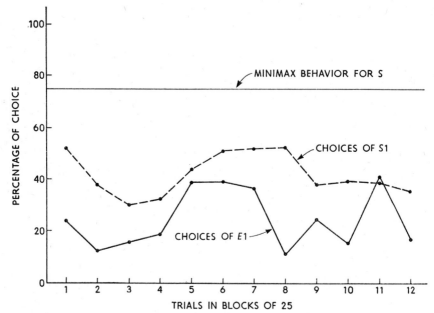

* The experimenter's choices of E1 are included in the figure.

jects chose S1 approximately 75 percent of the time.

Group N. The mean percentages of choice of S1 for the subjects of group N (presented in Figure 2), were similar to those of group O over the first 100 trials: S1 was chosen 37.8 percent of the time by the subjects of group O and 42.8 percent of the time by those of group N. After the 100th trial, when the experimenter played nonrationally against the players of group N, their choices of S1 increased rapidly, approaching the 75 percent line, but remaining, however, consistently below it. Over the last 200 trials, the mean percentage of choice of S1 was 65.1 percent; and the high point 74.4 percent. Comparisons of the obtained behavior with the minimax behavior indicate obvious and statistically significant differences.[9]

Analyses of the behavior of the individual subjects of group N over the final 200 plays of the game indicate that some did, on some blocks of trials, choose S1 with a frequency greater than 75 percent. The subjects could have exploited the weakness in the experimenter's play by choosing S1 100 percent (or perhaps only 80.0 to 90.0 percent) of the time. However, when the entire 200 trials are considered, only two subjects chose S1

[9] A *t* test led to a rejection of the null hypothesis ($a = 0.05$) that the choices of S1 (for the subjects of group N over the final 200 trials) were drawn from a population of responses in which the probability of choice of S1 was 0.75.

FIGURE 2

CHOICES OF S1 WHERE THE EXPERIMENTER PLAYED NONRATIONALLY ON THE
FINAL 200 TRIALS (Group N)*

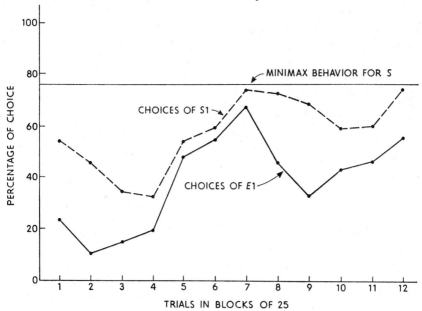

* Choices of E1 are included.

with a frequency greater than 75 percent; one subject chose S1 80.5 percent of the time, and another 76.5 percent of the time.

From the data presented in Table 1 (the percentages of the choice of S1 by the individual subjects of group N) it is obvious that, with one possible exception, the subjects did not exploit the weakness in the experimenter's play. Since the experimenter was playing nonrationally over the final 200

TABLE 1

PERCENTAGES OF CHOICE OF S1
OVER THE FINAL 200 TRIALS
BY SUBJECTS OF GROUP N

Subject Number	% Choice of S1
1	80.5
2	71.0
3	67.5
4	50.5
5	61.0
6	46.5
7	76.5
8	73.0
9	64.5
10	59.0

plays of the game against group N, the relationship of the subjects' choices to the minimax solution is a bit complicated and will be considered in some detail in the subsequent discussion.

The Game as a Probability Learning Situation. It is possible to subject the present data to analyses carried out in probability learning experiments. To do this, it is necessary to make some identifications. For group N on the first 100 trials, and for group O throughout, the probability of reward of the choice of S1 was 0.25; for group N on the final 200 trials, the probability of reward of the choice of S1 was 0.50.

Edwards [10] has offered a theoretical notion to explain behavior in probability learning situations in which reward and loss values are varied from zero and unit amounts. He offers a Relative Expected Loss Minimization Rule (RELM), based on Savage's concept of *regret* or *loss*, which is applicable to the present study. Edwards found considerable correspondence between his results and the predictions of the RELM rule.

When the rule is applied to the present data, it yields a prediction for group N over the final 200 trials. The rule predicts that subjects should choose alternative 2 more often than 1. The subjects of this study did just the opposite. The reasons for this are fairly clear and will be discussed below.

Although there does not appear to be any precise quantitative theoretical explanation of the subjects' behavior, there is one analysis of the data that yields an interesting observation. The experimenter's choices have been described variously as optimal and nonoptimal, with given numerical probabilities. Actually, he adopted two randomized strategies, one against group O and another against group N. This resulted in variations from trial block to trial block in the experimenter's choices of E1 and E2. The variations in behavior, together with the subjects' behavior, are presented in Figures 1 and 2. There appears to be a marked responsiveness of the subjects' choices to the random fluctuation in the experimenter's choices of E1. This responsiveness is even more marked in the case of group N, where the subjects' choices follow the shift in the experimenter's change from the optimal to the nonoptimal strategy. The reader can make more detailed observations to see the extent to which subjects were responsive to the trial block variation.

Responses to Questionnaire. The subjects' answers to questions about their manner of play indicated that most *did* believe they were opposed by a player who was responsive and attempting to win money from them. Sixteen of 20 stated that they used some plan of play in an attempt to increase their winnings; and the same number stated that the experimenter was responsive to their choices: what he did depended on their own choices. Eleven of the 20 stated they varied their choices in an attempt to influence the decisions of the experimenter.

---

[10] *Op. cit.,* pp. 177–88.

Discussion

The behavior of the subjects of group O indicates quite clearly that in a game requiring the use of a randomized strategy, the minimax model (which is primarily a normative model) is not adequate as a descriptive theory of behavior. Previous results indicated that, in a simpler matrix game with a saddle point, some people behaved as the minimax model prescribes. The current results indicate this may be the limit of rationality of intelligent individuals in two-person, zero-sum matrix game situations.

The interpretation of the behavior of the subjects of group N requires some consideration of the definition of rationality that was employed. As has already been indicated, game theory, including the minimax model, was created to prescribe what an individual should do on a single play of a game when in conflict with an opponent who is believed to be intelligent and rational. The game played by the subjects of group N cannot be said to be such a situation. The subjects played the final 200 repetitions of a game in which, if they had adopted the minimax strategy, their expectation was zero. However, in the course of play, they might have learned that they could increase their winnings by deviating from the minimax strategy.

We cannot say that a rational player should not have attempted to exploit the weakness in the experimenter's play by deviating from the prediction of the minimax model. It might be appropriate to say that after some experience with the experimenter's choices over the last 200 plays of the game, the subjects of group N should have chosen S1 and 100 percent (or 80 to 90 percent) of the time. But since the subjects were led to believe that they were being opposed by a responsive opponent who would exploit any obvious weakness in their play—such as the adoption of a pure strategy —such a prescription may not be appropriate. Since minimax theory does not prescribe how a player should exploit an opponents's weakness, it seems clear that the situation for group N was not a test of the minimax model as a descriptive theory.

In the two-person game played, if one player adopted the optimal strategy, as the experimenter did against group O, the expectation of the game was zero, no matter what the subject did. It might be argued that the subjects of group O had no incentive to be rational, since no matter what their choices were they obtained the same expected payoff. This fact, that subjects' choices do not affect their expectation, must be seen as characteristic of utilizing the minimax model as a descriptive theory. A strict interpretation of minimax theory requires that the subjects of group O adopt the optimal solution, if only to prevent the experimenter from exploiting any weakness in their play that might exist were they not rational. Thus the game played by the subjects of group O was a reasonable and demanding but not an uncomplicated test of the minimax model.

From observations of the subjects during the experimental session, and from their responses to the questionnaires, it was obvious that they did not perceive the task facing them as one in which they should find a systematic manner of playing the game, or a plan which would assure them of receiving the minimax value. Subjects tended to look for patterns in the experimenter's play and to anticipate his response on each trial in an attempt to win the small amounts of money involved. Many appeared to behave in a manner similar to humans making decisions in a probability learning situation.

The analyses reported above indicate that Edwards' RELM rule does not explain the behavior of group N over the final 200 trials. Edwards states that two tendencies make the RELM rule work. The first is a preference for high probabilities of reward, and the second is a preference for large amounts over small amounts. Neither of these tendencies could operate in the situation facing the subjects of group N. The experimenter adopted a 0.50–0.50 mixed strategy and the amounts of reward were identical, no matter which alternative the subject chose. In addition, S1 had a 1 cent loss associated with it, and S2 presented the possibility of a 9 cent loss. Given these factors, it is understandable that the RELM rule did not predict accurately. The present study should not be considered a best test of the rule. However, it should be recognized that, given these factors that would tend to make the rule fail, it *did* fail.

STUDY THREE: BEHAVIOR IN TWO, THREE-PERSON ZERO-SUM GAMES

The third study to be described gives us information about how certain groups of intelligent individuals behave in two, three-person conflicts which are described by the zero-sum game models. The two previous studies indicated that in social interactions described by the two-person, zero-sum models, people were in some situations rational and in other situations not rational. The present study, which follows in the line of the previous work, raises some new and interesting problems. The moment a third person enters a situation of social interaction, the alignment of two against one become possible. In fact, von Neumann and others believe that this is one of the central problems in understanding the significant features of three-person interaction.[11]

Unlike the two-person, zero-sum game, in the three-person, zero-sum

---

[11] In the three-person game being played by the United States, the Soviet Union, and the Mainland Chinese, a very significant feature has been the relationship between the two communist countries as it affects the United States. The nature of splits and coalitions on the international scene of course provides tempting game theory analogies, explored elsewhere in this volume and in more ambitious political theorizing. J. von Neumann and O. Morgenstern, *Theory of Games and Economic Behavior* (3d ed.; Princeton, N.J.: Princeton University Press, 1953).

game there is no generally accepted, unambiguous solution. A small number of three-person, zero-sum games have what we might consider precise solutions, but the larger number do not. A number of solutions of varying types have been offered for three-person games. Von Neumann and Morgenstern offer one. However, on examination, this solution can be seen as not giving a precise prescription of how a player should conduct himself; rather, it yields a class of solutions. Shapley has offered a value for three-person, zero-sum games whose meaning is somewhat ambiguous.

In the present study two games were used. One was a three-person game which has, what we may consider, an obvious, specific solution. The second was a three-person game which did not have a solution, in the sense that there was a precise prescription of play for each subject on every play of the game. The game selected virtually required the subjects to form coalitions, and, in the second game, to divide the winnings they obtained. The experimental situations enable us to study rigorously the aspects of the phenomena of conflict, cooperation, coalition formation and communication in three-person groups.

Method

The Games. Two, three-person, zero-sum majority games were employed. In the majority game each player (designated 1, 2, 3) by a personal move chooses the number of one of the two other players. If two choose each other's numbers, a couple or coalition is formed. Three distinct couples are possible; but on any one play of the game only one couple, or none at all, can occur. The coalition that forms wins an amount of money from the third player. In the first game, described by Table 2, all the winning coalitions received 6 cents from the third player. The rules of the game provided for a different distribution of the 6 cents among the winners. When the coalitions (1,2) and (1,3) formed, player 1 received 4 cents and players 2 and 3 received 2 cents. When coalition (2,3) formed, each player received 4 cents.

TABLE 2

GAME 1

Choice of Player			Couple	Loser	Payoff to		
1	2	3			1	2	3
2	1	1	(1,2)	3	+4	+2	-6
2	3	1	-	-	-	-	-
2	3	2	(2,3)	1	-6	+3	+3
3	1	1	(1,3)	2	+4	-6	+2
3	1	2	-	-	-	-	-

In the second game, which is described by Table 3, similar personal moves were made, coalitions formed, and payoffs went from the single player to the coalitions. This game involved coalitions of different strength. The coalition (1,2) received 10 cents from 3; (1,3) received 8 cents from 2; and coalition (2,3) received 6 cents from 1. The winning pairs had to decide, by the use of written communications, how to divide the winnings.

TABLE 3

GAME 3

| Choice of Player | | | | | Payoff to | |
1	2	3	Couple	Loser	Couple	Loser
2	1	1	(1,2)	3	-10	-10
2	3	1	-	-	-	-
2	3	2	(2,3)	1	- 6	- 6
3	1	1	(1,3)	2	- 8	- 8
3	1	2	-	-	-	-

Procedure. In both games, written communications among the players were permitted between moves. At the moment of decision, each player was uninformed of the choices of the others. Choices were made by placing the card with the player's number face-down on a table. The cards were then turned over simultaneously to determine the outcome of each of the 40 plays of the game.

Subjects. Forty-eight Harvard College undergraduates served as subjects. Eight groups of three played game 1, and eight different groups of three played game 2.

Materials. The materials used consisted of the following: (1) instruction sheets for each player; (2) red, white, and blue chips; (3) red, white, and blue choice cards, which contained the players' numbers; (4) blank, colored cards for communications; (5) scrap paper and pencils for each subject; and (6) $2.50 for each player in game 1 and $3.00 for each player in game 2.

Questionnaire. After the experimental session, each player gave a description of how he played the game.

Solutions. Solution notions in three-person, zero-sum situations are quite complex. For game 1, von Neumann and Morgenstern offer an informal but convincing solution. Players 2 and 3 should unite to take 3 cents each from player 1. The basic values of the von Neumann and Morgenstern solution a', b', and c' are all zero. The premium $\Delta/6$ to each player who is part of the coalition equals -3, and $-\Delta/3$ equals -6. The Shapley value for each player in game 1 is zero.

For game 2, the von Neumann and Morgenstern basic values are: $a' = +2$, $b' = 0$, $c' = -2$; $\Delta/6 = +4$, and $-\Delta/3 = -8$. For game 2, von Neumann and Morgenstern offer a solution that suggests that when coalition (1,2) forms, player 1 should receive 6 cents of the 10 cents, when (1,3) forms, player 1 should receive 6 of the 8 cents, and when coalition (2,3) forms, player 2 should receive 4 of the 6 cents. Other sets of imputations may be considered solutions for this game. As a result, solution theory, as presented by von Neumann and Morgenstern, offers no simple, unambiguous prescription as minimax theory does in the two-person, zero-sum game. In game 2, the Shapley value for player 1 is $+2$; for player 2 it is 0; for player 3 it is -2.

Results.

Game 1. Table 4 summarizes the outcomes of the plays of the game by the eight triples of subjects. Outcome 0 indicates that no coalition formed; outcome 1 indicates coalition (1,2) formed; outcome 2 indicates coalition (1,3) formed; outcome 3 indicates coalition (2,3) formed. The table presents percentages of occurrences of the four possible outcomes, in blocks of five trials, over the 40 trials. If the subjects were to conform to the von Neumann and Morgenstern solution, they should form coalition (2,3) 100 percent of the time. The data show that, in the first block of trials, this outcome occurred 50 percent of the time. On the last trials, outcome 3 occurred 77.5 percent of the time. This outcome occurred more frequently than any other: 70 percent of the time over all 40 trials. It is interesting to note that the no coalition outcome occurred at least as often as either outcome 1 or 2.

TABLE 4

DATA OBTAINED FROM PLAYS OF GAME 1

	Percentage of Occurance of Outcome			
Trials in Blocks of 5	0 No Coalition	1 (1,2)*	2 (1,3)	3 (2,3)
1–5	15.0	17.5	17.5	50.0
6–10	15.0	7.5	12.5	65.0
11–15	12.5	10.0	0	77.5
16–20	12.5	15.0	5.0	67–5
21–25	15.0	5.0	12.5	67.5
26–30	20.0	5.0	0	75.0
31–35	7.5	5.0	10.0	77.5
36–40	7.5	5.0	10.0	77.5
Mean	13.2	8.8	8.4	69.7

* (1,2) indicates player 1 and 2 chose each other's numbers and formed the winning couple.

Table 5 presents the amounts each player won or lost at the conclusion of the 40 plays of the game. If the players were perfectly rational (formed the [2,3] coalition on each of the 40 plays), player 1 would have lost $2.40 of his $2.50, and players 2 and 3 would each have won $1.20. In games (e) and (h), players 2 and 3 actually won the maximum amount they could. In game (c) they came quite close to this maximum amount. Only in game

TABLE 5

PAYOFFS TO PLAYERS OF GAME 1

Game	Amounts Won or Lost by Players (In dollars and cents)		
	1	2	3
(a)	−1.68	+0.80	+0.88
(b)	−1.40	+0.50	+0.90
(c)	−2.24	+1.16	+1.08
(d)	−0.84	+0.42	+0.42
(e)	−2.40	+1.20	+1.20
(f)	−0.24	+0.24	0.0
(g)	+0.02	+0.11	−0.13
(h)	−2.40	+1.20	+1.20
Mean	−1.40	+0.70	+0.70

(g) did player 1 win more than he lost. The mean values show that player 1 lost $1.40 and players 2 and 3 won 70 cents each.

Game 2. The relationships among the three players in game 2 are quite intricate. One might think that a simple way of resolving the conflict would be for players 1 and 2 to form a permanent coalition and divide their winnings equally. However, when this occurs, it immediately becomes obvious to player 3 that it is advantageous for him to form a coalition with one of the two others. He can make an offer to player 1 to form a coalition with him, from which player 1 can receive more than the 5 cents he can receive together with player 2. It is even advantageous for player 3 to offer player 1, 7 cents or even 8 cents. Thus player 1 is tempted to break his coalition with player 2 and to take the full 8 cents from player 3. Seeing this, player 2 can then make a more attractive offer to 3 or to 1. The process can be repeated.

The three players quickly learned to see the complexities of the situation. What occurred was instability: offer and counter-offer; acceptance, rejection, deception; and the "double cross." Coalitions formed and were changed; in not one of the eight games did a coalition form on the first trial and remain constant through all the 40 plays of the game.

Table 6 presents the percentages of occurrence of the possible outcomes in blocks of five trials. The no-coalition outcome occurred on 7.2 percent of the plays; outcome 1 occurred on 35.3 percent of the plays; outcome 2 on 18.1 percent of the plays; and outcome 3 on 39.4 percent of the plays. The outcome that occurred most frequently was 3, the one that yielded the smallest payoff to the winning coalition.

We may speculate a bit about such a result. It is possible that the same forces that led to the exclusion of player 1 from the coalition formation in game 1 were also effective here. Here player 1 was seen as the stronger or more exploitive individual. This led players 2 and 3 to unite against him to form their coalition quite frequently.

TABLE 6

DATA OBTAINED FROM PLAYS OF GAME 2

	Percentage of Occurrence of Outcome			
Trials in	0	1	2	3
	No			
Blocks of 5	Coalition	(1,2)	(1,3)	(2,3)
1-5	10.0	47.5	22.5	20.0
6-10	0	32.5	17.5	50.0
11-15	10.0	37.5	10.0	42.5
16-20	12.5	22.5	22.5	42.5
21-25	7.5	27.5	30.0	35.0
26-30	7.5	40.0	17.5	35.0
31-35	2.5	40.0	17.5	40.0
36-40	7.5	35.0	7.5	50.0
Mean	7.2	35.3	18.1	39.4

Table 7 presents the frequency of the divisions of the payoff the subjects decided upon. The divisions marked by asterisks include the solution mentioned previously. After each play of the game (there were 320 plays of

TABLE 7

DIVISIONS OF PAYOFFS IN GAME 2

Coalitions Formed and Possible Divisions of Payoffs			Frequency
	(1,2)	10 - 0[a]	0
		9 - 1	0
		8 - 2	4
		7 - 3	17
		6 - 4*	20
		5 - 5	65
		4 - 6	3
		3 - 7	0
		2 - 8	2
		1 - 9	0
		0 - 10	2
	(1,3)	8 - 0	0
		7 - 1	0
		6 - 2*	10
		5 - 3	16
		4 - 4	24
		3 - 5	1
		2 - 6	1
		1 - 7	5
		0 - 8	1
	(2,3)	6 - 0	5
		5 - 1	0
		4 - 2*	2
		3 - 3	93
		2 - 4	23
		1 - 5	3
		0 - 6	0
	0		23
	Σ		320

* Indicates a division of payoffs suggested by the von Neumann and Morgenstern solution.

[a] When coalition (1,2) formed, this division indicates player 1 received 10 cents and player 2 received 0 cents. Similarly, 0 - 10 indicates player 2 received 10 cents.

the game by the eight triples of subjects), two subjects had to decide how their winnings should be divided. Table 7 indicates the various possible divisions of the payoffs.

Since the solutions discussed give no precise prescription to the subjects how they should play the game and divide the winnings, it is difficult to prescribe which of the divisions of earnings should occur most frequently. Examination of Table 7 indicates that an equal division of the winnings was the most frequent outcome. On 297 of the plays of the game, some payoff occurred; on 23, no coalition formed. Of these 297 payoffs a total of 182 or 61.3 percent of the divisions were equal divisions. In more than half the cases the subjects decided to split their winnings evenly.

Discussion

The results of game 1 describe the behavior of three individuals in a situation where two have a clear incentive to unite forces to the detriment of the third. In a majority of choices the two do just that. However, in a sizable minority of choices this prescribed behavior did not occur. Observations of the subjects and their descriptions of the play offer a variety of reasons for this. Two can be mentioned.

Some subjects felt it was not fair to do this. In other cases, the fact that player 1 received the larger share of the winnings seemed to indicate that his position was one of special privilege or power, and some players 2 and 3 sought to align themselves with him. In fact, in a number of the games, player 1's position was seen initially as being advantageous, but as the relationships among the three players became clear, the weakness of his position became apparent.

The nature of game 2 made complex negotiation inevitable. The agreements, breaking of agreements, and bargaining that occurred, led to an interesting result. From observation of the subjects' behavior, their written descriptions of how they played the game, and their messages, it became obvious that in a number of games the players came to realize that a maximum return on one or two plays of the games was not important. It was far more profitable to enter into a stable, continuing agreement with one other player. Since defection was a possibility, and not an infrequent occurrence, the *intuitive notion of trust* was significant in determining which coalitions formed and held together. The subjects stated that they would enter into coalitions with the player they trusted, with the one they believed would not be tempted to defect from their coalition for a more attractive offer on the next play of the game.

When considering the results in relation to the solutions offered, it should be kept in mind that solution theory was designed to prescribe behavior on a single play of a game. However, the following statements can be made.

The Shapley value offers little help in the understanding of either the descriptive or prescriptive aspects of the two games played. If we require of a theory that it give a precise prescription of behavior, and that it be completely—or virtually completely—correct, then we must reject, as a *descriptive notion*, the von Neumann and Morgenstern solution for the three-person situations studied here.

However, if we wish to be a bit more charitable to our theories, we may concede that the von Neumann solution had a slight or modest success in predicting the behavior obtained from the plays of game 1. In game 2, the common notion that winnings should be divided evenly is more descriptive of behavior than the von Neumann solutions.

CONCLUSIONS

The three studies described in this chapter give us a picture of behavior of some intelligent individuals in a variety of zero-sum games. The picture is a mixed one. Nowhere can we say that individuals behave precisely as a rational theory prescribes. However, where the situation of social interaction and conflict is simple enough that mathematical theories can prescribe precisely a form of rational behavior, we sometimes find people actually behaving in such a way. This is true of the behavior obtained in the two-person, zero-sum game with a saddle point, and is also true in the first of the three-person, zero-sum games.

However, in the two-person mixed-strategy game (for group 0), the mathematical theory offers a specific randomized solution. It was quite obvious in this situation that subjects did not behave in this way. The notion of a randomized strategy is nonintuitive; and subjects not familiar with game theory do not learn to adopt this solution. In the second game of the three-person study, we reached a situation of social interaction and conflict in which the mathematical theory does not offer a precise prediction. It is not surprising, then, that the subjects exhibited varying types of behavior. In this situation an even division of winnings was the most frequent outcome.

The studies reported above are perhaps the simplest ones that could be done involving game theory notions. It is quite obvious that the mathematical theory was the primary stimulus for this work; the intent was to compare prescribed behavior with actual behavior. Now that these studies are completed, it appears that it is quite feasible to study situations of social interaction and conflict utilizing other game models. There are any number of more interesting small group situations that can be simulated by game models. Game theory abstracts many essential elements from situations of social conflict, and ingenious experimentation may provide insight into more important social conflicts.

A Model of Negotiation
12   and Some Experimental
Evidence *

OTOMAR J. BARTOS [†]

THE OBJECTIVE of this paper is threefold: to describe a model of negotiation, to present some preliminary findings bearing on the model, and to identify some of the problems encountered while formulating the model and applying it to the findings. No attempt will be made to discuss negotiation in general. Instead, only a model applicable to the given experimental design will be described. Since much of the discussion to follow is tentative, no attempt will be made to state all our ideas in a rigorous fashion.

Experiments

A total of 18 experiments was performed with a total of 30 subjects, all of them students at the University of Hawaii. Each of the 18 experiments involved 5 subjects discussing a five-point agenda. Maximum time allotted to each experimental (negotiation) session was two hours. Since each subject served in three different experiments, it is convenient to distinguish three different waves of experiments.

During the first and the third wave, all subjects played the roles of heads of state meeting at a Summit; during the second wave, each subject played the role of a U.S. Senator meeting as a member of a Senate committee. Because of lack of space, only the first wave will be described in some detail; [1] the second and third waves are similar in most respects.

Depending on his private values,[2] a given subject was assigned one of five possible roles:

---

* This paper is based on the pilot study conducted under the grant NSF G-16462 by the National Science Foundation.

† University of Hawaii.

[1] For a complete description of all three waves, see Otomar J. Bartos, "Negotiations in Small Groups," Honolulu, Hawaii (mimeographed report, 1960).

[2] A questionnaire designed to determine private values was administered to all subjects.

1. The head of (Communist) China.
2. The head of the Soviet Union.
3. The head of Great Britain.
4. The head of the United States.
5. The head of France.

The subjects met to discuss an agenda consisting of five proposals:

1. That total disarmament be put into effect.
2. That nuclear tests be banned.
3. That a system of inspection stations be established.
4. That a permanent UN police force be established.
5. That all nuclear weapons already produced be destroyed.

With each role was associated a set of five payoffs, one with each proposal, indicating how much the power of the given nation was to be increased or decreased if a given proposal were to be unanimously agreed upon by the five negotiators. The following payoffs were associated with the five roles:

	Disarma- ment (1)	Test Ban (2)	Inspection (3)	UN Police (4)	Destruction of Nuclear Weapons (5)
China .... (1)	—10	—10	—30	—30	70
USSR .... (2)	70	50	—30	—10	—10
GB .... (3)	—10	70	30	10	—30
USA .... (4)	—30	—10	70	50	—30
France .... (5)	30	—30	30	10	50

A given subject did not know the entire payoff matrix. He knew only one row of the matrix, the one associated with his role. Considerable care was taken that he remain ignorant of the other rows throughout the experiment. Each subject was told that the negotiation was not to be limited to the five proposals, that he could consider compromises; that is, the combinations of any two, three, four, or all five of the above proposals. He was then told that the payoff of a compromise would be the average (mean) of the payoffs included in the compromise. Finally, each subject was told that, should there be no unanimous agreement at the end of two hours, each negotiator would receive payoff of zero points.

The actual experimental session proceeded so that only one subject was allowed to speak at a time. The speaker at any point was determined by the rules of common courtesy. The principal investigator was present to explain additional rules of order whenever a need for such explanation arose.[3]

---

[3] For the description of the additional rules, see Otomar J. Bartos, "Experiments in Negotiation," Honolulu, Hawaii (mimeographed report, 1961).

Model of Negotiation: Preliminary Remarks

It is true almost by definition that the individuals who meet in a given negotiation session represent divergent interests. One of the fundamental problems of any theory of negotiation is to determine under what conditions and in what way the divergent interests become reconciled. In our experiments the condition of divergent interests was created by assigning to each of the five negotiators a different payoff function. However, the rules of the game assume that the payoff functions remain constant throughout negotiation.[4] But if it is true that the interests (payoffs) do not change, what does? Something must, at least in those cases in which the negotiators reach an agreement.

The fundamental assumption of our model is that the only thing that can change as a result of negotiation is each member's *expectation* concerning the outcome of the session. We shall call such expectation *subjective probability*.

The argument goes as follows: Assuming that some advantages to each negotiator are to be gained from reaching an agreement, he certainly will be "interested" in those outcomes that appear especially likely to be acceptable to the rest of the group, provided they are also acceptable to him. Indeed, if there are two outcomes that are equally acceptable to him, he will promote the outcome that appears to him to have a better chance of acceptance. But what outcome is "acceptable" to a given negotiator? It seems plausible to argue, in our experiments, that it will be only the policies that have for him non-negative payoff.[5]

On the other hand, the negotiator certainly will not simply "swim with the current" and support the policies that are most likely to be accepted. He wishes to influence the negotiation so that it steers towards the policies that are particularly favorable to *him*. Thus it seems plausible to assume that, given two policies with equal chances of acceptance, he will prefer the one which has higher payoff for him. These considerations are summarized in the first assumption of our model. We assume that a given negotiator will, at time t, prefer that policy for which the *product* of (his) subjective probability and (his) payoff is at a maximum.[6]

Given this assumption, we turn to subjective probability. Basically, there

---

[4] This assumption seems reasonable in many instances of actual negotiation. Often the negotiators do not speak for themselves, but represent a large organization or even a whole nation. It is hard to imagine, for example, that the interests of the United States are altered by what transpires during a negotiation session, even if the negotiators are heads of state.

[5] It will be recalled that a negotiator can always secure for himself 0 payoff by refusing to come to a unanimous agreement.

[6] Note that this assumption is consistent with our argument that a negotiator will never prefer a policy with a negative payoff.

are two ways in which subjective probability can be determined in a given experiment: We can either ask the subjects to tell us, for each time t, how likely they consider each of the possible outcomes, or we can make assumptions about the factors determining subjective probability.

Only the second approach is explored here.[7] Given this approach, we immediately encounter the problem of deciding whether all permissible policies should be viewed as mutually exclusive, or whether we should assume that, for some policies at least, there is an "overlap." The case in point are the compromises and the proposals "included" in them. Does it make sense to say that the proposals are elements of the compromise in which they are included? The argument in favor of such a view is the fact that the payoff of a compromise depends on the payoffs of the proposals included in it. The argument against such a view is that the proposals included in a compromise are different from the proposals considered on their own merit: The payoff of a proposal included in a compromise is a fraction of the payoff associated with the proposal when considered by itself.

We shall resolve this problem by assuming that the subjective probability of a compromise is a weighted sum of the probabilities associated with the k proposals included in the compromise, the weight being $1/k$.

The second problem associated with the concept of subjective probability is the identification of the variable or variables that cause it to change. It seems plausible to assume that changes in subjective probability are a result of what has been said during the negotiation session. But just how does a given speech affect the subjective probability of a given negotiator? In our experiments the problem is lessened since each speech must endorse one, and only one, permissible policy, f. Hence it is possible to characterize fully a given speech in terms of $f'^{(t)}$, the policy endorsed at time t.

But what impact does an endorsement have on the subjective probability associated with the policy that was just endorsed? Is it plausible to assume that, whenever policy f is endorsed, the subjective probability that policy f will be unanimously adopted will be increased? We make this assumption. It appears that this assumption is more realistic than the assumption that endorsement leads to a decrease of the corresponding subjective probability. And the assumption that it has no effect at all is not useful.

However, problems remain even now. Granted that endorsement leads to an increase in the corresponding subjective probability, can we assume that the size of the increase is always the same? No matter who the speaker is? No matter which policy is endorsed? Or at what time the endorsement is made? And no matter who the negotiator is whose subjective probability we are considering?

We tried to steer between assuming too much and too little. It seems

---

[7] For a discussion of, and some results concerning the first alternative, see Bartos (1961).

that the absolute minimum of variation one has to allow for concerns the personality of the negotiator, especially his suggestibility. Thus we assume that each negotiator is characterized by a "resistance factor" which determines the size of the increase in subjective probability subsequent to an endorsement. As far as the remaining aspects of the endorsement are concerned, we assume that they have no effect on the changes in subjective probability.

All these considerations are summarized in the second assumption of the model. The third and last assumption deals with the question of what subjective probability should be assumed to exist at the very beginning of the session, at time $t = 0$. It seems reasonable to assume that, since the negotiator in our experiments is ignorant of the payoff functions of the other negotiators, he will assign equal probability to all events that involve unanimous agreement by the rest of the group, the negotiators other than himself.

A Model of Negotiation: Assumptions

As indicated already, we shall refer to a set, F, of *permissible policies, f*. At each time, there is one policy that is endorsed by the speaker; and we shall refer to such a policy as the policy *actually publicly endorsed* at time t, and denote it by $f'^{(t)}$. We shall speak of a given negotiator's *resistance factor* and denote it by α_i.

We shall view time as being a discrete variable, $t = 1,2,3,\ldots$ However, within each time-interval, t, we shall distinguish two subintervals, t_1 and t_2. When we say that a certain speech was delivered at time t, we mean that it was delivered at time t_1. When we say that a certain subjective probability exists at time t, or that at time t negotiator i privately prefers a certain policy, we are referring to the second subinterval, t_2.

It will be recalled that each policy, f, can be a "compromise." The items that are included in a policy will be called the *permissible proposals, j*. In our experiments, there were five proposals j from which a total of 31 policies f could be formed.

We shall speak of *subjective probability*, $p_{ij}^{(t)}$, to refer to the probability assigned at time t by negotiator i to the event that the negotiators other than himself (the "rest of the group") will all endorse, in their final choices, policy f. It will be assumed that subjective probability obeys the axioms of the ordinary calculus of probability. In particular, it will be assumed that:

$$0 \leq p_{ij}^{(t)} \leq 1$$
$$\sum_j p_{ij}^{(t)} = 1.$$

We shall speak of the probability of private preference, $q_{ij}^{(t)}$, referring to the (objective) probability that negotiator i prefers, at time t, policy f. It will be again assumed that:

$$0 \leq q_{if}^{(t)} \leq 1$$

$$\sum_f a_{if}^{(t)} = 1.$$

Assumption 1. Let F^* be a subset of F, containing k policies f^*, such that:

$$v_{if*} p_{if*}^{(t)} \geq v_{if} p_{if}^{(t)} \tag{1}$$

for all f in F, f^* in F^*. Then:

$$a_{if*}^{(t)} = \frac{1}{k}. \tag{2}$$

Assumption 2. Let $f^{(t)}$ in F be any one policy permissible at time t; $f'^{(t)}$ in F the one policy publicly endorsed at time t; and let:

$r^{(t)}$ be the number of proposals included [8] *both* in $f^{(t)}$ and $f'^{(t)}$;
$k^{(t)}$ be the number of proposals included in $f^{(t)}$; $\qquad$ (3)
$k'^{(t)}$ be the number of proposals included in $f'^{(t)}$;

and let $\lambda_f^{(t)}$ be a function such that:

$$\lambda_f^{(t)} = \frac{5}{31} \frac{r^{(t)}}{k^{(t)} k'^{(t)}}. \tag{4}$$

Furthermore, let α_i be a number such that:

$$0 \leq \alpha_i \leq 1; \tag{5}$$

then [9]:

$$p_{if}^{(t+1)} = \alpha_i p_{if}^{(t)} + (1 - \alpha_i) \lambda_f^{(t+1)}. \tag{6}$$

Assumption 3. Let r be a proposal [10] included in policy f; k the number of r included in f. Then:

$$p_{if}^{(0)} = \frac{1}{w} \text{ for all } f \text{ in } F. \tag{7}$$

Comments

Let us assume for a moment that the following conditions prevail:

(i) There are no ties between policies f^*; that is:

$$q_{if*}^{(t)} = 1 \text{ for all } t.$$

---

[8] When speaking about the number of proposals that are in *both* f' and f, we are counting only those proposals that are included in f' and are also included in f.

[9] Note that Equation 6 is formally identical with Bush-Mosteller's stochastic model of learning. See Robert R. Bush and Frederick Mosteller, *Stochastic Models for Learning* (New York: John Wiley & Sons, Inc., 1955).

[10] The permissible proposals are referred to as proposals j. The proposals included in a policy f (in a compromise) are referred to as proposals r.

(*ii*) Whenever negotiator i speaks at time t, the policy he actually publicly endorses is the policy he actually privately prefers; that is, there is one negotiator i at each time t, such that:

$$f_i^{*(t)} = f'^{(t+1)}.$$

(*iii*) The order of speaking is given for the entire session; that is, we know the i for whom, at time t, the above identity between f^* and f' holds.

(*iv*) The resistance factor α_i is given for all i.

It is not difficult to show that under these conditions the private preferences of all negotiators, i, as well as their public endorsements, are all uniquely determined for the entire negotiation session. Given the payoff functions used in our experiments, condition i is satisfied in an overwhelming majority of cases. Although it would be preferable to make an *a priori* assumption about condition *iii*, it is possible to work with the order of speaking as it actually occurred in a given experiment. And we are willing to make assumption *ii*.[11]

Now we must make an assumption about condition *iv*. Ultimately we hope to be able to use information about i's personality to estimate α_i. For the present purposes, however, we shall assume that:

$$\alpha_i = \alpha_i^*,$$

where α_i^* is negotiator i's *optimal* resistance factor. Without offering a rigorous definition at this point, let us say that α_i^* has the property of leading to the best fit between the model and the experimental data.

Once we estimate α_i^* from our data for all i, we can predict the course of the entire negotiation session. However, this will not be done in this paper; at this preliminary stage we are interested merely in the question of how good is the fit between our theory and the data for each negotiator, taken individually.

Goodness of Fit

Since our model will be used to generate predictions about the preferences of the negotiators, the question is raised whether the fit between the predictions and the actual preferences is "good enough." There are several possible measures of the goodness of fit, and it is not easy to decide which measure should be chosen.[12] However, for the present purposes, we shall use a measure that is based on the fact that it is possible to speak of an "overlap" between the predicted and the actually preferred policy. Let the predicted policy f^* and the actually preferred policy f' be represented as

---

[11] Such an assumption amounts to postulating that our subjects be "naive" in the sense of expressing publicly what they privately prefer. With our subjects, who are not expert negotiators, we are willing to make this assumption.

[12] For a discussion of some of the problems, see O. J. Bartos, "Experiments in Negotiation."

five-element vectors (since in our experiments the number of proposals, m, is five). Let the two policies at time t be, for example:

$$f^* = (0,1,1,0,0)$$
$$f' = (1,1,1,0,0).$$

This means that the model predicts that the negotiator will, at time t, prefer the policy consisting of proposals 2 and 3, while in fact the negotiator prefers the policy consisting of proposals 1, 2, and 3. Clearly, the overlap in this case is 2, there being 2 proposals that are both in f^* and f'. We shall define a measure, O_m, such that:

$$O_m = \frac{1}{s} \left[\sum_{t=1}^{s} \frac{r^{(t)}}{m^{*(t)} m'^{(t)}} \right], \tag{8}$$

where:

$r^{(t)}$	is the number of proposals both in f' and f^*;
$m^{*(t)}$	is the number of proposals in f^*;
$m'^{(t)}$	is the number of proposals in f'; and
s	is the number of speeches during the negotiation session.

The reason for defining O_m in the way given by Equation 8 is that this measure is free from "model bias." For our purposes it is desirable that the measure not be affected if the model is biased toward (for example) predicting compromises that include all m proposals. It can be shown that the measure O_m has the property of:

$$E(O_m) = \frac{1}{m} ;$$

that is, that the expected value of O_m is $1/m$, no matter what bias the model has (m being the number of permissible proposals, j).

To illustrate the above, let set F be given by only three policies, two being proposals j, and the third the only permissible compromise. The payoffs associated with the three policies are:

$$v = \left(v_1, v_2, \frac{v_1 + v_2}{2} \right) .$$

Now let us suppose that we are considering a session that includes only three speeches, and that the actual preferences of the negotiator for time $t = 1,2,3$ are policies 1, 2 and 3; that is:

the actual series is $(1,2,3)$.

Now let us imagine that we have a model that has a bias such that it predicts only *one-proposal* policies. Clearly, such a model can generate any one of the following eight series of predictions:

Series 1: $(1,1,1)$	Series 5: $(2,2,2)$
Series 2: $(1,1,2)$	Series 6: $(2,2,1)$
Series 3: $(1,2,1)$	Series 7: $(2,1,2)$
Series 4: $(2,1,1)$	Series 8: $(1,2,2)$.

Now we use Equation *8* and the actual series to compute O_2 for each possible series:

Series 1: $(1+0+1/2)/3 = 1/2$ Series 5: $(0+1+1/2)/3 = 1/2$
Series 2: $(1+0+1/2)/3 = 1/2$ Series 6: $(0+1+1/2)/3 = 1/2$
Series 3: $(1+1+1/2)/3 = 5/6$ Series 7: $(0+0+1/2)/3 = 1/6$
Series 4: $(0+0+1/2)/3 = 1/6$ Series 8: $(1+1+1/2)/3 = 5/6$.

Let us now assume that the model generates each series with equal probability, 1/8. The expected value of O_2 then is:

$$E(O_2) = 1/8[(1/2)+(1/2)+(5/6)+(1/6)+$$
$$(1/2)+(1/2)+(1/6)+(5/6)] = 1/2.$$

Let us now consider a different model, one which has a bias such that it alway predicts a *two-proposal* policy. Obviously, such a model predicts only one series of preferences:

Series 1: $(3,3,3)$.

From Equation *8*, the value of O_2 is in this case:

Series 1: $(1/2+1/2+1/2)/3 = 1/2$.

Since Series 1 is the only series the model can generate:

$$E(O_2) = 1/2.$$

In other words, no matter what bias the model in fact has, the expected value of O_2 is 1/2. Since number of proposals is $m = 2$ in this illustration, it is clear that the measure O_2 satisfies the assertion that $E(O_m) = 1/m$.

Given the measure of fit, it remains to determine the criteria of "goodness." Of course, we can always use the classical approach and determine whether the discrepancy between the predicted and the actual preferences is attributable to chance. However, we should anticipate that a simple model, such as ours, will show discrepancies that cannot be accounted for by chance. What should we do in such a case? Should we discard the model? We think not. Instead, we shall adopt an alternative set of criteria by which we shall judge the goodness of fit. We shall consider the fit between predicted and actual preferences "good enough" if either:

1. The fit due to our model is better than the fit due to a comparable but simpler model, or
2. The fit due to our model is at least as good as a different, but comparable and equally complex model.

TWO SIMPLER MODELS

Our model assumes that the preference of a given negotiator is determined by the product of two variables: payoff and subjective probability. Clearly, it is possible to formulate two alternative models that are "comparable but simpler" by assuming that preference is determined solely by payoff (Model 1) or solely by the subjective probability (Model 2). Specifically, we can postulate the following two comparable but simpler models:

Model 1: Negotiator i prefers at time t that policy which has for him the highest payoff.

Model 2: Negotiator i prefers at time t that policy which has for him the highest subjective probability.

It is easily seen that if $\alpha_i = 1$, our model is identical to Model 1. Perhaps less obvious is the similarity between Model 2 and our model when $\alpha_i = 0$. To see this similarity, one notes that when $\alpha_i = 0$, our model predicts that the negotiator 1 prefers at time t that policy for which the product $v_{if}\lambda_f^{(t)}$ is at a maximum. Now if we use a special payoff function with our model, such that $v_{if} = k$ for all f (k being a constant), then our model predicts that policy for which function $\lambda_f^{(t)}$ is at a maximum. And it follows, from the way $\lambda_f^{(t)}$ is defined, that it will be at a maximum either for the policy that has "just been endorsed" at time t, or for any one of the proposals included in that policy.

Consequently, we shall assume that our model satisfies criterion 1 (above) if:

a) The optimal α_i, α_i^* is smaller than 1, and if
b) Goodness of fit for α_*^* is better than for $\alpha_i = 0$ and $v_{if} = k$ (for all f)

We now turn our attention to models that are comparable and equally complex. Undoubtedly, there is a larger number of such models, but the following model appears particularly promising.

Linear Regression Model

Let $v_{if}^{(t)}{}'$ be the payoff associated for negotiator i at time t with the policy publicly endorsed at time t, $f'^{(t)}$, and let b_1, b_2, and a be linear coefficients.[13] Then:

$$v_{if^{**}}^{(t)} = b_1 v_{if'}^{(t)} + b_2 t + a, \qquad (9)$$

where $v_{if}^{(t)}{}_{**}$ is the payoff associated with the policy presumed to be preferred at time t, $f^{**(t)}$.

This alternative model is deemed equally complex because it utilizes the same number of variables as our model. We feel that this linear regression model is particularly promising because it corresponds to the intuitively plausible view that preferences change as a function of time.

In particular, it seems plausible to assume that negotiation starts by each negotiator's stating "unreasonable" demands (i.e., demands most advantageous to him), and proceeds by each negotiator's "giving in."

Siegel and Fouraker[14] state a model in which the payoff associated with negotiator's preferences decreases at a decreasing rate. Cursory inspection of our findings suggested that it may be premature to assume that such relationship

---

[13] For a definition of the coefficients see, for example, Hubert M. Blalock, Jr., *Social Statistics* (New York: McGraw-Hill Book Co., Inc., 1960), p. 344.

[14] Sidney Siegel and Lawrence E. Fouraker, *Bargaining and Group Decision Making* (New York: McGraw-Hill Book Co., Inc., 1960).

exists between time and preferences.[15] It seems preferable to postulate linear relationship, leaving the direction unspecified for the time being. And this the multiple regression model does.

Until we can find a different and promising model, of equal complexity as our model, we shall assume that criterion *ii* of goodness of fit is satisfied if our model generates at least as good predictions as the linear regression model.

FIGURE 1

GOODNESS OF FIT FOR A CHOSEN NEGOTIATOR
(FIT MEASURED IN PAYOFF UNITS)

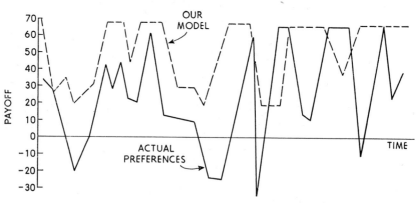

GRAPH A: OUR MODEL

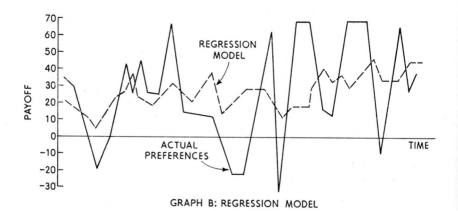

GRAPH B: REGRESSION MODEL

---

[15] See O. J. Bartos, "Experiments in Negotiation."

Findings

To test the adequacy of our model, an IBM 650 computer was used to perform the necessary computations. Since our approach at this point is exploratory, the simplest possible method was used to compute α_i^*, the optimal resistance factor for each negotiator. Six different values of α_i were considered: $\alpha_i = 1.0, .8, .6, .4, .2,$ and $.0$; and that α_i for which the measure of overlap, O_m, was largest,[16] was chosen.

The findings are exploratory in still another sense. Instead of using all 90 of the negotiator-records we obtained in the experiments (there were 30 subjects, each serving three times), we chose randomly a sample of 10 negotiator-records. The findings are based on this sample.

Three sets of experimental data served as the main input for the IBM 650:

1. The policy actually privately preferred by negotiator i at time t, for all t. (This information was secured by asking each subject to indicate which one policy he would endorse "now"—after each speech—if he were the very next speaker.)
2. The policy actually publicly endorsed at time t, for all t.
3. The payoffs to negotiator i associated with each permissible policy f.

FIGURE 2

GOODNESS OF FIT FOR A CHOSEN NEGOTIATOR
(FIT MEASURED IN OVERLAP)

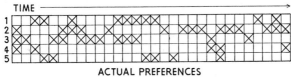

ACTUAL PREFERENCES

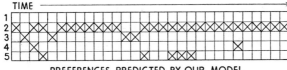

PREFERENCES PREDICTED BY OUR MODEL

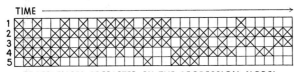

PREFERENCES PREDICTED BY THE REGRESSION MODEL

---

[16] For a more detailed description of the procedure, see O. J. Bartos, "Experiments in Negotiation."

Illustration. To facilitate the reader's understanding of our findings, Figures 1 and 2 present a rather detailed account with respect to one "typical" negotiator. Figure 1 presents the chosen negotiator's private preferences, actual (solid line) and predicted (broken line), in terms of the payoffs associated with the preferences. Figure 2 presents the same preferences in terms of the composition of the preferred policy. Graph A of Figure 1 compares the actual private preferences with the preferences predicted by our model. It turns out that this particular negotiator had a very low resistance factor, either $\alpha_i^* = .2$ or $\alpha_i^* = 0$. Hence the predicted preferences represent a kind of "symmetrical balance" between the chosen negotiator's payoff function and the payoff (to him) of the policy "just endorsed" publicly.

The optimal resistance factor for this particular negotiator is either .2 or 0 because, for these two values of α_i, the measure of goodness of fit, O_m, was the same and larger than for any other of the six values of a_i considered. (The six values of α_i considered were 1, .8, .6, .4, .2, 0.)

The "symmetrical balance" referred to above occurs whenever $\alpha_i = 0$. Under these conditions our model predicts that the negotiator will prefer that policy for which the product $v_{if}\lambda_f{}^{(t)}$ is at a maximum. And the dependence of function $\lambda_f{}^{(t)}$ on the speech "just-endorsed" publicly is given by Equation 3.

Graph B of Figure 1 compares the actual preferences with those predicted by the alternative model, the linear regression model. The predictions shown in Graph B are based on the regression equation:

$$v_{ij}^{(t)}** = .332\, v_{ij'}^{(t)} + 1.14t + 7.4.$$

The interesting fact about this equation, and Graph B, is that both suggest an "unreasonable" behavior by the negotiator: he tends to "demand" more payoff as time goes by, not less. This is shown both by the general upward trend of the broken-line curve in Graph B and by the fact that the coefficient associated with t is positive, $b_2 = +1.14$.[17]

Figure 1 gives a picture of the negotiation that may be quite easy to comprehend. Nevertheless, this figure is deceptive in one respect: it suggests that the goodness of fit is about as good for our model as it is for the alternative linear regression model. But this is not so: our model results in a much better fit ($O_m = .4472$) than does the linear regression model ($O_m = .2669$). Figure 2 does not suffer from this deficiency; a glance at Figure 2 shows that there is indeed a greater overlap between our model and the actual preferences than there is when the regression model is considered.

The reason why Figure 1 is deceptive merits some comment. One may note in Figure 2 that the regression model has a heavy bias: it tends to predict policies that are compromises, that include several proposals.

---

[17] Of the 10 negotiator-records included in the sample chosen for analysis, 7 were of this kind; i.e., had positive b_2. This finding casts some doubts on the "intuitive" conception of negotiation.

This "compromise-bias" manifests itself in Graph B of Figure 1 in that the predicted preferences tend to cluster close to low payoffs. The reason for this clustering is that, given the definition of a compromise, the more proposals a compromise includes, the closer it tends to fall to the payoff associated with the compromise including all five proposals. In the present illustration the payoff associated with the policy including all five proposals is $+16$.

This fact has one important consequence: The closer one comes to the payoff of $+16$ (in the present illustration), the more policies one encounters. Thus a model with a compromise-bias generates predictions which, by pure chance, are fairly close to the actual preferences in most cases, *when "closeness" is measured in terms of payoff*. And Figure 1 suggests measurement of goodness of fit in terms of payoff.

These were some of the considerations that led us to adopt the bias-free measure, O_m. Note that by adopting this measure we emphasize that the important thing for a model of negotiation is to predict accurately the composition of the preferred policy (i.e., to predict exactly which proposals are included in it), not the payoff associated with it.

Goodness of Fit: The Whole Sample. The very first question one may wish to have answered is the classical question of whether the discrepancy between the actual and the predicted preferences is too large to be attributable to chance.

To provide a basis for answering this question we shall present two measures:

1. The measure of perfect overlap: $\text{Max}(O_m)$. This measure results when we take the actual preferences of a negotiator and assume that our model predicts exactly those preferences.
2. The measure of actual overlap: $O_m^\cdot$. This measure results when we take as given both the actual preferences of a negotiator and the preferences in fact predicted by our model.

The values the two measures assume for the 10 sample cases are given in Table 1.

TABLE 1

Group	Role	$\text{Max}(O_m)$	$O_m^\cdot$	$R_m^\cdot$
2	3	.547	.271	.205
7	2	.450	.419	.877
8	3	.722	.447	.473
10	4	.804	.565	.604
12	1	.747	.448	.453
12	3	.684	.570	.764
13	3	.458	.284	.325
13	4	.377	.342	.801
14	4	.879	.636	.642
15	1	.843	.623	.658

It will be noted that values of $\text{Max}(O_m)$ are not constant from row to row. This is due to the fact that $\text{Max}(O_m)$ depends on the composition of the policy actually preferred by i: The larger the number of proposals negotiator i tends to include in the policy he actually prefers, the lower is $\text{Max}(O_m)$.

Given this fluctuation of the upper limit of O_m, the actually found values O'_m are somewhat misleading. It is useful to transform O'_m into a measure that equals 1 when $O'_m = \text{Max }(O_m)$ and 0 when $O'_m = 1/m$.[18] It is clear that the following measure, R'_m, has these properties:

$$R'_m = \frac{o'_m - \dfrac{1}{m}}{\text{Max }(o_m) - \dfrac{1}{m}}.$$

The last column of Table 1 contains the value of R'_m.

Inspection of the values of R'_m reveals that in none of the 10 cases considered is there a perfect overlap between actual and predicted preferences, since none of the 10 values of R'_m is 1. Although we shall not offer a test of statistical significance at this time, it appears that the difference between the actual and the predicted preferences is too large to be due to chance.

However, it also appears that our model performs better than in a random fashion, since none of the R'_m equals 0. Again, the difference between the predicted preference and the randomly generated preferences appears to be too large to be attributable to chance. Thus we are justified in turning our attention to the criteria of goodness of fit defined for the case when the discrepancy between prediction and findings is too large to be attributable to chance: we shall compare our findings with the values generated by models 1 and 2 and by the alternative linear regression model. Table 2 contains the relevant data.

TABLE 2

MEASURE OF OVERLAP R'_m

Group	Role	Our Model	Model 1	Model 2	Regression Model
2	3	.205	.106	.016	.241
7	3	.877	.877	—*)	.849
8	3	.473	.330	.199	.128
10	4	.604	.604	.315	.119
12	1	.453	.136	.710	.410
12	3	.764	.484	.483	.254
13	3	.325	—*)	.311	—*)
13	4	.801	.801	.060	.269
14	4	.642	.642	.176	.582
15	1	.658	.658	—*)	.294

*)Value of R'_m is smaller than 0.

As before, the large values of R'_m indicate considerable overlap between

[18] We have argued that the expected value of O_m is always $1/m$. It seems reasonable to take this value as the origin, since $1/m$ would be found if our model generated predictions randomly.

the predictions and the actual preferences. The largest R'_m for a given row is underlined in Table 2. Several observations are pertinent:

1. Only in one case did the regression model generate better predictions than our model.
2. Only in one case did Model 2 generate better predictions than our model. (It will be recalled that Model 2 predicts that the negotiator always prefers the policy with the highest subjective probability.)
3. In none of the cases did Model 1 generate better predictions than our model. However, in five cases it generated predictions just as good. (Model 1 predicts that the negotiator will always prefer the policy with the highest payoff.)

The last observation merits comment. First of all, it is not accidental that Model 1 never does a better job than our model because Model 1 is actually a special case of our model (the case when $\alpha_i = 1$), and it can never do a better job of predicting than our model. Second, we have postulated that our model will do better than either Model 1 or 2. Hence the cases in which our model does equally well as Model 1 should be counted as "evidence" against our model.

Discussion

What does all this evidence amount to? Just how good is our model of negotiation? It is to these questions that we now turn. First of all, we note that our model does not appear to predict the actual process of negotiation well enough to allow us to attribute to chance whatever discrepancies are found.

However, when we look at the alternative models, our model is not doing too badly. It certainly is doing better than generating prediction randomly. And in three of the ten cases it does a better job of predicting than any one of the alternative models.

In this respect our model is superior to both the regression model and to Model 2. The regression model exceeds the other models in accuracy in only one case, and so does Model 2. Thus we are left comparing the adequacy of our model with that of Model 1. And we find that there are disturbing as well as encouraging observations to be made in this case.

On the disturbing side, we note that Model 1 predicts that the negotiator always prefers the policy with the highest payoff. This is disturbing because, according to the rules of the game, the payoff function of a given negotiator remains constant throughout the session. Hence Model 1 predicts that the negotiator never changes his preference. Moreover, Model 1 predicts that the negotiator prefers throughout the session the policy that has the highest payoff for him. If Model 1 were to be taken seriously—as a reasonable model of negotiation behavior of all negotiators meeting at a session—it would follow that they either never reach an agreement, or that they agree to start with. Both implications are unreasonable since, in many instances, negotiators will reach agreement after prolonged discussion. To make things even worse, all five cases in which Model 1 equalled our model actually ended in unanimous agreement.

On the brighter side, we observe that, after all, Model 1 is a special case of our model (while Model 2 or the regression model is not), and hence we are quite justified in limiting our study to our model alone. Second, we may add that, in those five cases in which Model 1 equals our model, the negotiators in fact often privately preferred the policy with the highest payoff. Third. we note that three of the five cases occur in the third and last wave of the experiments (groups 13, 14, and 15). If, after we analyze all the 90 negotiator-records we have, we find that such cases indeed occur most frequently in the last wave of experiments, we might be justified in concluding what is already suggested by some additional evidence: that our subjects were somewhat tired of our experiments when they participated in them for the third time (as all did in the third wave), and hence their records were less accurate.[19]

In the analysis that will follow in the near future, we shall try to discover the conditons under which our model becomes the special case of Model 1; that is, under what conditions $\alpha^*_i = 1$. This will be a part of our broader investigation, designed to relate differences in α^*_i to factors such as negotiator's rating as a "good" negotiator (supplied by his fellow negotiators), his popularity, his background, etc., as well as to such formal considerations as the nature of the payoff function given by the experimental rules.

POSTSCRIPT

Since the writing of the above paper, "A Model of Negotiation and Some Experimental Evidence," further theoretical and experimental work has been done. As a result, some of the puzzling findings can now be accounted for.

Perhaps the most puzzling finding of the paper is that the model often predicts that the negotiator never changes his preferences (see "Discussion"), an obviously incorrect prediction. The reason for this prediction now is clear, and has been traced to a fundamental weakness of the model.

The model implies that agreement always will be reached on a policy that is "best" (has the highest payoff) for some negotiator. The model precludes, for example, the possibility of agreeing on a policy that is "second best" to everybody. To see that this is so, consider the following payoff matrix, involving two negotiators and three policies:

---

[19] It will be recalled that we are using negotiator's *private* preferences, and that these were obtained from the records kept privately by each negotiator.

Policies

	1	*2*	*3*
Negotiator 1	$10	$8	$2
Negotiator 2	$ 1	$4	$10

Now suppose that Negotiator 1 starts the session. According to the model, he endorses Policy 1 (his "best" policy). It is clear that, depending on his resistance factor, α, Negotiator 2 responds either by endorsing his best policy, 3 (if his resistance factor is high), or by endorsing Policy 1 (if his resistance factor is low). It is clear that he will not endorse Policy 2 at this time because the utility of this policy has to be lower that that of Policy 3. But the utilities in fact are as follows:

$$u_{22}^{(1)} = \left[\alpha_2 p_{22}^{(0)}\right] v_{22} = \left(\alpha_2 \frac{1}{3}\right) \$4 = \alpha_2 \frac{4}{3};$$

$$u_{23}^{(1)} = \left[\alpha_2 b_{23}^{(0)}\right] v_{23} = \left(\alpha_2 \frac{1}{3}\right) \$10 = \alpha_2 \frac{10}{3}.$$

(It will be recalled that, according to assumption 3, $p_{ij}^{(0)} = 1/3$ for all three policies, f.)

Now consider a sequence of endorsements of an arbitrary length, such that policy f was never endorsed during the sequence. It is clear that p_{22} keeps on decreasing as time goes by during this sequence. Policy 3 may or may not have been endorsed during this sequence, but even if it had not been endorsed at all, p_{22} will never be larger than p_{23} if it was not larger at the beginning of the sequence. Since the payoff associated with Policy 3 is larger than the payoff associated with Policy 2, ($\$10 > \$4$), the utility associated with Policy 3, u_{23}, will always (during this sequence) be larger than the utility associated with Policy 2, u_{22}. Hence Policy 3 will always be preferred to policy 2 during this arbitrary sequence.

And it is not difficult to see that this sequence will in fact be of infinite length, since (as shown above) it holds for its very first member that $u_{23} > u_{22}$. In other words, Negotiator 2 will never endorse policy 2. Using a similar argument, it can be shown that Policy 2 will never be endorsed by Negotiator 1 either; and that, indeed, only the "best" policy (such as Policy 1 or 3 in our illustration) can become the basis of unanimous agreement.

This implication of the original model was not recognized at the time of writing. Since then it has been discovered (from the analysis of the data) that repeated endorsements of the same policy by the same negotiator lose effectiveness with each repetition; that is, there is a point at which repetition no longer increases the subjective probability. This fact can be incorporated in the model in several ways, the most attractive of which appears to be the assumption that any policy "not as yet" endorsed by anybody has a constant subjective probability associated with it, and that only the policies that have already been endorsed by at least one person can have "decaying" subjective probabilities attached to them.

On a more positive side, it has been shown that the model described in this paper is essentially correct: it predicts that the most recent speeches are most influential—and these predictions were fully supported by the findings.[20] Thus it seems that, with a modification, the model of negotiation here described is sound. Further theoretical and empirical investigations are being conducted [21] and will be reported in later publications.

---

[20] See O. J. Bartos, "A Model of Negotiation and the Recency Effect," a paper read at the 1963 meetings of the American Sociological Association, Los Angeles, Calif.

[21] Under the grant by the Air Force Office of Scientific Research, AFOSR–62–314.

13

Structured Programs in Their Relation to Free Activity within the Inter-Nation Simulation *

HAROLD GUETZKOW [†]

ELSEWHERE, Snyder has located the simulation of relations among nations within the broader context of work in international relations.[1] Brody has analyzed the variety of games, exercises, and simulations which have been developed within international relations itself.[2] Guetzkow has provided an overall description of an inter-nation simulation which has been developed at Northwestern University.[3] Noel gives details as to how this particular simulation was evolved to meet theoretical needs.[4] In this essay, it may be helpful to attempt a somewhat rigorous summarization of the assumptions involved in the development of the programs used within the inter-nation simulation. These structured postulates then may be examined as they relate to the emergence of the free activities of the decision-makers operating within the framework of the programmed assumptions. The analysis which follows presents a summarization of the

* This essay assumes some familiarity with details of the operations of the international simulations, as sketched elsewhere (see Guetzkow footnote 1, below).

Many of the ideas utilized in the simulation were developed in staff meetings of the Program of Graduate Training and Research in International Relations at Northwestern University. Mr. Robert C. Noel made especially significant contributions to the development. Many thanks also are due to Messrs. Chadwick F. Alger, George I. Blanksten, R. Barry Farrell, Daniel Levine, Denis G. Sullivan, and Richard C. Snyder. The programs were formalized for this essay by Mr. William R. Caspary. The work was supported by Contract AF 49(638)–742, Air Force Office of Scientific Research, AFOSR–TN–61. This essay, while presented initially at Cambria Pines, appears in more recent, developed form as Chapter Five in Harold Guetzkow, Chadwick F. Alger, Richard A. Brody and Richard C. Snyder, *Simulation in International Relations: Developments for Research and Teaching* (Englewood Cliffs, N.J.: Prentice-Hall, Inc., 1963), pp. 103–49; (c) 1963. Reprinted by permission of Prentice-Hall, Inc.

† Northwestern University.

[1] Richard C. Snyder, "Simulation in the Perspective of Recent Trends in the Study of International Relations," in Guetzkow, *et al., Simulation in the Study of International Relations* (Englewood Cliffs, N.J.: Prentice-Hall, Inc., 1962).

[2] Richard A. Brody, "Varieties of Simulation in International Relations Research," in Guetzkow, *et al.*

[3] Harold Guetzkow, "A Use of Simulation in the Study of Inter-Nation Relations," *Behavioral Science, Vol. 4, No. 3* (July, 1959), pp. 183–191.

[4] Robert C. Noel, "Evolution of the Inter-Nation Simulation," in Guetzkow, *et al.*

theoretical model developed in the simulation during 1958 and 1959.

GUIDEPOSTS IN THE CONSTRUCTION OF THE INTER-NATION MODEL

The relations among nations are embodied in the simulation by the postulation of programs of operation with respect to the internal functioning of the several nations constituting the overall inter-nation system. Using these programs, the decision-makers of each nation then freely develop relations between their states as they deem appropriate, given their unfolding circumstances. It is possible to vary the assumptions made within the programs, as Noel has demonstrated.[5] Such changes in the operating postulates should result in variations in the unprogrammed activities which emerge as the nations relate to each other within the developing overall system.

The simulation is grounded in explicit specification of a basic set of variables and programmed relations among them. But because of the use of human beings as decision-makers in the system, a variety of additional factors—and relations among them—are incorporated but implicitly in the representation. Together, these two kinds of factors and their relationships produce an operating environment for the decision-makers which is designed to be isomorphic to the environment in which foreign policy decision-makers operate within the system of nations of the world.

During the course of our early work on the simulation, an option was available to attempt to program the entire model. Instead, programs were postulated only for limited intra-national activities, such as office holding and revolution. An advantage which we hoped to gain in the use of human participants (rather than computing machines) as decision-makers was their potential ability to out-think the simulators themselves. Later it may seem fruitful to program more of the behavior of the system than has been done in the representations to be described below. But perhaps the development of a completely programmed inter-nation simulation must wait until the men behind the computers have developed further the self-programming capacity of their machines.

In constructing the simulation, whole sets of variables in the complex of national and international life are represented by simplified, generic factors, supposedly prototypic of more elaborate realities. For example, the gamut of groups and processes through which decision-makers gain and maintain political office within a nation is represented in the simulation by the relation of the decision making participants to their so-called "validators." This one programmed relationship, which will be described in detail below, provides a condensed version of a gamut of real-life activities, similar to the way in which probability distributions are used by simulators to represent elaborate, underlying mechanisms which are too complicated to detail.

---

[5] *Ibid.*

Yet these prototypic variables, be they of determinant or stochastic form, constitute the core of the simulation. One important part of the task of this essay, therefore, is to delineate these core variables. No attempt, however, will be made at this time to enumerate the implicit variables—those of personality and of organization expectation—which are carried into the simulation by the persons participating as decision-makers. Uncovering such factors must await experimental work with the simulation.

Once the core variables have been posited, interrelations among them are then programmed through assumptions which assert what happens when the magnitude of one of the variables is changed. For example, when the probability of office holding reduces to certain levels, validator support is considered as questionable in a program which determines whether or not the decision-makers continue to hold office. These calculations for determination of office holding are assumptions postulated to simulate processes involved in the "orderly and disorderly transference of political power," as will be displayed below.

Another important part of the task of this essay is to state the assumptions embodied within the programs of the inter-nation simulation. The prescribed programs actually used in making the calculations in the internation simulation are presented after each "Programmed Assumption."

The core variables and their programmed assumptions constitute the foundations of the simulation. The activities which emerge from these postulated conditions, generated as the participants react to their simulated environments, consist of such things as arms races, trade systems, and international organizations. But because this unfolding is not prescribed, it is possible to formulate hypotheses (as contrasted with the programmed assumptions) about these developments. And just because these free activities are not prescribed, a description of their operation depends upon our insight in isolating the important variables which undergird these unprogrammed developments and in hypothesizing the interrelations which exist between them and the core variables. This essay will provide examples of how the core variables and their programmed interrelations generate free variables, which in turn may be hypothesized as being linked to the foundational structure of the simulation.

Although an attempt will be made to enumerate all the core variables and all their programmed interrelations, no such coverage can be attempted at this stage in our understanding of the inter-nation simulation for the free activities. Hence, the essay will have an imbalance, with the free variables and associated hypotheses being described in a rather fragmentary manner. At some later time it may be possible to present a more complete analysis of the inter-nation simulation in both its programmed and its unprogrammed features. The reader will decide whether it is fruitful at this time, despite the incompleteness, to describe the way in which the programmed characteristics of the simulation—in conjunction with the personal characteristics and organizational expectations of the decision-makers—create the free activities of the inter-nation simulation.

DECISION-MAKERS AND THEIR NATIONS

Actions within the inter-nation simulation originate through individuals and groups. The human beings participating in the simulation represent the decision-makers within national political systems. A group of two or three to five or six decision-makers, along with their resources and capabilities, operate as the nation. Some or all of these nations, in turn, may combine to form supra-groups, such as regional and universal organizations.

Core Unit: Decision-Makers. These are humans who develop and choose among alternative policies and actions at the nation or inter-nation levels.

Core Unit: Nations. These are groups of validated decision-makers, operating within a political-military-economic system, which are capable of amalgamation and splintering.

Free Unit: Supra-Units. These are supra-national groups of nations, developing and operating various structures, with capabilities derived from national units.

The simulation thus consists of components at three levels: individuals (decision-makers), groups (nations), and supra-groups (alliances and international organizations). Some of the assumptions and hypotheses which follow are concerned with relations within the level of the phenomena being considered; others relate components at one level to those at another level.

Organizational Relations among Decision-Makers

One individual initially is designated central decision-maker. He is responsible for overall national policy, both domestic and international. With him are associated other decision-makers, who constitute the nation's government. The central decision-maker possesses final authority in all decisions, within the limits set by the risk of losing his office and the constraints imposed by his associates. The exercise of final authority by the central decision-maker simulates the fact that there is usually a recognized head of state or someone exercising ultimate political power.

Core Variable: Authority. The command of each central decision-maker is honored by the simulation-director, even though the decisions of the associated national decision-makers be at variance in some way with the former's directives.

Free Variable: Delegation of Authority. The central decision-maker may delegate various amounts of authority within particular domains to his associated decision-makers, either informally or formally.

The mechanical reconciliation of conflicts among the decision-makers of a nation by the simulation-director attempts to simulate the exercise of actual power within a political system, which by definition resides within the "central" decision-maker. There is freedom within the delegation of authority for its abuse, if the central decision-maker does not institute adequate controls. A central decision-maker may lose partial control of his decisions until his authority is re-established by his personal control of the nation's decision-forms or by confrontation of disobedient associates so that they are reversed or even disqualified from participation in the exercise by the simulation-director. In a run with foreign students, the "European" nation was divided internally, one of the external decision-makers secretly having joined force with the decision-makers in the "South American" state. Advantage was taken of delegated authority to sabotage the effectiveness of the central decision-maker's activities before the perfidy was discovered and accreditation revoked by the latter.

Free Variable: Division of Labor among Decision-Makers. It is possible for the central decision-maker to use his authority to organize his associates so that each performs different tasks within the nation.

Some participants may become internal decision-makers, specializing in economic or military matters. Others may serve as external decision-makers, focusing upon the international affairs of their nation. They might regularly conduct negotiations with other nations. They might operate the international organizations. The lack of prescribed structure among the decision-makers, except for the allocation of prime authority to the central decision-makers, allows freedom for the participants in the evolution of their decision-making roles.

Note how the two free variables are related to the core variable, in this instance, authority. The participants are given definite instructions that the central decision-maker holds the ultimate power within his nation "by definition." But the utilization which is made of this "programmed" authority by the decision-makers depends upon such unprogrammed features of the simulation as their personality characteristics and developments within their situation. "Delegation" and "division of labor" are but two of an array of free variables which might be discovered within the operation of the simulation.

It may be that a division of labor gradually develops within the nation, in response to the relations of a country to other nations within the system. In one run, for example, an external decision-maker in ERGA [6] became concerned with the economic aspects of his state's relations to two other nations. His counterpart focused his attention upon security affairs, working closely with the central decision-maker concerned with force. In another run of the simulation, the central decision-maker in OMNE re-

---

[6] It has been our practice in the simulation to designate the nations by fictitious names or by single letters.

stricted the role of his external ministers to representing and reporting, allowing them little scope for policy development. In yet another run, the central decision-maker, or "prime minister," turned over almost all internal functions to a trusted associate so that his full attention could be devoted to foreign affairs.

Unprogrammed Hypothesis No. 1   Insufficient delegation of authority within a nation produces inter-nation crises because of lag in the decision-making activities of the nation.

Unprogrammed Hypothesis No. 2.   The number of decisions demanded of a nation by both internal and external relations is greater than the capability of one decision-maker.

The core variable of authority permits the central decision-maker of any nation to amalgamate his nation with others—by agreeing to have his decisions subject to a supra-national unit. The core variable of authority also allows for a situation in which the central decision-maker relinquishes control to an antagonistic power. The processes of amalgamation and occupation will be discussed in more detail at a later point in this exposition.

Should the researcher/teacher want to explore the implications of a more complex decision making organization, the simulation can be so adapted. For example, by restricting direct communications among the national decision-makers to occasional internal conferences interspersed with longer periods of indirect, written communication among them, significant characteristics of hierarchical organizations can be simulated. Even in the present representation of Foreign Office operation, the need for coordination among the decision-makers is apparent, especially when they are "abroad" for prolonged periods in international conferences or organizations. Misunderstandings among the decision-makers result from differences in perspective among the decision-makers on a particular international problem.

The manner of organization of internal activities also may have external consequences. Specialization among the decision-makers creates coordination problems for other nations. In one run, the senior external decision-maker of UTRO specialized in the development of a grand alliance system, which competed with alliances among smaller nations. But the smaller nations had not designated particular decision-makers as "opposite numbers" to UTRO's diplomat, who had great trouble developing a series of bilateral negotiations. Or, another way, the internal authority within each state creates consequences for the external affairs of all other states. Communications between states have bogged down noticeably in runs characterized by insufficient delegation of authority by the central decision-makers. During one of the 1958–59 runs, dangerous risks were incurred by UTRO because of its slowness in responding to urgent pleas from its allies in a time of crisis.

Office Holding

By definition the exercise of power in political decision making situations within a nation depends upon formal or informal office holding, be it *de facto* or *de jure*. Office holding is a mainspring of the inter-nation simulation. Although no attempt has been made thus far to represent accession to office, an endeavor is made to simulate vital characteristics of the process of remaining in office. Alger (1962) has inserted an aspiring office holder in the simulation to represent forces of political opposition.

Core Variable: Office Holding (pOH). This is the *de jure* right, as recognized by the simulation-director, to make the decisions of the nation with respect to both internal and external affairs.

The retention of office by the central decision-makers depends upon their ability to elicit "validation" of their office holding in competition with countermoves by aspiring decision-makers. For purposes of the simulation, this validation process consists in gaining and retaining the support of elites and interest groups within their nation, along with sufficient compliance among all its inhabitants to secure implementation of political decisions. Validation is expressed as a mathematized set of relations between the consequences of the decisions made within nations and the chances of remaining in office.

The validators within such a process may be conceived as individuals and groups in the nation's political system who occupy positions of influence outside the formal governmental structure. Through their situations of power, they influence the chances for office retention by the decision-makers in the nation. In a democracy, the validators might be voters and interest groups. In an autocracy, the validators might be some oligarchic elite or military junta. In all governmental systems, however, it seems there must be some minimal compliance by the peoples as a whole, even if it is only passive acceptance rooted in apathy.

Core Variable: Validator Satisfaction (VS_m). This is the acceptability of the central decision-maker's program to those with power to authenticate his office holding.

The demands of the validators are postulated to arise from two sources.

1. The nation must satisfy the basic needs of its peoples; and, in our "satisfaction with regard to consumption" (VS_{cs}) variable, an attempt was made to encompass the whole gamut of living needs of the validators, from bare necessities for the peasant and workman to luxuries for the guardians of the palace or members of the cabinet.
2. The nation also must satisfy the needs of its people with regard to their feelings of national security (VS_{ns}).

In later parts of this essay, details of these validating components will be described. For the moment overall validation of office holding may be viewed as a function of the extent to which these prototypic needs are satisfied. The emphasis given various needs may vary over time within a nation, just as they may vary from nation to nation.

Programmed Assumption No. 1: Relation of Validator Satisfaction to Office Holding. The probability of continuing in office depends upon the extent to which the decision-makers of the nation satisfy their validators.

This assumption is programmed as follows:

$$pOH = a(b-DL)VS_m + c(DL-d),   \qquad (1)$$

where pOH is the probability of continuing office holding, and VS_m is mean overall validator satisfaction. When DL, or "decision latitude," is thought of as a constant.[7] Equation 1 is linear, that is, of the form $pOH =$ a constant, times VS_m, plus another constant. The constants were chosen so as to allow use of simpler calculation routines, given the arbitrary scale values assigned to VS_m and DL, as follows: $a = .01$; $b = 11$; $c = .1$; and $d = 1$.

The relation between the validating process and office holding is presented in Figure 1. Validation is conceptualized as a duo-stage process by which decisions regarding consumption standards and force capability are translated into measures of validator satisfaction (Figures 1a and 1b). These measures then are combined into a single index (VS_m), which in turn determines the probability of holding office (pOH [Figure 1c]). Undoubtedly, the programs represented in these graphs are only approximations of the complex functions which may hold in society.

In operating the simulation, graphs are not given to the participants, although the general form of the functions is revealed. In making explanations, each component is described on an 11-point scale. The two components are averaged into a single index on an identical 11-point scale (see Table 1a).

The transformation displayed in Figure 1c is explained as the relationship of Table 1a to Table 1b. When overall validator satisfaction is high, likelihood of retaining office tends to be greater; when overall validator satisfaction is low, the likelihood of retaining office tends to be less.

Programmed Assumption No. 2: Relations of Overall Validation to Component Validations. The validators are satisfied to the extent to which their national security and standards of living are realized.

$$VS_m = (.5 \ VS_{cs} + .5 \ VS_{ns})   \qquad (2)$$

where VS_{cs} represents consumption satisfaction for validators deriving from their living standards, and VS_{ns} represents satisfactions deriving from national security. These terms will be defined more adequately on pages 176 and 179, respectively.

It is possible to inject some of the effects of an opposition party into the simulation through the use of a participant who makes critiques of the

---

[7] Definition of decision latitude as a variable is made in the section below.

FIGURE 1

THE VALIDATION OF OFFICE HOLDING

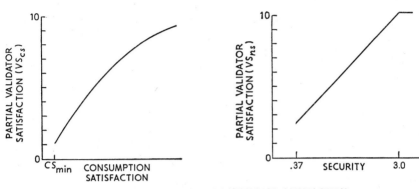

BASES FOR THE GENERATION OF VALIDATOR SATISFACTION

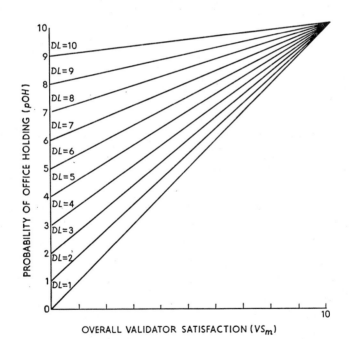

OVERALL VALIDATOR SATISFACTION (VS_m)

RELATIONSHIPS BETWEEN OVERALL VALIDATOR SATISFACTION
(VS_m) AND CHANCES FOR HOLDING OFFICE (pOH), FOR
VARYING LEVELS OF DECISION LATITUDE (DL)

performance of the decision-makers serving as office holders. In Noel's description of the January 1959 runs, he explains how we asked individuals to stand by, ready to take over when the decision-makers lost office. Alger has worked out procedures to consummate a transfer of power to an opposition group.[8] An aspirant office holder makes his own decisions, parallel to those made by the office holders. He functions without the operating responsibilities imposed on the official decision-makers. The extent to which the aspirant's decisions prove to be potentially more adequate in meeting the needs of the validators serves as an indicator of the amount to which validator satisfactions provided by the central decision-makers are diluted because of alternatives provided by an opposition.

Perhaps the validation process is the best example of our endeavor to build essentials into the simulation by the use of so-called "prototypic" variables. The probability that particular individuals continue in office in real life is an elaborate, ill-understood process. Yet, it seems that the decision making in domestic and foreign affairs is dependent upon a number of factors, two of which we intuitively assert may be taken as representative of a wider gamut. The decision-makers may endeavor to retain office by favoring one source of validation over another, representing the way in which practical politicians may cater to one validating group rather than another. A running competition with the aspirant decision-maker would make it necessary for those in office not only to satisfy their validators, but to come to decisions which compare favorably with the promises of an opposition which has none of the responsibilities of office holding. In this way, the simulation creates a conceptual environment for the decision-makers which basically typifies variables which are seen as motivating office holding in political life.

Decision Latitude

In the real world the relationship between validator satisfaction and office holding varies widely from nation to nation, depending upon the forms of the internal government. In some cases, the decision-makers for certain periods of time have wide latitude in making their decisions, regardless of how their validators respond. In other instances, the decision-makers have little latitude; they find their office holding is very sensitive to changes in the overall satisfaction of their validators.

These differences in decision latitude are represented in the simulation by varying the functions relating satisfaction of office holding in Figure 1c. The participants are given a scale which indicates the sensitivity of their validators to their decisions, as presented in Table 1.

---

[8] Chadwick F. Alger, "Use of the Inter-Nation Simulation in Undergraduate of International Relations," in Guetzkow, *et al.*

TABLE 1

SCALE FOR MEASUREMENT OF DECISION LATITUDE

	10	Complete decision latitude
	9 ⎫	
	8 ⎬	High decision latitude
	7 ⎭	
	6 ⎫	
(DL) *Decision Latitude*	5 ⎬	Moderate decision latitude
	4 ⎭	
	3 ⎫	
	2 ⎭	Low decision latitude
	1	No decision latitude

Core Variable: Decision Latitude (DL). The degree to which the probability of office holding of the decision-makers depends on changes in validator satisfaction.

Programmed Assumption No. 3: Relation of Office Holding to Decision Latitude. The higher the decision latitude, the less immediately is office holding subject to validator satisfaction. (See explication in Equation 1, above, where *DL* now is allowed to vary.)

The nation's decision latitude changes slowly, sometimes being dependent upon factors quite beyond the control of the office holders, and at other times responding directly to decisions or communications made by the nation's principals. Changes in the freedom of the decision-makers due to exogenous factors are stochastically developed by the simulator. These are programmed to occur randomly, resulting in a change in the decision latitude of one unit either in an upward or downward direction. These changes in decision latitude may be thought of as occurring for reasons outside the control of the central decision-makers, such as shifts in leadership among the validators, changes in mass media, and so forth.

Programmed Assumption No. 4: Stochastic Variations in Decision Latitude. Each period there is random modification in the decision latitude of each nation. Changes of plus or minus one unit or zero are equally probable.

But the central decision-maker may himself induce changes in his decision latitude, never exceeding one unit down or up in a period. These changes incur direct consequences. When the decision-makers become more sensitive to their validators by decreasing their decision latitude, there is a momentary flush of satisfaction. These are but temporary increases which dissipate during the period as the validators become accustomed to the new sensitivity of the office holders. When the decision-makers wish to increase their decision latitude, not only is there a momentary increase in dissatisfaction (of one or two units for each unit increase in decision latitude), but there are moderate decreases in the basic capabilities of the nation during the period following the change. These latter changes may be taken to represent effects of the dissatisfaction felt by validators who control production, as well as by those "influentials" who now participate less actively in the production of basic goods and services. The decreases in validator satisfaction are temporary, disappearing as the validators become accustomed to the restraints enforced by their government.

Programmed Assumption No. 5: Relation of Changes in Decision Latitude to Validator Satisfaction. Decision-maker initiated increases in decision latitude induce temporary decreases in validator satisfaction.

$$\triangle VS_m = e(\triangle DL), \tag{3}$$

with the restriction that $e = -1$ when $D < 8$, and $e = -2$ when $DL \geqq 8$. The delta sign ($\triangle$) indicates changes in VS_m and DL; and in this case the unit change in DL upward or downward is initiated by the central decision-maker. The change in the value of the constant e, from 1 to 2 when the DL is 8 or above, is intended to assert that the validators will be relatively more sensitive to changes in DL when the decision latitude already is high.

Consider the joint operation of Programmed Assumptions Nos. 4 and 5. If the stochastic change of Programmed Assumption No. 4 happens to be downward during the same period in which the central decision-maker of a nation (via Programmed Assumption No. 5) decides to increase his decision latitude by a unit, the two changes will balance and there is no change in VS_m. Sometimes the direction of the two changes may coincide, so that when $DL < 8$, VS_m is determined only by the action of the central decision-maker.

Programmed Assumption No. 6: Relation of Changes in Decision Latitude to Basic Capabilities. Increases in decision latitude induce a corresponding decrease in the nation's basic capability.

$$\frac{\triangle BC}{BC} = f \triangle DL, \tag{4}$$

where $f = 5$ percent when $DL < 8$, and $f = 10$ percent when $DL \geqq 8$. Basic capability (BC) units represent undifferentiated capital resources of the nation (described under National Capabilities, below). The $\triangle DL$'s of this equation may be stochastic or initiated by the decision-makers.

Thus, associated with changes in decision latitude are direct effects of exogenous changes (Programmed Assumption No. 4), mixed with both direct (Programmed Assumption No. 5) and indirect (Programmed Assumption No. 6) effects of endogenous changes. Our purpose in this medley is to create a decision environment in which our participants are partially in control of their relation to their validators, and at times are subject to the vicissitudes of the political, economic, and social forces in their societies.

The decision to vest authority within an individual, rather than within a small internal group, was dictated by our interest being centered on the interrelations among the nations, rather than in the internal functioning of each of the states. However, an effort was made to represent constraints upon these decision-makers, constraints which seem always to exist in na-

tional political systems—whether they be totalitarian or democratic—
through the limitations on office holding as extended by the validators and
through restrictions in decision latitude. Thus, the validation and decision
latitude functions are designed to represent such constraints as those imposed by courts, legislative bodies, and bureaucratic inflexibilities.

The use of stochastic processes in these programs is analogous to their
use by operations research analysts in their simulation of physical systems.
Whenever the variables involved in a given consequence are numerous
and complicated—and thereby at times little understood—it is possible to
represent the resultant by a probability distribution of random numbers.
This stochastic representation later may be replaced by a more adequately
detailed program which gives rise to the desired consequent by other than
random means. Our use of prototypic variables to represent a complex network of poorly delineated variables parallels this employment of stochastic
or random determinations in the inter-nation simulation.

Orderly and Disorderly Transference of Power

The mechanisms of the transference of power from one set of public
office holders to another is of central interest to the political scientist. When
overall validator satisfaction is quite low, there would be some chance that
disorder might occur, possibly with immediate loss of office. When overall
validator satisfaction is high, the more orderly and regularized devices for
the transfer of power from one set of office holders to the next would prevail. Yet, even when there is great likelihood for losing office, decision-
makers in the real world retain office because of nonpredictable circumstances. These hypotheses again are embodied in the simulation by the use
of probabilistic devices, this time for the determination of office loss.

Core Variable: Determination of Office Holding (pOH). At periodic
or intermittent times, a determination of office holding is made within each
nation. This determination may result in continuation of the same decision-
makers in office, or provide for their replacement.

Core Variable: Determination of Occurence of Revolution (pR). When
a determination of revolution is made, the result may be revolution or no
revolution.

Core Variable: Determination of Outcome of Revolution (pSR). When
a revolution occurs, the decision-makers may or may not lose office.

The simulation is divided into periods. To date, we have employed
periods ranging from 45 to 75 minutes in length. At the beginning of each
period the office holders are informed of the likelihood of retaining office.
To simulate more routinized, orderly shifts in the occupants of positions
of power in a nation, regular bi-period or tri-period determinations of office
holding have been employed. The ruling is made on the basis of the average
likelihood of office holding over the past two or three periods (see Equa-

tion 1). The span over two or three periods gives the participant the ability to take short-run gambles with his validators if, in the longer run, he can maintain high enough satisfactions to keep his chances for holding office sufficiently great. But even when his chances are high at the times of these regular determinations, there still will be some occasions when office is lost.

For example, in a run in 1958, central decision-maker P lost office when the random numbers were applied, even though his scale value of 9 indicated nine chances out of ten that he would retain office. Due to the vagaries of politics—"perhaps there was a scandal of political import in his immediate family"—he lost office, even though his decision making had induced much satisfaction in his validators.

The stochastic determinations in the simulation represent the full scope of causes which may terminate office holding in real life. The rarer events, such as death in office from assassination or ill health, occur even when there is much overall support for a regime. The common causes of office loss, as in *coup d'états* and narrow losses of elections, occur when there is less than full support for a particular set of office holders. By varying the probabilities of office holding, these differences in real world situations are reflected in the inter-nation simulation.

The "risk of revolution" is encountered within a nation when overall validator satisfaction drops to or below a threshold of 3 units (see "Revolution Threshold" in Table 2a). The impact of disorder is determined immediately on a probability basis. If there is no revolution, the decision-makers retain office and the orderly process for the transference of power prevails, despite the low validator satisfaction. If disorder terminates in revolution, then a second stochastic calculation is involved to determine the outcome of the revolution itself.

Programmed Assumption No. 7: Relation of Regularity in Office Determination to Validator Satisfaction. If the satisfaction of the validators is above the critical threshold of 3 units, there is periodic determination of office at regular intervals.

Programmed Assumption No. 8: Relation of Occurrence of Revolution to Validator Satisfaction. If the satisfaction of the validators is below the critical threshold of 3 units, there is an immediate determination of whether a revolution has occurred.

Note how the combination of programs for the determination of office holding and revolution imply that although a government in the short run may be threatened by revolution, should it maintain immediate power during the disorder, its chances for holding office might be still relatively good because of the past satisfactions of its validators. The choice of the levels of probability involved in determining the outcome of revolution will be explained in detail in a later discussion of the use which may be made of force capabilities. Suffice it to say here, internal controls may be applied by the decision-makers to lessen the chances of the success of the revolution, no matter how immediately dissatisfied their validators are.

If the change in office is induced by orderly or disorderly procedures, once the calculation yields office-loss, the central participant yields his

TABLE 2
SCALES FOR THE MEASUREMENT OF VALIDATOR SATISFACTION AND CHANCES FOR OFFICE HOLDING

TABLE 2A. SCALE OF VALIDATOR SATISFACTION
(Same for VS_m, VS_{cs}, and VS_{ns})

(VS) Validator Satisfaction

10	Maximum satisfaction
9, 8	High satisfaction
7, 6	Moderately high satisfaction
5	Indifference
4 { Revolution	Moderately low satisfaction (moderate
3 { Threshold	dissatisfaction)
2, 1	Low satisfaction (high dissatisfaction)
0	Minimum satisfaction (maximum dissatisfaction)

TABLE 2B. SCALE OF CHANCES FOR OFFICE HOLDING

(pOH) Probability of Office Holding

10	Certainty of office holding
9, 8	High likelihood of office holding
7, 6	Moderately high likelihood of office holding
5	Even likelihood of holding or losing office
4, 3	Moderately low likelihood of office holding
2, 1	Low likelihood of office holding
0	Certainty of losing office

decision making office and is replaced in the simulation by another. Perhaps the greatest impact of the motivational setting of the simulation is felt in this situation. When the office holders are strangers to each other (except for the interaction which occurs in the simulation itself), less than powerful motivations are aroused. But when the simulation consists of adults who make their profession in foreign policy decision making, their interest in retaining office is keen. Loss of office is loss of face among participant-colleagues with whom they will be in contact over the years ahead. Long-term operation of one's nation was taken as a sign of outstanding decision making ability in one run of the simulation involving such professionals.

Unprogrammed Hypothesis No. 3.   Because the associated decision-makers of a government hold office on the authority of the central decision-maker, there is a tendency to replace at least some of the associated decision-makers upon transfer of power from one central decision-maker to another.

In establishing and maintaining the relations of their nation to others, the decision-makers seek to use the results to keep themselves in office. These efforts may indeed redound to the well-being of the nation's population, as when a comparative advantage arises from foreign trade to increase validator satisfaction. Or the external effort may simply reinforce the leaders' elite position with concomitant decreases in the well-being of their peoples; for example, through the display of great force, which thereby assures an increase in the probability of office holding. External relations, then, may be motivated by a felt need for office holding, regardless of the consequences for the external system.

Free Variable: Decisions on External Affairs.   These are decisions with respect to relations of the nation to other nations.

Free Variable: Office Holding Needs.   These are considerations thought important by decision-makers in retaining office.

Unprogrammed Hypothesis No. 4   The considerations related to office holding tend to dominate the considerations deriving from external relations in national decision making.

There is controversy as to the genesis of policy change in foreign affairs, some arguing that basic policy shifts come only through change in the office holders. The fact that office holders are transient (often in the short and at least in the long run) is important in the relations among nations. Because the nation's interests and the policies implementing them are subject to the interpretations of its office holders, national goals and strategies are subject to change as the office holders change. As individuals with different personality needs and different political ideologies take office, the goals and strategies of the nation in its relation to other states reflect such changes.

Free Variable: National Goals.   These are the objectives, implicit or explicit, toward which the decision-makers attempt to direct their nation's behavior.

Free Variable: National Strategies.   This is the plan of means, implicit or explicit, by which the decision-makers attempt to achieve national goals.

Unprogrammed Hypothesis No. 5.   When different decision-makers take office, national goals and strategies change.

Unprogrammed Hypothesis No. 6.   When different decision-makers take office, overall satisfaction of the validators may be developed through changed emphasis on the components of validator satisfaction.

The fact that "all things pass" produces powerful pressures within international systems for "staying" until there are shifts in the office holders of the other nations, *vis-a-vis* one's capacity to retain office. "Staying" tends to induce important limits and potentials in the relations of nations. Because office often is retained by continuation of the same general pattern of external relations which have aided office retention in the past, remaining in office tends to produce conservative, status quo tendencies. Because change of office holders often is accompanied by changes in the bases for office retention, it is at this time that rearrangements of the complex relations among states may be attempted.

Free Variable: Continuation in Office. This is the number of consecutive periods during which a decision-maker holds office.

Free Variable: Similarity of Decisions. This is the extent to which the substance of decisions is repetitious in content, from time to time.

Unprogrammed Hypothesis No. 7. The longer decision-makers continue in office, the greater the tendency for similar decisions.

Many consequences of the changes in office holding flow from uncertainties introduced into complex organizations by personnel changes. Role expectations are generated not only in terms of position demands, but also in terms of the personal characteristics and styles of the nation's representatives in their behavior in bilateral and multilateral contacts. Changes destabilize expectations in the larger system. These uncertainties in expectation make prediction of the behaviors of opposite numbers difficult. Hence, errors in decision making are more likely.

Free Variable: Stability of Behavior Expectations. This is the extent of constancy which is expected in the anticipated behaviors of a unit.

Unprogrammed Hypothesis No. 8. The longer decision-makers continue in office, the more constant will others expect their behaviors to be.

Unprogrammed Hypothesis No. 9. The longer decision-makers continue in office, the greater is their adequacy in achieving their national goals in inter-nation affairs.

Unprogrammed Hypothesis No. 10. The more unstable the expected behavior of others, the greater is the chance of error in the nation's decision making.

National Capabilities

All kinds of resources, physical and human, are subsumed in the inter-nation simulation under the concept of "basic capability." The size of a nation's basic capability accumulation reflects the nation's overall ability to produce all goods and services, be they used for consumption or for the exercise of physical force in internal or external affairs.

Units of basic capability at the disposal of the nation's decision-makers may be allocated to the development of further basic capability (as exploration for oil fields, investment in more efficient factories, or in the training of scientists and engineers), or for research and development. Because of obsolescence, deterioration, and resource exhaustion, all nations must devote parts of their basic capability to regeneration if they desire to maintain a constant level. Growth, stagnation, and retrogression will occur, depending upon the amounts allocated over time to the development and renewal of the nation's basic capabilities.

Core Variable: Basic Capability (BC). This is the nation's overall ability to produce goods and services, be they used for replacement of or for addition to the basic capability itself, or for consumption in living or in arms.

Core Variable: Generation Rates. This is the rate at which basic capability allocated to different sectors of the economy generates, with a lag of one period, new basic capability units, force capability units, and consumption satisfaction units.

Core Variable: Depreciation of Basic Capability. This is the rate at which basic capability depreciates each period, due to depletion, obsolescence, and deterioration.

Programmed Assumption No. 9: Stochastic Variation in Depreciation of Basic Capability. In each period, depreciation may occur in the amount of basic capability.

The values .02, .05, and .10 for the depreciation rate are equiprobable. The relative magnitude of the depreciation has no relation to the amount of basic capability possessed by the nation.

The nation consumes its own goods and services at varying standards of living. A minimum portion of the nation's basic capability must be devoted each period to the production of goods and services for consumption. This minimum changes from time to time, increasing as the basic capability of the nation increases, decreasing as the nation becomes depressed. The increases, however, are programmed to be a decreasing percentage of the total as the "gross national product" increases. The minimum consumption represents that allocated of necessity by the government to provide for the supply and manning of the nation's productive capability.

The minimum requirement further represents the amount of consumption which the people of the nation, despite government action, are able to devote to ther own maintenance, as in the peasants' hidden poultry or grains, and in the laborers' pilferage of clothes or fuel. These minima are such that they yield little validator satisfaction. For consumption above the minimum the validator satisfaction increases with the ratio of consumption satisfaction to the minimum living standard. The goods created for use in living are conceived in the simulation as being entirely expended, with no carry-over from period to period.

Core Variable: Consumption Satisfaction (VS_{cs}). This is the gratification provided to the nation's population through goods and services.

Core Variable: Minimum Living Standards (CS_{min}). The decision-makers of the nation must provide at least minimal living standards for its people.

Programmed Variable: Maximum Living Standards (CS_{max}). The maximum units of consumption which could be allocated by the nation in a given period to living standards; that is, $CS_{max} = BC$ x *Generation Rate* for CS's.

Programmed Assumption No. 10: Relation of Consumption Satisfaction to Utilization. The goods and services produced by the nation's capability are completely expended at the end of any period, without holdover.

Programmed Assumption No. 11: Relation of Minimum Consumption Standards to Basic Capability. The minimum consumption standards of the nation increase as the basic capability of the nation to produce satisfying goods and services increases.

$$CS_{min} = g \, CS_{max}, \qquad (5)$$

where the product of the *BC*'s and the generation rate for *CS*'s may be thought of as the maximum living standards (CS_{max}) for the nation, should all its basic capability be put into consumption. The parameter g in this equation is defined by Programmed Assumption No. 12, which follows.

Programmed Assumption No. 12: Relation of Level of Minimum Living Standards to Basic Capability. The percentage of total capability required to fulfill minimum living standards decreases as the potential to provide consumption increases.

$$g = 1 - \frac{CS_{max}}{h}, \qquad (6)$$

where h is an ultimate limit, beyond which the maximum consumption could not ever go, and representative of a fully satiated population of maximum density. In the runs conducted to date, this ultimate limit has been arbitrarily set at 380,000 *CS*'s. When the nation is so wealthy that its maximum living standards might approach its ultimate limit, the constant g approaches zero. This indicates that the then minimum living standards of the state may be met by allocating only a tiny fraction of its basic capability to *CS*'s.

Programmed Variable: Validator Satisfaction with Respect to Consumption Satisfaction (VS_{cs}). This represents the satisfactions attained by the nation's validators from the amount and distribution of goods and services.

Programmed Assumption No. 13: Relation of Validator Satisfaction to Consumption Satisfaction. This assumption may be thought of as consisting of three parts:

1. For consumption near minimum living standards, validator satisfaction depends on the relation of consumption satisfaction to minimum living standards.
2. Once minimum living standards have been met, larger and larger increases in consumption are necessary to produce corresponding changes in validator satisfaction.
3. This saturation effect is more prominent for wealthier nations.

The effects of Programmed Assumption No. 13 are incorporated in a quadratic equation in the inter-nation simulation. It is reasonable to conceive that when minimum living standards are but barely met (i.e., when the CS in any period equals CS_{min}), the validators are minimally satisfied (i.e., $VS_{cs} = 1$). Part 1 of the assumption then may be represented as the first term of a quadratic equation:

$$VS_{cs} = h(CS/CS_{min}) + j. \ldots \tag{7}$$

When consumption is near minimum living standards, that is, VS_{cs} equals 1, and CS/CS_{min} equals 1 (as $CS = CS_{min}$), then Equation 7 becomes $1 = h + j$. By transposing terms, $j = 1 - h$. Using this value for j and rearranging terms, Part 1 of Programmed Assumption No. 13 may be stated as:

$$VS_{cs} = 1 + h(CS/CS_{min} - 1). \ldots$$

As CS increases above CS_{min}, the saturation effect of Part 2 may be obtained by substracting a squared term from Equation 7 as follows:

$$VS_{cs} = 1 + h(CS/CS_{min} - 1) - k(CS/CS_{min} - 1)^2 \tag{8}$$

According to Part 3 of our assumption, however, the effect is more prominent for wealthier nations, so that the constant k then should be made to depend upon the relation of CS_{min} to CS_{max}. This may be done easily enough so that the final quadratic expression for Programmed Assumption No. 13, including all three of its parts, with appropriate constants to handle the transformation of units into VS_{cs}'s, is as follows:

$$VS_{cs} = 1 + h(CS/CS_{min} - 1) - m(CS_{max}/CS_{min}) (CS/CS_{min} - 1)^2 \tag{9}$$

Although the decision-makers must meet the bare minimum living standards for survival of their nation, their allocations of basic capability for strategic purposes may very from zero to amounts determined by the nation's security needs. The ability of the nation to use force as a threat or for actual warfare depends upon its current level of "strategic capability." Although one's strategic capabilities may be carried over from period to period, the loss each period is large because of high obsolescence and operating costs. The reductions are erratic, depending upon military breakthroughs, weapon developments, and so forth. Because there is lag in the conversion of basic capability to strategic abilities, preparedness policies demand standing forces, despite their drain on the nation's resources. Validator satisfaction is based on the strength of a nation and its allies in relation to the strength of the enemy.

Core Variable: Force Capability (FC). This is the coercion that is available for the control of external and internal affairs.

Core Variable: Military Costs. This is the obsolescence and wear (depreciation) as well as the resources consumed and labor involved in operating a military establishment.

Programmed Assumption No. 14: Relation of Levels of Force Capability to Military Costs. The costs of the force capability of the nation change over time, the percentage amounts varying randomly within given ranges from time to time.

The values of 20, 30 and 40 percent for the rate of depreciation of force capability within a period are equiprobable.

Programmed Assumption No. 15: Time Lag in the Availability of Force Capability. Despite the period lag involved in the creation of force capability, the force in existence is available for immediate use.

Programmed Variable: Validator Satisfaction with Respect to National Strength (VS_{ns}). The extent to which a nation's validators feel secure in their military position *vis-a-vis* other nations.

Programmed Assumption No. 16: Relation of Validator Satisfaction to Level of Force Capability. Validator satisfaction is directly related to the ratio of the force strength of the nation and its allies *vis-a-vis* the strongest nation or group of nations not allied with it, within limits, as follows:

Top limit: when a nation with its allies is many times stronger than non-ally nations or groups;
Bottom limit: when a nation with its allies is insignificant in its strength *vis-a-vis* its non-allies.

$$VS_{ns} = p \; \frac{\overset{\text{for allies}}{\sum (FC - FC_{ic} + .5 \; BC)}}{\underset{\text{for others}}{\sum (FC - FC_{ic} + .5 \; BC)}} + a, \qquad (10)$$

where $p = 4.3$ and $q = .28$, and arbitrary constants permit the manipulation of FC and BC units within the same equation. The FC units without subscript represent the total coercive power of the nation, from which is subtracted that part which is devoted to internal controls, FC_{ic}, a variable which is treated immediately below. The force capability available for external use, and a measure of the overall basic capability of the nation, are added for the nation and its allies, constituting the numerator of the ratio of strength represented in Equation 9. The corresponding sum, which supplies the denominator for the comparison, is gathered for all non-allies. If the nation has no allies, the comparison is made between itself and the total of all other nations. Whenever the ratio is greater than 3, VS_{ns} is considered to have reached its maximum. When the absolute level of a nation's FC's is less than 500, the nation is considered disengaged from the armaments race. Its VS_m is then considered as equivalent to VS_{cs}, rather than the combination of VS_{cs} and VS_{ns} assumed in Equation 2.

The underlying capability decisions made each period by the central decision-maker therefore are interdependent. The sum of the allocations made each period to consumption, force, and renewal or improvement of the basic capability is constrained always by the basic capability available from the previous period. In this way, the simulation attempts to represent the allocative choices facing top decision-makers concerned with domestic and foreign affairs.

Unprogrammed Hypothesis No. 11. The decision-makers of a nation will allocate their various capabilities so as to increase their chances for retaining office and for implementation of their nation's goals.

Prevention and Consequences of Revolution

Now that capabilities have been described, it is possible to enumerate further details about one of the important political processes within the simulation-revolution. As noted above, when the validator satisfactions descend below the revolution threshold, a two-step program is invoked: first, a determination is made of whether there is or is not a revolution, and secondly, if there is a revolution, its outcome is decided.

The chances of having a revolution, once the critical threshold of validator dissatisfaction is reached, are determined stochastically in the simulation, the probability of revolution varying directly with the insensitivity of the decision-makers to validators, that is, varying with decision latitude. When the decision-makers are not sensitive to their validators, then attempts at revolution are substituted for more orderly political processes. But the likelihood of revolutionaries precipitating upheaval will also depend upon the chances that they might succeed in taking over the government.

Programmed Assumption No. 17: Relation of Occurrence of Revolution to Decision Latitude and Outcome of a Revolution. The risk of having a revolution, be it eventually successful or unsuccessful, is related directly to the nation's decision latitude and the chances of the revolution being successful.

$$pR = (r\,DL + pSR)/s, \tag{11}$$

where $r = .1$ and $s = 2$. The programmed variables DL (decision latitude) and pSR (probability of a successful revolution) have been defined above (pp. 169 and 171, respectively).

The chance of being successful in revolution, should one occur, is also determined stochastically in the simulation. However, it is possible for the central decision-makers to use the nation's force capability to increase the government's chances of crushing a revolution. The central decision-maker may reserve up to 33 percent of his force capability for application as internal control measures during any period of the simulation. The application of force units to control the demands of the rebelling validators during periods of upheaval represent such devices as riot suppression forces, secret police, and paramilitary activity.

Core Variable: Internal Controls (FC_{ic}). This is the force capability which is applied internally for reducing the chances of revolutions being successful.

Programmed Assumption No. 18: Relation of Outcome of Revolution to Internal Controls. The chances for a successful revolution, should one occur, is reduced directly by the percentage of force capability which is applied to internal controls.

$$\text{Where } t = 2, \; pSR = 1 - t(FC_{ic}/FC). \tag{12}$$

This last hypothesis indicates that although reduction in validator satisfaction may release or trip a revolution, its outcome actually is not dependent upon the level of validator satisfaction. The potential success of the revolution is specified as dependent upon the amount of forceful opposition the government is prepared to give to the revolutionary effort.

Costs of the force capability, as programmed in Programmed Assumption No. 14, remain the same whether the force is applied to internal controls or for purposes of foreign affairs. Should a revolution occur, the entire allocation of force units is consumed.

Programmed Assumption No. 19: Utilization of Internal Force during Revolution. When a revolution occurs, the whole force capability devoted to internal controls is expended during the revolution.

Note the flexibility in policy decision-makers have with respect to their validators, *vis-a-vis* the possibility of revolution with their nation. By keeping validator satisfaction high, the government may almost insure its perpetuation in office, incurring, at most, orderly changes. By operating their government so as to insure themselves sufficient decision latitude, approaches to the revolution threshold may be forestalled (Equation 1). Or, should revolutionary outbreaks occur, the decision-makers within a nation may apply direct force internally, thereby attempting to suppress the revolt (Equation 11).

Unprogrammed Hypothesis No. 12. Decision-makers will tend to prevent the outbreak of revolutions in the first place, rather than depend upon their suppressive force to control revolution once it has been set in motion.

But revolutions are not without cost, even if they should be successfully suppressed. Not only is there a loss of the force capability which was applied internally, but the economic life of the nation is disrupted so that its basic capability is reduced.

Programmed Assumption No. 20: Depletion of Basic Capability due to Revolution. The basic capability of a nation is depleted by a given amount at the conclusion of each revolution.

$$\triangle BC = -0.2\,BC \tag{13}$$

Revolutions also have their gains. After each revolution there is an immediate increase in overall validator satisfaction, part of which continues during the subsequent period. In the case of a revolution which has been crushed, the rise in overall satisfaction occurs because the opposition has been silenced and suppressed. In the case of a revolution which has been won, the rise in overall satisfaction occurs because the new government now is operated by men of greater popularity. Eventually, however, these revolutionary gains are dissipated, as when the decision-makers confront their validators during more normal times.

Programmed Assumption No. 21: Increase in Validator Satisfaction due to Revolution. At the conclusion of each revolution there is a rise in validator satisfaction.

$$\triangle VS = +2 \text{ units}$$

A "silent" revolution also is programmed within the simulation. Consider further the joint operation of Programmed Assumptions Nos. 4 and 5 (pp. 169 and 170), and note again the potential opposition between a stochastically induced decrease in decision latitude and the staus quo, or even an increase desired by the decision-makers of a nation. If the stochastic process resulting in decreases in latitude for the decision-makers is considered as an effort by the validators to gain internal freedoms, then the simultaneous operations of Programmed Assumptions Nos. 4 and 5 represent the resistance of the ruled to their rulers. This silent revolution may be controlled, however, if the decision-makers are willing to utilize force capabilities—beyond those already allocated for "stand by"—against violent revolution. By the application of additional preventative "police" measures internally, resistance to the status quo or to increases in decision latitude may be suppressed.

Programmed Assumption No. 22: Force Capabilities Applied Internally to Silence Opposition to Increases in Decision Latitude and to Suppress Deviation from the Status Quo. By allocation of force capability, FC, decreases in decision latitude may be prevented and increases in decision latitude may be imposed.

In addition to the FC_{ic} already allocated, some u percent of FC's must be applied to break the resistance of the validators. When validators attempt to decrease DL, or when decision-makers endeavor to increase the decision latitude, u is programmed at 5 percent. The value of u increases to 10 percent when there is simultaneous effort to change DL in opposite directions. These values of u double to 10 percent and 20 percent, respectively, when the $DL \geqq 8$.

Nationalism

An important ingredient in validator satisfaction within nations is the esteem with which nations are held by the peoples of the world. A constellation of variables is invoked in explaining the role of world opinion, nationalism, and other social processes in building esteem. To date, we have no core variables in the simulation with which to program the feedback of national pride into the validation process. Our two failures in programming feedbacks from the inter-nation system itself into validator satisfactions is described by Noel.[9]

However, there are unprogrammed feedbacks from the interaction to the decision-makers themselves. The participants become strongly identified with their own nations, feeling intense rivalries and being sensitive to grievances. Among the external decision-makers representing different nations, status hierarchies develop based on such considerations as the nation's capabilities, the skill of the decision-makers in the conduct of their nation's affairs, and the ideological force with which the nation's diplomacy is conducted. These feelings of esteem extend beyond that of friendship, since sometimes a *coup de maître* is the beginning step in a switch of allies.

The following hypotheses suggest the rich isomorphism with reality which has been produced by unprogrammed developments in runs of the simulation.

Unprogrammed Hypothesis No. 13. The greater the feeling of identification of the decision-makers with the importance of their states, the greater sensitivity will they feel about their status relations within the inter-nation system.

Unprogrammed Hypothesis No. 14. The less secure the decision-makers feel about their tenure in office, the greater sensitivity will they feel about their status relations within the inter-nation system.

Unprogrammed Hypothesis No. 15. The greater the esteem with which a nation is regarded in the inter-nation system, the greater are the chances that developments in the inter-nation system may redound indirectly to increase the probability of continuation in office by its decision-makers.

Can one gain perspective on the way in which the model has been constructed to this point by examining the differentiation between the programmed assumptions and the unprogrammed hypotheses? The distinction between the core and free variables discussed above is analogous to the differences between the programmed and unprogrammed relationships among the variables. The programmed assumptions are hypotheses structured into the foundation of the simulation. Although they constitute the basic postulations of the operations which constitute the simulation, they can be changed from time to time should they prove at variance with increases in our understanding of processes within the real world to which they are supposedly isomorphic. The unprogrammed hypotheses are speculative formulations of the way in which self-developed features of the simulation operate.

It would be possible to transform some of the unprogrammed hypotheses into the simulation as programmed assumptions. For instance, one

---

[9] *Op. cit.*

might develop a program rule for increasing the nation's decision latitude whenever there was rapid decrease in validator satisfaction, a not unreasonable proposal in that governments often take self-defense measures which inhibit orderly change procedures when their populations begin creating public disorders. Contrariwise, it would be possible to relax an assumption, allowing the variables involved to operate without a structured program. An instance might be developed by eliminating a program which imposes direct costs in basic capabilities whenever there is an increase in decision latitude, as now is operative in Assumption No. 6.

Were this made the case, an unprogrammed relation between basic capabilities and decision latitude could develop, nevertheless. Decision-makers generally might be prone to operate with higher decision latitudes, were they able to obtain latitude without cost. This in turn might induce them to take more risks with their nation's basic capabilities, inasmuch as they could (with more latitude) be less sensitive to the standards of living of their people. Such risks might pay off well—or result in impoverishment of the nation's basic capabilities. Thus, although a programmed assumption was eliminated, the same core variables might still be related to each other through unprogrammed processes.

Is it possible to program a free variable into a core variable by making an appropriate assumption? For example, could one formally link the esteem variable into the probability of office holding, as possibly intimated in Unprogrammed Hypothesis No. 15? It seems the answer is negative. Although one can speculate about the impact of core variables on free variables (and vice versa) by means of unprogrammed hypotheses, one cannot program one's hunches into the simulation unless one already has defined core variables for incorporation into the new assumptions. It will be noted that the programmed assumptions of this essay consist of relationships between core variables.

RELATIONS AMONG NATIONS

Our effort has been confined so far to a description of the nations and the variables—both core and free—through which the decision-makers operate within the simulation. Now attention may be turned to relations among the nations. The first focus will be upon the interaction processes themselves in the political, economic, and military spheres. Later, the development of supra-national institutions will be examined. On occasion, in the first part of this essay, the interrelations among nations were incorporated integrally into the operation of the simulation, as in the dependence of satisfaction with respect to national security upon the levels of arms of one's neighbors (Programmed Assumption No. 19). But in the main, with the exception of the rules for communication and war, interaction between states is generated in unprogrammed ways by the decision-makers themselves, as this second part of the essay demonstrates.

Communications

Characteristics of the communications existing between states yield important consequences for their behaviors. Implicit in our description of the simulation to this point has been the existence of communicative exchanges within nations and between them. An attempt has been made within each run to have all the communications between nations, whether oral or written, routed through external decision-makers. Ten to thirty decision-makers send a tremendous number of messages over a period of 15 to 45 hours. If the decision-makers do not organize themselves adequately within their nation, the unit becomes "paper-logged," with consequent failures in communication. Sometimes the neglect of requests by other powers is interpreted as disrespect and an indication that the notes from a nation are considered insignificant, or not worthy of top-level attention.

Core Variable: Conferences.   These are oral communications involving two or more decision-makers within the same nation and between nations.

Core Variable: Messages.   These are written communications from one decision-maker to another, within the same nation and between nations.

An important difference between sets of inter-nation communication patterns is whether they are bilateral or multilateral. If the former, the communications are restricted to the two nations involved. When the multilateral exchanges include less than all the nations, as in the case of the trilateral exchanges, decision-makers often are unaware of what is going on in the other parts of the system. This tendency toward ignorance sometimes is strengthened by a division of labor among the two to five decision-makers within the nation, so that, even though one of the participants receives a message from another nation, his failure to communicate it internally to others in his government may result in important errors of omission in the actions of the other decision-makers.

These areas of ignorance induced the experimenters to augment the direct exchanges among the decision-makers with a communications system external to the nations themselves: a "world newspaper." Journalists were introduced into the simulation to present information about inter-nation events to all decision-makers simultaneously through a mass medium. Issues of the "world newspaper," made every 15 to 30 minutes during the run, provide communications among the decision-makers which otherwise only the most elaborate and costly intelligence operations could assemble.

The mass media provide knowledge about the international system, so most decision-makers know the gross outlines of what is going on within the world. Space is given for the insertion of press releases and communiques by the decision-makers of any nation. The development of non-secret treaties are publicized through issues of the press, be they concerned with economic, military, or ideological matters. The proceedings of open conferences are reported in summary so that non-attenders may receive dispatches of progress being made or learn of stalemates and conflict. A special statistical supplement is included in the report from time to time, summarizing the information on changes in validator satisfaction, in economic well-being, and containing some statistics on force capability. "Extra" editions are prepared when there is a turnover in government. Although no radio or television apparatus was used in the simulation, the printed media served as a surrogate for the "mass media."

Core Variable: Mass Media. Regular reports contain information about states of the inter-nation system, as well as releases issued by the decision-makers; their contents are open and circulated to all members of all nations.

During one of the runs, professional editors operated two competing presses. By taking sides with particular blocs, the two papers helped develop propaganda quarrels among the nations. In fact, when one of the blocs was conquered through a devastating war, the deposed decision-makers continued participating in the world complex by starting a "rebel" newspaper.

Some information circulates in the communication nets among the decision-makers as rumors or secret reports. It is possible for the decision-makers to issue messages which are false, or merely speculative. Decision-makers classify some of their messages as RESTRICTED. Receivers sometimes find it advantageous to violate the secrecy. At times this creates severe distrust, especially when strategies are divulged in the course of on-going negotiations. A stochastic leakage of restricted messages is part of the newspaper operation. Without favoring any particular nation, these "intelligence reports" allow decision-makers to weave a web of conjecture from partial information which is gleaned by tapping one out of every five of the restricted exchanges.

Core Variable: Restricted Messages. These are messages whose existence and contents are known only to the sender and receiver.

Programmed Assumption No. 23: Relation of Leakage of Restricted Messages to Volume of Messages. Inasmuch as restricted messages are leaked stochastically, the greater the volume of restricted messages, the greater will be the revelation of secret information to the mass media. The message leakage rate is 20 percent, or every fifth message.

Although no formal espionage operation is included in the simulation, it is fascinating to see how external decision-makers attempt to gain information by posting "observers" at conferences, even when they refuse to have formal representation of their nation at the conference table for reasons of diplomacy. An external decision-maker at times will attempt to ingratiate himself with an ally by communicating supposedly secret information obtained from non-members of the alliance.

Because news is communicated in terms of who said what when, and to whom, the internal and external communication systems help create prestige hierarchies among the decision-makers. These hierarchies of esteem have great import for the operation of influence patterns in the simulation world, as they do within the real world. It is revealing to note how a prestigious nation, once its central decision-maker has spoken, can change the policies of less influential nations.

Unprogrammed Hypothesis No. 16. Communication failures due to overload are interpreted by decision-makers as deliberate signs of disrespect and neglect.

Unprogrammed Hypothesis No. 17. When there is a preponderant use of bilateral rather than multilateral and mass media channels for communication, there is more distrust and suspicion among the decision-makers of the world.

Unprogrammed Hypothesis No. 18. Standards for judgment of national achievement develop in the course of inter-nation communication, thereby defining the "social realities" of the system.

Inequalities among Nations

To anyone surveying the more than 100 independent countries of the real world, an outstanding characteristic of the array is found in their differences. An attempt has been made to incorporate some of this rich variety of the real world in the simulation. The nations may be distinguished from each other by virtue of different weightings of the core factors. Basic differences may be reflected in variations in decision latitude. Authority might be shared, instead of centralized in one decision-maker. Some nations might be designated as having higher or lower thresholds for revolution than others. In some, the office holder determinations might be made at regular, relatively short intervals; while in others, the determination might be made only after revolutions, following (for example) life-tenured monarchies. It is possible to distinguish one nation from the others through the validation process, by using different weights for the contributions of the components of satisfaction to office holding (Figure 1). One nation, for example, might have a more demanding consumption standard; the validators in another nation might want higher levels of national security.

Different weightings are employed to symbolize inequalities among the nations with respect to their capabilities. Some of the nations are construed as "have-nots" with meagre capabilities; others are rich. These differences among the nations are induced in two ways: by starting the nations with different accumulations of basic and force capability, and by assigning differential "generation rates" for the production of goods and services used for the standard of consumption and for strategic purposes.

For example, in the 1959 run the initial conditions characterizing nation ERGA were designated as 10,000 basic capability units, with an accumulation of 500 force units. The analogous parameters for nation INGO were

16,000 and 2,400. The rates at which these nations could generate consumption satisfaction units from their basic capability units were 1.0 and 1.5, respectively; the generation rates for force units were .5 and 2.00. In the programmed equations constituting the intra-nation system, some 30 parameters are utilized.

These inequalities among the nations produce important differences in the unprogrammed relations among the nations. Further inequalities, of course, emerge from the ways in which the decision-makers use their resources. In one run in 1958, the decision-makers in nation S lost their top position as wealthiest nation. In another run, nation M rose to a position as one of the two nations with the dominant strategic capabilities. It is feasible to go further by introducing slowly, or suddenly—to correspond to an important technological breakthrough—changes in the generation rates during the course of the historical development of nations. For example, during one of the exploratory runs, a middle-size nation was allowed to "develop" nuclear power, which increased its force capabilities tenfold.

The employment of differences in the weightings yields important leverage for using the simulation in the study of international relations. By setting the weightings to correspond to the configurations found in today's system of nations, contemporary problems in foreign affairs may be studied. By resetting the weightings, it is possible to represent historical situations. Perhaps as important is the potential development of simulation analyses based on weightings which have not yet existed in the world of real affairs. This latter possibility may be the most significant heuristic value to be obtained from the simulation. Research leading to better understanding of the possible in the development of world affairs, unbounded by current practices, may lead to unimagined innovations in international relations.

Although at first the participants within a nation feel they are the United States, or nineteenth century Britain, or perhaps contemporary Yugoslavia, these identifications with historical or existing nations gradually lose their potency. The simulated nations seem to take on color and characteristics unique to themselves. Then the participants vividly contrast their own nations with those of the real world. Suppose we attempt to set the weightings in our functions as they are found in real nations. Further, suppose each nation is manned by persons of the nationality of the nation being represented. Then, if the model simulates adequately, participants of a given nationality should feel themselves conceptually to be operating in their own "home country" when they serve as decision-makers for their home nations.

Armaments: Defensive and Aggressive Use of Force

In the exploratory runs undertaken to the first of 1960, the decision-makers tended to make great use of their force capabilities in handling their external problems. As noted earlier, validator satisfaction derived from a given level of strength, for a nation is programmed to depend upon its relation to the strength of its non-allies (Assumption No. 19). The relationship, however, is considered to have a ceiling effect in that validator satisfaction reaches its maximum when the strength of a nation is three or more times that of its strongest potential enemies. Likewise, there is a floor effect, for when the nation's strategic capability is a small fraction of that of the strongest potential enemy, its validators become indifferent to the nation's strategic capability in world affairs.

Free Variable: Alliance. This is a written treaty, explicitly authorized by central decision-makers to provide military aid and/or support to another nation in case of the latter's involvement in military activity. (There is no enforcement of these treaties by the simulation-director.)

The effectiveness of strength as a factor in foreign relations depends on the uses to which it may be put. So the simulation provides opportunities for its symbolic employment both in aggressive and defensive ways. The decision-makers within each nation project war plans of an offensive and/or defensive nature, which may be revised from period to period. These plans specify the amounts of force which may be directed against particular nations. The plans provide for target selection, directed toward the basic capability of the other unit and/or toward his military forces.

The attack, counterattack, and defense plans may be kept quite secret, or they may be exhibited as part of a deterrent strategy. Sometimes the nations will stage war exercises or make displays of strength. The central decision-makers may systematize response plans analogous to the von Schlieffen plan; or they may develop automatic response plans, resembling those contemplated for nuclear warfare. The arrangement allows significant variation in the use of force in both limited or more global ways. Since the decision-makers are allowed to ally themselves freely, the possible combinations are great. By building war into its rules, the simulation accommodates a wide range of the use of strength for purposes of threat and intimidation.

The war programs of the inter-nation simulation are still in need of marked revision. However, a general outline of the waging and consequences of war in this exercise can be sketched at this time.

In the making of war, the routines may be phased so that there are opportunities for varying levels of engagement in battle. When a nation goes to war, rallying to the national cause is portrayed through increases in validator satisfaction. The war itself may engage less that the total resources of the system, so that during its conduct there is time for threats and counterthreats, for peace proposals and counterproposals. During these periods, other nations come to their decisions as to whether they will or will not enter the struggle. Sometimes a "neutral" will attempt to mediate the conflict.

Core Variable: War. This is the use of force capability by one or more nations against one or more other nations.

Programmed Assumption No. 24: The Relation of the Making of War to Validator Satisfaction. Whenever a nation makes war against another (or others), its validator satisfaction is temporarily increased.

$$\triangle VS_m = 2 \tag{15}$$

The hardware intricacies of war itself are abbreviated in the simulation because interest does not center on nonpolitical aspects of violent conflict. The outcomes of the contests of strength depend stochastically upon the relative basic (BC) and force (FC) capabilities of the nations. It is possible to allow consequences to vary in severity, from partial to total destruction. If the nation is not totally destroyed, its decision-makers may surrender, negotiate an armistice, and eventually sign a peace treaty with the victor(s). An occupation may be arranged, in which the winning power exercises authority within another nation, through implementation of its decisions with respect to the internal and external functioning of the nation.

Included among these decisions is the possibility of reparations and tribute. Of course, there is internal opposition to an occupying force, which over time may become acute enough to engage the revolution mechanism against the occupying power (as it is sometimes evoked against an indigenous national government). The rules also permit other nations to overthrow the occupying forces through a "war of liberation."

Core Variable: Determination of Outcome of War (pOW). When a determination of the outcome of a war is made, the result may be victory or defeat.

Programmed Assumption No. 25: Outcome of War as Related to Relative National Strengths. The winning or losing in each phase of a war is determined stochastically, with the chances for winning proportional to the relative strength of each side at the beginning of each phase of the war.

$$pOW = \frac{(FC - FC_{ie} + .5\ BC)\ \text{adversary}}{\sum (FC - FC_{ie} + .5\ BC)} \tag{16}$$
$$\text{for all}$$
$$\text{nations in}$$
$$\text{war}$$

The adversary may be a single nation or a group of allied nations.

Core Variable: War Destruction (WD). The amounts of the basic and force capabilities of a nation which are destroyed during each phase of a war are proportional to the force capabilities applied by the adversary in the course of each phase.

Programmed Assumption No. 26: War Destruction as Related to Force Capabilities Applied in Course of War. The war destruction suffered by any nation is proportional to the force capabilities applied by its adversary.

$$\frac{\triangle FC}{FC} \text{ and } \frac{\triangle BC}{BC} = \frac{FC \text{ adversary}}{\sum FC} \tag{17}$$

in target nation   for all nations
in war

Whether the percentage destruction is suffered in FC's or BC's—or both—depends upon the targeting decision of the adversary.

Unprogrammed Hypothesis No. 19. When the members of a coalition are historically united in terms of ideology, they will come to the defense of one of their members when the latter is attacked by outside forces, either directly through participation in an on-going war or later through a war of liberation.

The following example of the above hypothesis was found in one run in which three nations operated as "tightly reigned" states, as reflected in their high decision latitudes. When one of their number clashed with a "democratic" nation, the other two immediately came to its aid. The decision-makers in the "totalitarian" bloc simply could not understand why the other nations, which continued to operate with low decision latitudes period after period despite opportunities for increasing their decisional latitudes, wished to remain "democratic."

Perhaps the intertwining of the internal and external processes within an inter-nation system is nowhere as well represented in the simulation as in the utilization of the force capabilities of the nations. As has been demonstrated in the history of military aid in the real world, the arms of a country may be used by its decision-makers to control its own peoples, as well as against the peoples of other nations. The intimacy of the reciprocity of domestic and foreign policy is embodied in the inter-nation simulation in the internal control and war programs.

Interaction Patterns: Conflict and Cooperation in War and Peace

Interest in developing an operating model of inter-nation relations stemmed in part from the belief that mathematical and vernacular languages, as they exist today, seem to limit (for different reasons) our ability to handle abstractions. It was hoped that the central heuristic value of this kind of exercise would reside in its representation of inter-group processes, which we simply are unable to program adequately, given our present state of knowledge.

Enfolded within the capabilities are the sinews of war and peace. Quests for high standards of living, given differential rates of production, may eventuate in trade, in loans, or in aid. Fear for national security may produce alliances and arms races. Although the capabilities seem at first directed only toward fulfillment of validator satisfactions, they too become significant bases for external activity.

There are variations in the degree to which interactions stabilize in the form of structured organizations. Let us now explore the way in which the interactions about peace and war yield entanglements in the relations among our simulated nations. In the following section, the more formalized, complex organizations which may evolve in the simulation will be discussed.

The decision-makers can and do make informal and formal agreements on many subjects. Sometimes these agreements are simply *de facto* working arrangements which develop tacitly in the course of the interactions. For example, in an early exploration run one of the external decision-makers in state P informally helped an external decision-maker of state G arrange a multilateral conference among the nations. Sometimes the agreements are more formal, being registered with each nation's signature. Some of the treaties are secret, and some are publicized. Some treaties even involve definite commitments of force capability units to other nations, for purposes of aggression against another nation or group of nations, or for collective security.

Unprogrammed Hypothesis No. 20. When agreements are well publicized throughout the international system, there is less miscalculation of national intentions.

Much interaction is generated among the nations because of the differences in their abilities to transform one capability into another. The economic "law of comparative advantage" induces trade, which often is sporadic but sometimes takes a more stable, long-term form with formal exchange agreements. Because of the impoverishment of some nations, loans are arranged between them and the wealthier countries. These loans may be interest bearing or free. Agreements may be made to provide that basic capability be sent abroad to generate returns at the rates of the nation within which the investment is made. During both the summer and winter simulations of 1959, outright grants of aid were made, sometimes military (in force capability units) or economic (in basic capability units) in form, and sometimes of an emergency nature (in consumption satisfaction units). The aid arrangements at times became part and parcel of security alliances.

Unprogrammed Hypothesis No. 21. The more mutual trust among nations, the more likely will the law of comparative advantage operate.

No attempt was made to further complicate the economic features of the simulation by introducing a formal monetary system. With three "commodities" (basic capability, consumption satisfactions, and force capability), transactions by barter seem to be made without awkwardness. In one exploratory run during 1958, the basic capability units operated for the nations' decision-makers as a "gold standard" in determining "prices" used in international transactions. Since there is no explicit private sector of the national economies, the usual need of governmental decision-makers for trade restrictions in the forms of tariffs, exchange controls, and quotas is not present.

But trust and suspicion are generated in these interactions. Some nations become reliable and trustworthy; others are suspect and perceived as crafty. During the simulation runs it is possible, at the end of each period, to ask the decision-makers to rate each other nation in terms of its trustworthiness. Mutual trust can be generated, even when the decision-makers are overtly unconcerned with each other's welfare when certain situational conditions hold. One such condition is the state of affairs in which there is opportunity for each party to know what the other will do before committing itself to irrevocable choice. The entanglements arising from economic and military matters generate ideologies among the nations, which seem in some cases to have created much trust and, in other cases, considerable hostility and feelings of threat.

Unprogrammed Hypothesis No. 22. At any level of congruence or conflict of national goals, the greater knowledge each nation has of the other's actions, the greater the mutual trust.

Inter-Nation Organizations

When the volume of transactions among the nations becomes stable and sufficiently large, and is spread over considerable time periods, the interactions occur through formal inter-nation organizations.

Unprogrammed Hypothesis No. 23. Members of an alliance, which exists but for a single purpose under ad hoc *conditions, gradually will begin meeting periodically for increasingly broad purposes.*

It is intriguing to note how inter-nation collectivities, thus evolved, tend to develop an autonomy of their own, so that the delegate members no longer act solely in terms of their national reference groups but develop bases of action within the international organization itself. The organization may be consultative or it may be given decision making power of its own by delegation of national power from the member states. The evolutions sometimes are followed by devolutions, so that an overall effect of waxing and waning is experienced.

Free Unit: Inter-Nation Organization. A formally chartered supra-unit among three or more nations.

Unprogrammed Hypothesis No. 24. Inter-nation organizations tend to develop, over time, an increasing amount of autonomy of their own, to the extent that they are successful in achievement of their substantive goals.

In the course of the 1959–60 runs, two formal inter-nation organizations were created by the external decision-makers acting in behalf of their nations. During one run, an underdeveloped nation induced the other nations of the world (except one) to establish an international bank. Each period the member nations made contributions in basic capabilities to a fund thereafter to be entirely controlled by the bank's board, consisting of external ministers from the contributing states. Before the simulation was terminated, the poorer countries of the world had been given loans, resulting in decided increases in the stability of their governments.

During another run, two large powers established an international grant-in-aid corporation to which the dissident smaller powers, flirting with aggressive national policies, might apply for grants-in-aid. The external ministers who manned the corporation, however, squabbled so much among themselves that, before the terms of the grants were formulated, the smaller countries experienced internal disorders, with many changes in their decision-makers. The disagreements among the great powers and the disorders within the smaller powers eventuated in a world war. It was interesting to note that the postwar peace treaty provided, among other things, for reestablishment of an international grant-in-aid corporation, this time with a worldwide membership on its board.

During a third run, in Alger's International Organizations course, the students found themselves unable to build a viable international bank, even though considerable effort was devoted to the enterprise.

Unprogrammed Hypothesis No. 25. Most basic changes in the international system take place when there are simultaneous changes in office holders within several of the nations.

Unprogrammed Hypothesis No. 26. When there are changes in office holders within the several nations within a short period of time, the decision-makers find the behavior of each other more unpredictable.

Because of the relatively short duration of our runs up to this point in the exploration, there has been little time for the international organizations to consolidate. Each of our nations has needed opportunity to worry through its internal problems. Although both the bank and the corporation began establishing rules for their own internal operation, no attempts have been made yet to erect a court or legislature for the establishment of inter-nation law. When the runs are extended in duration, the nations may develop uni- versus multi-functional organizations. It also is possible then that regional organizations may emerge to compete with universal complexes. Patterns of interrelationship will develop among the various inter-nation organizations themselves. It should even be possible to note how world community norms develop ahead of—or lag behind—the building of legal and political institutions among the nations. Because the central decision-makers may turn over parts or even all of their decision making to supra-national groups, it is possible to have federations and/or world governments.

Unprogrammed Hypothesis No. 27. When the decision-makers of a nation are intensely involved in meeting internal problems, there is little growth of inter-nation organizations.

Unprogrammed Hypothesis No. 28. Inter-nation organizations established for single purposes tend to be less viable than those established for multi-purposes.

Unprogrammed Hypothesis No. 29. The norms of conduct of states which develop within an inter-nation organization tend to be applied to relations among all states, whether they are members or not.

The relation of the decision-makers to their own nations plays an important role at the international level. In the simulation runs to date, we have evidence of the problems involved in the relation of the foreign mission to the home foreign office. When the external environment is rich with international activities, how can the external ministers keep their communications to their internal ministers adequate? One of the external decision-makers for state K had much trouble in a particular run because he acted as a plenipotentiary. The reactions of other states to nation K's inconsistency in policy lost K its membership in a newly forming alliance.

Discussion

One essay cannot handle all the problems which the construction of the simulation raises. But some of these are so pressing that it may be useful to mention them, even if they cannot be solved at present.

Although no explicit reference has been made to the scholarly literature of international relations, the constructors of this operating model have steeped themselves in this body of speculation. Hence, we have borrowed freely from many others as guides to our formulation. Perhaps more attention should have been devoted within the essay to justification of our decisions, indicating the rationale employed in making each individual choice. As yet, no formalized criteria have emerged to provide guidance for our exploitation of the work of others. For instance, no sampling technique seemed appropriate to guide our selection of core variables. Sometimes detailed rationalizations of the choices must be provided. It is important that a firmer embedding of our model within the studies of international relations be attempted, so that an almost total reliance upon an intuitive grasp of this literature may be circumvented.

Has the choice of a simulation which mixes men with computed programs been sound? An all-computer simulation would obviate the implicit contents introduced in the inter-nation simulation by the use of human decision-makers. An all-man simulation *without* intra-nation programs, on the other hand, perhaps would bring the form of the simulation too close to a face-to-face group. As the simulation stands now, it seems to be a composition of computer and men so that the inter-group relations which emerge from its operation are somewhat isomorphic, from a subjective point of view, with the phenomena one encounters in the inter-relations of real nations.

But have not our omissions of important features of the real world developed incapacitating artificialities within the simulation? How can the motivational stress of a game be compared with the deadly struggles for power which exist within and among the governments of the world? For example, has not our positing of authority within the central decision-maker induced an unrealistic security for the holders of power? And how is the impact of geography displayed? Because of the short time duration of the simulation, are not the historical factors—especially as they operate through tradition—being short-circuited? Perhaps most puzzling of all, how does the mixture of men and computers distort the time relations within the system? The participants function in terms of biological, or real time. The machines compress time so that some 70 minutes of game time are made analogous to a year of life time. These problems certainly must be given close attention.

If the simulation is to be of heuristic value, as Snyder contends,[10] its ability to produce unprogrammed consequences which are isomorphic to reality must be checked thoroughly. For example, Alger unexpectedly found that in several underdeveloped nations in the runs in his International Relations course, the aspirant decision-makers consolidated their efforts with those of the decision-makers in office, evolving "one-party" nations. It seemed that such nations felt they could not afford the luxury of opposition among their decision making groups. Work on the validity of the simulation is imperative at this time. When such validity is demonstrated, then one's use of the simulation for exploration in unchartered areas, such as the n-country problem, will be more justifiable.

In Table 3 a summary is presented of the core variables involved in the simulation. No similar list is made for the free variables, inasmuch as only

TABLE 3

SUMMARY OF CORE VARIABLES FOR INTER-NATION SIMULATION

Political Core Variables	Page	Military Core Variables	Page
Authority of Decision-Makers	162	Force Capability (FC)	178
Office Holding	165	Military Costs	178
Validation Satisfaction (VS_m)	165	Strength Satisfaction (VS_{ns})	179
Decision Latitude	169	Internal Controls (FC_{ic})	180
Determination of Office Holding		Alliance	189
(pOH)	171	War	190
Occurrence of Revolution (pR)	171	Outcome of War (pOW)	190
Outcome of Revolution (pSR)	171	War Destruction (WD)	190
Economic Core Variables		*Communication Core Variables*	
Basic Capability (BC)	176	Conferences	185
Generation Rates	176	Messages	185
Depreciation/Attrition Rates	176	Restricted messages	186
Consumption Satisfaction (VS_{cs})	176	Mass Media (Newspaper)	186
Minimum Living Standards (CS_{min})	176		
Maximum Living Standards (CS_{max})	176		

[10] *Op. cit.* Also see his "Some Recent Trends in International Relations Theory and Research" in Austin Ranney (ed.), *Essays on the Behavioral Study of Politics* (Urbana, Ill.: University of Illinois Press, 1962), pp. 103–71.

illustrative examples were presented in the body of the text. Neither should the 26 programmed assumptions, which attempt to exhibit all the assumptions within the simulation, be compared with the unprogrammed hypotheses, which also are only illustrative. The task ahead, of making explicit the implicit contents generated by the programmed assumptions within the inter-nation simulation, is a large one. It will be worthwhile only if the simulation demonstrates its potential as a heuristic device in the acquisition and application of reliable knowledge about international relations.

Summary

Individual and group components of the inter-nation simulation are meshed into an operating model through both structured programs and free, self-developing interactive processes. In general, programmed assumptions are used for setting the foundations of the simulation, thus providing operating rules for the decision-makers whereby they may handle the political, economic, and military aspects of their nations. On the other hand, with the exception of the rules for the conduct of war, there are no programs prescribing the relations among the nations. The basic strategy used in the construction of the simulation has been to allow free development of the inter-nation relations, without restrictions other than those implicit in the characteristics of the nations themselves. Illustrative hypotheses are offered to indicate the richness of the relations of the structured programs to the free activities within the inter-nation simulation.

PART V

Group Behavior: Process and Performance

Can I ever be
                Just me?
Is he, like me
Or she, like me?
                Driftwood
In
A Human Sea?

F.M.

14 Effect of Group Size on Group Performance

Herbert Solomon *

IN THIS PAPER an analysis of the relationship of group size to group performance in verbal recall is offered. The analysis is based on data obtained from an experiment conducted several years ago to explore the tenability of a model proposed for group behavior in verbal recall. In retrospect, this analysis emerges as a "well placed" step in what might be a textbook discussion of how the course of theorizing and experimentation could proceed in the examination of small group behavior in problem solving. An account of this experiment, and the thinking and previous experimentation that led to it, is given in Lorge and Solomon.[1] Before we look into the results and implications, let us briefly examine the sequence of events that led to this study.

In 1932, a paper by M. E. Shaw compared individual and group performance in the solution of complex problems.[2] One of these was the Tartaglia (missionary-cannibal) transportation problem, and Shaw deduced that, in this situation, groups of size four performed better (3 solutions out of 5) than individuals (3 solutions out of 21). A suggestion for the better performance, advanced by Shaw, was that a positive personal interaction among the members of the group produced this effect. One inference here is that two or more individuals working together can make each other produce more than any one of them could ever produce working alone.

Sometime in 1953, my colleague, Irving Lorge, who was initiating an investigation of the effect of group size on problem solving for the Air University at Maxwell Field inquired about statistical tests for differences in proportions. What he had in mind was a "probabilistic look-see" at the observed differences—in the Shaw data—in proportions of successful solutions in individual and group performance. It was obvious from the Shaw

* Stanford University.

[1] I. Lorge and H. Solomon, Chapter 15 in *Mathematical Methods in Small Group Processes* (eds.: Criswell, Solomon, and Suppes) (Stanford, Calif.: Stanford University Press, 1962).
[2] M. E. Shaw, "Comparison of Individuals and Small Groups in the Rational Solution of Complex Problems," *American Journal of Psychology*, Vol. 44 (1932), pp. 491–504.

data that her groups did better than individuals, and classical statistical tests for looking into the differences between proportions demonstrated this. What was not so obvious was Shaw's basis for the suggestions made as to why the differences existed.

This rather routine query on statistical techniques led to two models of group behavior, which we proposed and analyzed in an attempt to relate group and individual performance.[3] The first simply stated that a group solved a problem if any individual in the group could solve the problem (i.e., personal interaction was not a factor). The second model allowed for ability interaction and stated that if a problem could be solved in stages, then the group would solve the problem if any individual in the group (not necessarily the same one) could successfully pass the group through each stage. The second model is substantively the same as the first.

Briefly, we are saying that if P_g is the probability of group solution, and P_I is the probability of individual solution, then:

$$P_g = 1 - (1 - P_I)^k ,$$

where k is the number of individuals in the group. This is the model of group behavior we are going to explore in free-recall verbal learning.

Both models were surprisingly good and gave parsimonious explanations of the data obtained by Shaw. Since her experiment occurred some 20 years before our models were suggested, we have a situation where there is no possibility of forcing experimental conditions to fit a model in which some theory builders might have a vested interest. On the other hand, the development of the models suggested new experimentation.

As a next step we designed an experiment in which the same problem—similar subjects but different group sizes—was employed. Here one might say we now have a vested interest to see that a theory we proposed is not violated by new data. The results [4] were not as dramatic as one could hope for, and led, through an additional experiment,[5] to an examination of environmental variables not previously considered. In fact, it was only the passage of 25 years that made it necessary for us to look at the environmental variable. Accounting for the additional variable in our second experiment seemed to make the original conjecture more tenable again. At least it salvaged the use of the model as a base-line argument from which deviations would serve as a warning to seek the influence of other variables.

---

[3] Lorge and Solomon, "Two Models of Group Behavior in the Solution of Eureka-type Problems," *Psychometrika*, Vol. 20 (1955), pp. 139–48.

[4] Lorge and Solomon, "Individual Performance and Group Performance in Problem Solving Related to Group Size and Previous Exposure to the Problem," *Journal of Social Psychology*, Vol. 48 (1959), pp. 107–14.

[5] Lorge and Solomon, "Group and Individual Performance in Problem Solving Related to Previous Exposure to Problem, Level of Aspiration, and Group Size," *Behavioral Science*, Vol. 5, No. 1 (1960), pp. 28–38.

The Model

This rather simple model:

$$P_g = 1 - (1 - P_I)^k,$$

arises in the examination of some other settings where "behavior" is treated in a combinatorial manner. Here again, it serves as a base-line whose violation is usually caused by a group interaction behavioral variable, which we will discuss briefly before returning to our main development. This model is also used in the evaluation of missile reliability and is receiving a great deal of attention in those quarters because of some difficult estimation problems whose solutions will also benefit the behavioral applications of the model. We will discuss these implications. Note that the time dimension is not an explicit parameter in this model (as it will be in the verbal recall model which follows this digression).

Zajonc and Smoke [6] arrive at this model in the following way. Suppose N individuals are available to us for remembering H items of information, and what is especially important for us is that each item is remembered by an individual when its recall is required. How can the H items be allocated over the N individuals so as to maximize the probability of recall of each item?

Let p_{ij} be the probability that item i is remembered by individual j, and assume $p_{ij} = p$, i.e., is the same for all individuals and items. Assign h items at random to each of n individuals where $H/N = h/n$. Obviously, p should be written $p(h)$ since it depends (inversely) on the number of items to be remembered by an individual. Thus:

$$P = 1 - [1 - p(h)]^n$$

is the value to be maximized, since it is the probability that at least one of the n individuals will remember an item assigned to the group. From this vantage point, Zajonc and Smoke then discuss optimal allocations.

Deutsch and Madow arrive at this model through an assessment of the machinery by which top executives may achieve their posts by random decision making (spurious wisdom) rather than through ability.[7] Let p equal the probability of a correct decision and let n equal the number of independent decisions a bureaucrat makes in his career. The value of n is usually small, but if he is correct each time, the bureaucrat gains a reputation for great competence. The probability of n correct decisions by an

[6] R. Zajonc and W. Smoke, "Redundancy in Task Assignments and Group Performance," *Psychometrika*, Vol. 24, No. 4 (1959), pp. 361–69.

[7] Karl W. Deutsch and W. G. Madow, "A Note on the Appearance of Wisdom in Large Bureaucratic Organizations," *Behavioral Science*, Vol. 6, No. 1 (1961), pp. 72–78.

individual is p^n, and, correspondingly, the probability of at least one mistake is $1 - p^n$.

Suppose there are m bureaucrats; then the probability of at least one mistake by m bureaucrats is $(1 - p^n)^m$, and thus:

$$P = 1 - (1 - p^n)^m$$

is the probability that at least one of n bureaucrats makes all decisions correctly. If in a university there are about 50 department heads, for each of whom there is a record of action on 8 major decisions, and the probability for each of being correct on any decision is 1/2, we can expect two with perfect records. Thus if a new dean is to be chosen on this basis, it could very well be a department head who based each of his eight decisions on the toss of a coin.

In both of these two situations, and in the problem solving discussion, the model serves as a baseline from which the effects of individual interaction in the group may be measured. This baseline enumerates the eligible sets of elements in the group (produced by specific combinatoric action on individual items) and the relative frequencies for each set. One is usually not in the fortunate position of knowing the values of the parameters of the model. Also, we have made simplifying assumptions which reduce the number of parameters for which information is needed. More realistically, the format is:

$$P = 1 - (1 - P_1)(1 - P_2) \ldots (1 - P_k),$$

or, equivalently:

$$1 - P = (1 - P_1)(1 - P_2) \ldots (1 - P_k).$$

Estimates of these parameters are available from past or present experimentation or observation, or they must be obtained by new investigation. The fact that estimates replace the parameters adds more uncertainty and increases the analytical problems encountered in checking the tenability of a model. When estimates are obtained by statistical sampling, through experimental design or simulation, confidence intervals for the parameters may be generated.

Relating knowledge of confidence intervals on the P_i's to a confidence interval for P, or vice versa, is a tricky problem. The former is receiving much attention from workers in missile reliability. When reliability of a missile depends on a series structure (i.e., every component must operate for the missile to function) then the probability, P_M, that it will not function is:

$$P_M = 1 - (1 - P_1)(1 - P_2) \ldots (1 - P_k),$$

where $P_1, P_2 \ldots P_k$ represent the probabilities that each component will not function, or:

$$1 - P_M = (1 - P_1)(1 - P_2) \ldots (1 - P_k).$$

The reliability researchers assume confidence intervals are available for the component P's and from this would like to produce a confidence interval for P_M. Their efforts and results will be useful to the model in its behavioral contexts. Actually, in the problem solving situation confidence intervals can be obtained directly for P as well as $P_1 P_2, \ldots P_k$ by experimentation, but questions of tenability are made easy only when $P_1, P_2, \ldots P_k$ are all assumed to be equal.

In the situation discussed by Zajonc and Smoke, confidence intervals for $p(h)$, given h, could be obtained by experimentation for each of the N individuals, but then their relation to confidence intervals for n (the optimal number in each group) and consequently for P (the maximum probability) are still to be resolved. The same is true for confidence intervals for m (the number of bureaucrats) in the Deutsch-Madow setting, under the assumption that confidence intervals for the probability of a correct decision by an individual are obtained. These estimation problems and their effect on tenability questions require further work.

A next step was to explore the universality of the model. Since the subjects available to college professors are somewhat unchangeable, we decided to pursue a completely different problem solving situation. The subject of verbal recall appealed to us because a model for individual behavior in verbal recall had already been advanced by Miller and McGill,[8] and this model described process (i.e., behavior over time).

Accordingly, an experiment in individual and group behavior in verbal recall was conducted (Lorge and Solomon[9]). Individual subjects and groups of three were employed. However, the data resulting from this experiment also permits some study of the central topic of this paper. Analysis of tenability of the model as group size varies is advanced if we permit the formation of "concocted" groups as a contrast to "interacting" groups. The performance of a concocted group is simply the pooling of the individual performances of, say, three individuals, picked at random. From our data, we examined concocted groups of 2, 3, 4, 5, and 6, and thus are in a position to see how well our baseline model does, especially with regard to group size.

In our experiment, an interacting group of size three was studied. However, our model is such that its tenability depends on no interaction between individuals except for pooling of individual abilities. Thus if two or more individuals in a group can together recall a word that neither would get alone, the results would depart from those hypothesized. Actually, the second Lorge-Solomon pooling model could account for this (if recall of a word by two or more interacting individuals can be viewed as recall in stages, and this would have to be ruled out before a non-ability pooling

[8] G. A. Miller and W. J. McGill, "A Statistical Description of Verbal Learning," *Psychometrika*, Vol. 17 (1952), pp. 369–96.

[9] *Op. cit.* (1962).

factor could be admitted). This phenomenon would manifest itself by the superiority of interacting groups over concocted groups.

On the other hand, if groups do better simply because each member of the group recalls different sets of words, thus permitting a big advantage in group performance just by pooling, then the model is operating. If concocted groups or interacting groups, or both, do worse than the model predicts, then another investigation is required.

Free-Recall Verbal Learning Model

The Miller-McGill model reproduces some free-recall verbal learning data in a rather simple, brief, and elegant way. The data is discussed in Bruner, Miller, and Zimmerman,[10] although some of the data were obviously available to Miller and McGill several years before publication. Lists of 8, 16, 32, and 64 monosyllabic words were prepared and phonetically counterbalanced to reflect average frequencies of occurrence. These were presented so that, in effect, the individuals faced a random ordering of the lists of words 8, 16, 32, or 64 times, depending on whether the length of the list to be recalled at each trial contained 8, 16, 32, or 64 words, respectively.

The subjects were given from 4–6 seconds between word-list presentations for writing their responses. It appeared from the experiment that 8-word lists and 16-word lists would receive 100 percent recall after a number of trials, but that the asymptotes of the learning curves for the 32-word and 64-word lists would fall below 100 percent recall.

Miller and McGill provide this explanation for all the experimental data for individual responses. Assume each word has the same initial probability of recall, and that all words are of the same difficulty for any specified individual. Also assume that learning leads to 100 percent recall. This removes the estimation of one parameter from the model, namely the asymptote of the learning curve for the individual. Then define a random variable:

$$x_{i,j,n} = \begin{cases} 1 \text{ if subject } i \text{ does not recall word } j \text{ on trial } n, \\ 0 \text{ otherwise,} \end{cases}$$

and write:

$$p_{i,j,n} = Pr\{x_{i,j,n} = 1\}.$$

Then let learning take place as follows:

$$p_{i,j,n+1,} = \begin{cases} p_{i,j,n} \text{ if } x_{i,j,n} = 1, \\ \alpha_i p_{i,j,n} \text{ if } x_{i,j,n} = 0, \end{cases}$$

[10] J. S. Bruner, G. A. Miller, and C. Zimmerman, "Discriminative Skill and Discriminative Matching in Perceptual Recognition," *Journal of Experimental Psychology,* Vol. 49, No. 3 (1955), pp. 187–92.

where α_i $(0 < \alpha_i < 1)$ is the parameter describing learning rate for subject i. Thus the probability of non-recall decreases if recall occurs, but is unchanged if non-recall occurs and poor learning rate is associated with large values of α.

Also assume that $p_{i,j,0} = p_{i,0}$; that is, the probability of initial non-recall (or, equivalently, initial recall) is the same for every word. Thus two parameters, $p_{i,0}$ and α_i, determine the learning data for the ith individual. A good description of this model can be found in Chapter 10 in Bush and Mosteller.[11] This account includes methods of estimating the two parameters from the data.

The estimate for p_0 for an individual is:

$$\hat{p}_0 = N/N_0 \, ,$$

where N is the number of words in a list, and N_0 is determined (as follows) from an individual's responses. For each word, use the data on trials up through the trial on which recall first occurs, and record the number of trials preceded by zero recalls. Sum these for all words, and the result is N_0. This is also the maximum likelihood estimate for p_0, and the asymptotic variance of $\hat{p}_0$ is:

$$\frac{p_0^2 (1 - p_0)}{N} \, .$$

This is smaller (by a factor of p_0) than the variance of the usual binomial estimate, and is due to the fact that data after the initial recall trial may be used until recall is achieved.

Under the assumption that p_0 is known for an individual, the parameter α for that individual is estimated by:

$$\hat{\alpha} = 1 - \frac{\log_e p_0}{T_2} \, ,$$

where T_2 is the mean number of non-recalls per word over all trials for the individual. (This nomenclature is taken from the Bush-Mosteller book.)

In the experiment in which groups of individuals repeated the Bruner-Miller-Zimmerman experiment, the resulting data were analyzed to see if the Lorge-Solomon model for group behavior is applicable. Let us assume that for group learning, non-recall by a group of k subjects occurs if, and only if, all the individuals in the group fail to recall the word. Thus we are dealing with a group random variable X, similar to the one just described for individuals, x_i.

---

[11] R. Bush and F. Mosteller, *Stochastic Models for Learning* (New York: John Wiley & Sons, Inc., 1955).

Let $X_{j,n}$ represent group response for the jth word on the nth trial; then:

$$X_{j,n} = \begin{cases} 1 \text{ if } all \text{ individuals do not recall the } j\text{th word on the } n\text{th trial,} \\ 0 \text{ otherwise; or:} \end{cases}$$

$$X_{j,n} = \prod_{i=1}^{k} x_{i,j,n} .$$

Let

$$P_{j,n} = Pr\{X_{j,n} = 1\}.$$

Thus

$$P_{j,n} = \prod_{i=1}^{k} p_{i,j,n} ,$$

where $P_{j,n}$ is the probability that a group of k individuals does not recall the jth word on the nth trial. Then, the learning axiom proposed by Miller-McGill for individual subjects implies that:

$$P_{j,n+1} = \begin{cases} P_{j,n} \text{ if } X_{j,n} = 1, \\ \gamma P_{j,n} \text{ if } X_{j,n} = 0, \end{cases}$$

where γ is the learning rate parameter for the group; and we write

$$\gamma = f(\alpha_i).$$

Thus the model for a group of k individuals is identical to the model for a single individual, except that the assumption of the Lorge-Solomon model has replaced $p_{i,0}$ by P_0, and α_i by γ, which is some function of the α_i. As an initial function we will try:

$$\gamma = \prod_{i=1}^{k} \alpha_i .$$

As previously mentioned, an account of the experiment and data are reported in Lorge and Solomon [12] (and Table 1 in this paper is reproduced from that chapter). A total of 111 individuals, who also formed 37 groups of three individuals each, participated in the experiment in which a list of 25 words was to be recalled in each of 25 trials. The words were randomly mixed for each trial, and two different but equivalent lists were employed since individuals recalled alone and then in groups, or vice versa. In Table 1 the estimated $p_{i,0}$'s and α_i's for each individual are given, and the estimated P_0's and γ's are given for each group. In addition, there is a column for $\prod p_{i,0}$ and $\prod \alpha_i$, so that differences with P_0 and γ can be viewed. Also, a

---

[12] *Op cit.* (1962).

TABLE 1
ESTIMATES OF PARAMETERS FOR GROUP AND INDIVIDUAL LEARNING
(From Experimental Data)

Group	α_1	α_2	α_3	$\alpha_1\alpha_2\alpha_3$	γ	p_{01}	p_{02}	p_{03}	$p_{01}p_{02}p_{03}$	P_0
301	.777	.893	.475	.330	.586	.769	.782	.510	.307	.556
901					.494					.333
302	.871	.729	.884	.561	.841	.868	.593	.760	.391	.429
902					.650					.467
303	.882	.824	.859	.624	.917	.688	.625	.844	.363	.457
903					.745					.400
304	.866	.908	.870	.684	.839	.680	.742	.822	.415	.429
904					.811					.415
305	.652	.804	.700	.367	.651	.733	.727	.680	.362	.529
905					.494					.333
306	.853	.877	.863	.646	.767	.853	.739	.765	.482	.667
906					.817					.579
307	.806	.836	.838	.565	.800	.864	.745	.733	.472	.529
907					.862					.415
308	.869	.875	.852	.648	.772	.767	.762	.786	.459	.662
908					.742					.478
309	.898	.778	.786	.549	.724	.778	.613	.718	.342	.455
909					.651					.314
311	.809	.790	.859	.549	.692	.908	.814	.810	.599	.467
911					.669					.671
312	.836	.870	.865	.629	.861	.784	.821	.901	.580	.510
912					.826					.636
313	.864	.824	.777	.553	.687	.872	.871	.762	.579	.510
913					.728					.671
314	.701	.857	.827	.497	.759	.642	.855	.852	.468	.500
914					.558					.489
316	.844	.859	.653	.473	.803	.886	.847	.736	.552	.538
916					.551					.607
317	.884	.790	.839	.586	.869	.795	.711	.844	.477	.538
917					.645					.579
318	.841	.856	.871	.627	.749	.782	.714	.721	.403	.442
918					.740					.442
319	.846	.725	.747	.459	.704	.820	.776	.625	.398	.385
919					.505					.529
320	.838	.859	.653	.470	.816	.829	.745	.786	.485	.333
920					.589					.538
321	.891	.846	.821	.619	.694	.855	.817	.800	.559	.538
921					.747					.613

TABLE 1 (Cont'd)
ESTIMATES OF PARAMETERS FOR GROUP AND INDIVIDUAL LEARNING
(From Experimental Data)

Group	α_1	α_2	α_3	$\alpha_1\alpha_2\alpha_3$	γ	p_{01}	p_{02}	p_{03}	$p_{01}p_{02}p_{03}$	P_0
322	.837	.774	.838	.543	.655	.758	.833	.750	.474	.400
922					.689					.400
324	.862	.873	.747	.562	.754	.767	.836	.765	.491	.400
924					.683					.593
325	.839	.868	.868	.632	.849	.808	.826	.680	.454	.467
925					.782					.489
326	.840	.762	.860	.550	.757	.791	.839	.688	.457	.368
926					.647					.520
327	.805	.860	.870	.602	.639	.625	.883	.692	.382	.455
927					.642					.467
328	.882	.872	.514	.395	.775	.820	.636	.657	.343	.385
928					.421					.385
329	.868	.831	.795	.573	.744	.830	.810	.730	.491	.564
929					.717					.613
330	.835	.834	.760	.529	.581	.870	.718	.696	.435	.385
930					.676					.442
331	.886	.902	.704	.563	.849	.739	.714	.520	.274	.607
931					.681					.273
332	.764	.855	.882	.567	.753	.671	.836	.832	.467	.564
932					.621					.510
333	.539	.879	.797	.378	.572	.556	.636	.556	.197	.688
933					.410					.172
335	.882	.911	.840	.675	.734	.704	.753	.652	.346	.680
935					.755					.455
336	.833	.876	.852	.622	.826	.714	.784	.791	.443	.607
936					.771					.368
337	.771	.866	.859	.574	.639	.676	.750	.776	.393	.586
937					.775					.351
338	.851	.852	.818	.593	.786	.832	.711	.827	.489	.657
938					.631					.556
339	.900	.653	.861	.506	.725	.688	.684	.700	.329	.547
939					.537					.467
340	.836	.876	.697	.510	.783	.750	.838	.647	.407	.619
940					.526					.455
342	.821	.844	.885	.613	.712	.782	.762	.700	.417	.579
942					.723					.529

value of γ, which is estimated for a "concocted" group of three, is given, along with the value for the interacting groups. Here reference is made to the recall scores of the same three individuals in the interacting group when they performed as individuals, and when the following is done to achieve the concocted group.

Assume they are now performing as a group, and lump their individual performances to secure a group response. For example, if one or more individuals in the concocted group recalled the jth word in the ith trial, then the score of 0 is recorded; otherwise a score of 1. This concocted group action therefore gives no chance for group interaction to aid in recall of a word not achieved by any subject in the group, but obviously it does permit the group to do as well as the best recaller of each word on each trial. In Table 1 an interacting group (group performance during the experiment) is identified by a 300 designation, and a concocted group by a 900 designation. For example, the scores for 306 are for the group of three individuals acting together; the scores for 906 are the scores for the concocted group composed of the same three individuals who performed as individuals and were then lumped together.

Concocted Group Size and Group Performance

It is apparent from Table 1 that the deviations $(P_0 - \Pi\, p_{i,0})$ and $(\gamma - \Pi\, \alpha_i)$ for interacting groups and concocted groups composed of three individuals are such that some knowledge of the sampling variability of these deviations must be gained in order to look into questions of tenability. We are omitting the caret ($\wedge$) above [e.g., $(\hat{P}_0 - \Pi\, \hat{p}_{i,0})$], in what follows, and in the tables, but let us remember that the values are based on sample data and thus have sampling error, as well as possible bias due to an incorrect model. If the deviations were quite small—or large—our efforts might better be placed in an immediate reevaluation of the model. On the other hand, the magnitude of the deviations must be viewed in terms of the variability expected from natural sampling fluctuations in a random variable. An analytical study of the variability and distribution theory for these deviations is underway.

Because we have complete scores for each of 111 individuals, it is possible for us to observe concocted groups of different sizes. As mentioned in a prior paragraph, concocted groups of size $k = 2, 3, 4, 5,$ and 6 individuals were manufactured by random lumpings of the 111 experimental subjects. While many runs of size k can be obtained from 111 individuals, approximately $111/k$ runs were performed for each group of size k in order to conform to what would be available in a regular experiment. It is tedious to compute the concocted group responses for each value of k, and so this also limits the number of runs, although a computer could probably ease this burden. Thus 37 concocted groups of size three were obtained, and from these group responses 37 observations of the random variables $(P_0 - \Pi p_{i,0})$ and $(\gamma - \Pi \alpha_i)$ were computed.

In Table 2, the mean, mean deviation, and standard deviation of the 37 sample observations are listed. A second set of 37 concocted groups was obtained by random sampling, and the same procedure was repeated. The results for this sampling are also given in Table 2. This was done for the other group sizes, and the results are listed in Table 2 for four repetitions of 19 runs for groups of size six; three repetitions of 23 runs for groups of size five; three repetitions of 29 runs for groups of size four; and two repetitions of 59 runs for groups of size two.

TABLE 2

RELATIONSHIP BETWEEN GROUP SIZE AND THE DIFFERENCES $(P_0 - \Pi p_{i,0})$ AND $(\gamma - \Pi \alpha_i)$ IN CONCOCTED GROUPS

k	n	$\dfrac{\Sigma(P_0-\Pi p_0)}{n}$	$\dfrac{\Sigma\lvert P_0-\Pi p_0\rvert}{n}$	$\sigma_{P_0-\pi p_0}$	$\dfrac{\Sigma(\gamma_i-\Pi\alpha_i)}{n}$	$\dfrac{\Sigma\lvert\gamma_i-\Pi\alpha_i\rvert}{n}$	$\sigma_{\gamma-\pi a_i}$
6A	19	.05063	.05800	.0549	.11253	.14368	.1373
6B	19	.03021	.04832	.0501	.14511	.18300	.1733
6C	19	.04142	.05321	.0494	.14674	.16368	.1122
6D	19	.02593	.06444	.0753	.16781	.18325	.1755
5A	23	.04965	.05626	.0492	.13691	.14909	.1065
5B	23	.05739	.07252	.0664	.12830	.13726	.1160
5C	23	.03813	.05537	.0531	.14069	.15954	.1255
4A	29	.02472	.05562	.0705	.12607	.13772	.1029
4B	29	.02066	.05941	.0716	.12641	.13283	.0859
4C	29	.02402	.07174	.0818	.15356	.15420	.0962
3A	37	.04727	.06143	.0539	.11076	.11076	.0487
3B	39	.01140	.05348	.0643	.11136	.11196	.0591
2A	59	.00441	.03603	.0454	.07485	.07688	.0337
2B	59	.00839	.03578	.0465	.07351	.07765	.0387

In Table 2, the mean increases with group size for $(P_0 - \Pi p_{i,0})$, and the standard deviation is relatively stable as group size varies between two and six. For the deviation $(\gamma - \Pi \alpha_i)$, both the mean and the standard deviation increase with group size. Thus by simulation of a reasonably large population of individuals (111 subjects) for whom recall responses are available for 25 words on each of 25 trials, we have (in Table 2) some idea of the mean difference and the variability of the difference between group response and the Lorge-Solomon group conjecture for the Miller-McGill model, under the assumption that $\gamma = \Pi \alpha_i$.

In Table 2 there is an average estimated standard deviation of approximately .055 for $(\gamma - \Pi \alpha_i)$ for groups of size three, and approximately .058 for $(P_0 - \Pi p_{i,0})$. Applying this to Table 1, we have a measure for viewing the observed differences for both interacting groups and concocted groups of size three. It is possible that the assumption $\gamma = \Pi\alpha_i$ grants too favorable a learning rate to the group, and that a modification which will decrease the learning rate and still be a reasonable function of the α_i's should be sought.

It is apparent that further analytical work on both variability for the postulated model and revision of the model will be useful and should be developed before any new experimentation on group behavior in verbal recall is attempted.

Diffusion

15 in Incomplete Social Structures *

James S. Coleman [†]

ONE of the most pervasive processes in the study of social behavior has been the process of diffusion: diffusion of ideas, of technology, of cultural traits, of rumors, of opinion, of fads and fashions, and of population itself. Some social theorists have, in fact, made diffusion their central mechanism of social change (Tarde in 1903 [1] and Pemberton in 1936,[2] along with many early social anthropologists), and many others have examined empirical cases of diffusion (McVoy in 1940,[3] Kniffen in 1951,[4] Ryan and Gross in 1943,[5] Coleman, Katz and Menzel in 1957,[6] Hagerstrand in 1952,[7] and Lionberger in 1954 [8]). The empirical investigations have covered a remarkably wide range of topics, from hybrid corn (Ryan and Gross), to automobiles (Hagerstrand), to the practice of boiling drinking water (Wellin, 1955 [9]).

This body of research has resulted in a considerable cumulation of general knowledge about the way diffusion in human populations proceeds.

---

* This chapter, following its presentation at the Cambria Pines Conference, was published in James S. Coleman, *Introduction to Mathematical Sociology* (New York: The Free Press of Glencoe, 1964), chapter 17.

[†] Johns Hopkins University.

[1] Gabriel Tarde, *The Laws of Imitation* (New York: Henry Holt, 1903).

[2] H. E. Pemberton, "The Curve of Culture Diffusion Rate," *American Sociological Review*, 1936, Vol. 1, pp. 547–66.

[3] Edgar C. McVoy, "Patterns of Diffusion in the United States," *American Sociological Review*, 1940, Vol. 5, pp. 219–27.

[4] F. Kniffen, "The American Covered Bridge," *Geographic Review*, 1951, p. 114.

[5] Bryce Ryan and Neal Gross, "The Diffusion of Hybrid Corn in Two Iowa Communities," *Rural Sociology*, 1943, Vol. 8, pp. 15–24.

[6] James Coleman, Elihu Katz, and Herbert Menzel, "The Diffusion of an Innovation among Physicians," *Sociometry*, 1957, Vol. 20, pp. 253–70.

[7] Torsten Hagerstrand, "The Propagation of Innovation Waves," *Lund Studies in Geography* (Series B, Human Geography [1952], No. 4).

[8] Herbert F. Lionberger, "The Relation of Informal Groups to the Diffusion of Farm Innovation in a Northeast Missouri Farm Community," *Rural Sociology*, 1954, Vol. 19, pp. 233–430.

[9] Edward M. Wellin, "Water Boiling in a Peruvian Town," in Benjamin Paul (ed.), *Health, Culture, and Community* (New York: Russell Sage Foundation, 1955).

For example, diffusion processes appear to differ sharply as the unit of adoption varies, say from an individual to a community. In fluoridation of water systems, for example, the unit of adoption is circumscribed by the district served by a common water supply: ordinarily a city or town. In the diffusion of automobiles, the unit of adoption is the individual purchaser. In the former case, processes of community decision making and social conflict come into play which are absent in the latter. Or, as another situation, it is evident from several studies that different media of transmission perform different functions in leading to adoption of an innovation: interpersonal communication plays more nearly a role of influence, or legitimation of the new attribute, while mass media often play more nearly an informative role.

Despite these complexities, social diffusion has attracted the attention of some mathematically inclined persons. Quantitative variables are provided quite naturally by the process in the form of *time* and *number of persons* who have adopted it and, in some cases, in the form of geographic area. Stuart Dodd,[10] Anatol Rapoport,[11] Hagerstrand,[12] De Fleur and Larsen,[13] and others have had some success in developing mathematical models to describe the gross aspects of cases of diffusion.

By far the most sophisticated mathematical work and the most serious empirical studies have been in medical epidemics. Basically, two types of models have been developed for describing two different situations (see Bailey [14]). One describes diffusion (i.e., contagion) of a disease throughout a population and assumes complete intermixing of the population, with the rate of propagation (or, in stochastic models, the probability of infection in a given short period of time) proportional to the product of the number of infectives and the number of susceptibles. The other describes contagion within households, utilizing a chain of binomial distributions to describe the probability of 2, 3, 4, and more infections in the household stemming from an initial infective. Both types of models have had considerable success in describing the progress and distribution of a communicable disease in the two contexts in which they are applicable.

One of the assumptions made by nearly all models of social diffusion is that of a completely intermixed population. In person-to-person diffusion (as contrasted to constant-source diffusion), the models assume that the

---

[10] Stuart C. Dodd, "Diffusion Is Predictable: Testing Probability Models for Laws of Interaction," *American Sociological Review* (December, 1955), Vol. 20, p. 392.

[11] A. Rapoport, "Spread of Information through a Population with Socio-Structural Bias: I. Assumption of Transitivity," and "II. Various Models with Partial Transitivity," *Bulletin of Mathematical Biophysics*, 1953, Vol. 15, pp. 523–33 and 535–44, respectively.

[12] T. Hagerstrand, "On Monte Carlo Simulation of Diffusion" (Lund, Sweden: University of Lund, 1960 [mimeograph]).

[13] Melvin H. De Fleur and Otto N. Larsen, *The Flow of Information* (New York: Harper, 1958).

[14] N. T. J. Bailey, *The Mathematical Theory of Epidemics* (London: Charles Griffin, 1957).

number of contacts between the haves and have-nots is proportional to the product of the numbers of each. In a population where each person had equal numbers of contacts with each other person, such an assumption correctly describes the situation, for the product of n_1 and n_2 (the numbers of haves and have-nots, respectively) is equal to the number of *relations* that exist between the two groups. But when this assumption is not true (as it never is in human populations), then a serious bias may be introduced by it. For if diffusion begins with one person, then the person he diffuses to will not be a random person; he will usually be in contact with many of the same people as was the first person. A result of this is that, as diffusion proceeds, the group of haves may be people who have a great many contacts with each other, but few with the have-nots. At that point, the number of relations across the have/have-not boundary may be far fewer than would be implied by the model, and in fact the diffusion might die out. More generally, the departure of social structures from complete intermixing always slows the diffusion, and, in general, slows it differentially at different stages of the process.

I will not review the small body of investigation into diffusion in incomplete structures, but two authors' works should be mentioned: Rapoport attempted to incorporate a "distance bias" in otherwise random communication nets,[15] but this work has not continued in fruitful directions; and Hagerstrand[16] has simulated on a digital computer the geographic spread of a farm innovation with striking success, using data on geographic mobility as the communication structure.

Stochastic and Deterministic Models with Complete Intermixing

The principal work in social diffusion to date has started out with the deterministic or stochastic version of a classical growth model. In deterministic form it may be expressed:

$$\frac{dn_1}{dt} = kn_1n_2 \, , \qquad (1)$$

where n_1 is the number of persons who have adopted, n_2 is the number of have-nots, and k is the coefficient of conversion. The assumption behind this model is that the potential for diffusion is proportional to the number of pair relations between the haves and have-nots, which is simply the product n_1n_2. Implicitly, this assumes that the item spreads through its users, and that each user is in contact with all non-users. This equation gives rise to the familiar logistic curve of adoption over time.[17]

---

[15] See Rapoport, footnote 11.

[16] *Op cit.* (1960).

[17] This equation, and the stochastic one as well, can be usefully modified by adding another term to account for diffusion from some constant source (e.g., advertising). In the deterministic equation this would be $+ k_2n_2$, where k_2 is the coefficient of conversion from the constant source.

In the stochastic version of the same process, the rate of change of the probability p_i, that there are i "haves," is considered. Thus, for each state i there is a differential equation expressing the probability as a function of the probability of being in states i and $i - 1$, and of the product of the number of haves and have-nots (i and $n - i$ when the group is in state i):

$$\frac{dp_i}{dt} = -(n - i)ikp_i + (n - i + 1)(i - 1)kp_{i-1}. \qquad (2)$$

Even such an apparently simple process is not simple for analytic solution since it is not close to being Markovian, as the products in Equation 2 make clear. (See Bailey for the solution of a slight variant of this model.[18]) Despite its complexity, it provides no more aid for social structures that are not completely intermixed than does the deterministic version. In order to treat such structures it is necessary to somehow modify the assumption that the driving force for the process is proportional to the product of the number of haves and have-nots. It is to this task that we now turn.

Incomplete Social Structures: Small Separate Groups

The major aspect of empirical structures that causes diffusion to go astray is not a randomly spread incompleteness but the fact that these structures turn back on themselves. The friends of my friends are likely also to be my friends—far more likely than their frequency in the total population would predict. As a consequence, the diffusion may spread only to a tight little in-group. What is required, then, is a model that approximates such in-groupness so that the structural characteristics of a given system can be taken into account. (Obviously, to mirror the full complexity of such structures would require detailed measurement followed by a simulation with the structure mapped onto the memory of a computer.)

After many false directions, two approaches appear to show considerable promise. The first approach approximates the actual structure by assuming a number of discrete groups, *within* which communication is complete but *between* which it is absent, or nearly so. The first and simplest form of the model has the following assumptions, treated here in the form of two-person groups:

1. The population of n persons is assumed to be composed of $n/2$ pairs of persons in full communication with one another, but without communication to others.
2. If one member of the pair is a have, the second has a transition rate (analogous to a transition probability) of β for becoming a have in a small increment of time, dt.
3. In addition, independently of the other member of the pair, each person has a transition rate α for becoming a have, due to outside communication from some constant source.

---

[18] *Op. cit.*, p. 39.

4. All individuals and all pairs are alike.

We may then use these assumptions to write a stochastic process characterizing the two-person group. The group may be in one of three states:

State 0: both members have-nots;
State 1: one member have, one have-not;
State 2: both members haves.

The process for the probability of being in state 0, state 1, and state 2 may be described by three differential equations:

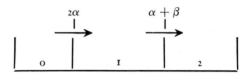

Or:

$$\frac{dp_0}{dt} = -2\alpha p_0 \tag{3}$$

$$\frac{dp_1}{dt} = 2\alpha p_0 - (\alpha + \beta)p_1 \tag{4}$$

$$\frac{dp_2}{dt} = (\alpha + \beta)p_1 \tag{5}$$

The group has a transition rate 2α for moving out of state 0, or simply the sum of the transition rates for the two members. When it is in state 1, its transition rate out is simply the transition rate of the member who is still a have-not, $\alpha + \beta$. Since the groups are continually seeded from the start by the constant source (i.e., through α), we would ordinarily be interested in the case with initial conditions: $p_0 = 1$, $p_1 = 0$, $p_2 = 0$.

These equations may be solved by first solving the equation for p_0, using its solution in the equation for p_1, and so on. The solution for the probability that at any time t a pair is in state i [19] is:

$$p_0 = e^{-2\alpha t} ; \tag{6}$$

$$p_1 = \frac{2\alpha(e^{-2\alpha t} - e^{-(\alpha + \beta)t})}{\beta - \alpha} ; \tag{7}$$

$$p_2 = \frac{\alpha + \beta}{\beta - \alpha}(1 - e^{-2\alpha t}) - \frac{2\alpha}{\beta - \alpha}(1 - e^{-(\alpha + \beta)t}). \tag{8}$$

These equations show the probability of a pair being in any state at a given time, so that by multiplying by the total number of pairs, $n/2$, we find the expected number of pairs in each state.

The progress of diffusion through the population of individuals is given by:

---

[19] For the special case when $\beta = \alpha$, substitute α for β in the original equations (3, 4 and 5), which are then easily solved.

$$E(n_1) = E(\text{groups in state 1}) + 2E(\text{groups in state 2})$$

$$= \frac{n}{2}p_1 + 2\frac{n}{2}p_2 \; ; \text{ or} \tag{9}$$

$$E(n_1) = n\left[1 - \frac{\beta}{\beta - \alpha}e^{-2\alpha t} + \frac{\alpha}{\beta - \alpha}e^{-(\alpha + \beta)t}\right]. \tag{10}$$

(Alternatively, the probability of an individual being a have at time t is given by the expression in brackets.)

To note how the process of diffusion is affected by this pairwise structure, we examine this equation at the extremes. If the interpersonal diffusion parameter, β, approaches zero, so that diffusion within the pair is non-existent, then the last term of Equation 10 becomes $e^{-\alpha t}$, and the next to last term drops out, so that the expected number of haves is:

$$E(n_1) = n(1 - e^{-\alpha t}). \tag{11}$$

This is the equation for constant-source diffusion in the *absence* of any inter-personal contact whatsoever.

If, at the other extreme, β approaches infinity, so that diffusion from one member to the other is almost immediate, the last term drops out, and Equation 10 becomes:

$$E(n_1) = n(1 - e^{-2\alpha t}). \tag{12}$$

This again is identical to a constant-source diffusion, but with an individual transition rate of 2α rather than α—so that the pair is acting just as a single person, but with "two sets of eyes in his head." Figure 1 shows the cumulative expected proportions of haves for various values of α and β.

FIGURE 1

CUMULATIVE EXPECTED PROPORTIONS OF
"HAVES" FOR VARIOUS VALUES OF α AND β

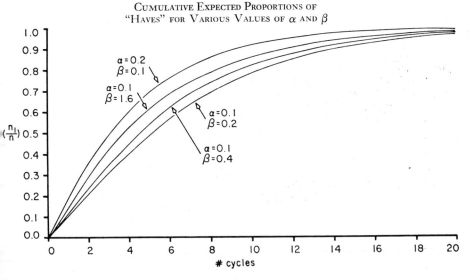

FIGURE 2

FIRST USE OF NEW DRUG BY DOCTORS WHO SHARE OFFICE AND
DOCTORS WHO PRACTICE ALONE

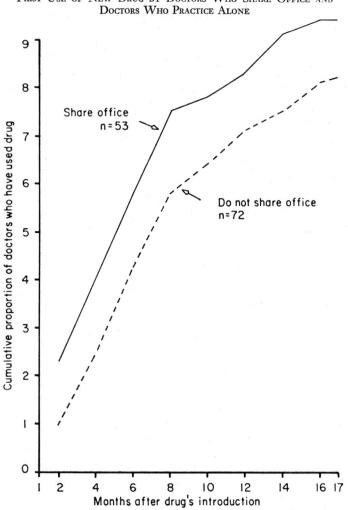

Months after drug's introduction

An interesting example of this kind of structure in operation occurred in a recent study of physicians introducing new drugs (carried out by the author and others in 1957 [20]). Some of the doctors shared offices with a partner, while others practiced alone. In examining the date of first use of the drug by these two sets of doctors, the curves of first use (shown in Figure 2) were found. The upper curve represents the cumulative proportion of adopters for the doctors with partners, while the lower curve represents the cumulative proportion of adopters for those who practiced alone.

[20] Op. cit. (Coleman, Katz, and Menzel).

Initially, we were puzzled at the shape of the office-partner curve: although it shows a higher rate of diffusion than that for the doctors who practiced alone, its *shape* is no different; it contains no suggestion of the inflection point shown by the logistic curve of interpersonal diffusion, and exhibited by doctors in the same study who were integrated into the larger social network of physicians. But equations 10, 11, and 12 show why: The social structure of isolated pairs does not transform a constant-source diffusion process into one showing the characteristic logistic form, but maintains essentially the same form, with merely a higher diffusion rate.[21] These data should not be taken as good for purposes of fitting this model, but merely as illustrative of an effect of social structure on diffusion that was inexplicable until the above process was understood.

Models for a combination of interpersonal and constant-source diffusion in other complete structures of this sort (e.g., size 3,4, . . .) are possible as well, proceeding along the lines of the pairwise structure. The models become increasingly more difficult to integrate, although use of the Laplace transform reduces the work.

However, rather than follow out this model for structures with larger groups, I want to introduce a slight modification of a more interesting sort. This modification puts back in a little more of the complexity of an empirical structure by allowing some communication between persons in different groups. In the model above, each person had a transition rate from the constant source, and, depending on the state of his partner, one from him as well. It is possible to add a third transition rate, proportional to the total number of persons who are haves.

Each person has a transition rate toward adoption γn_1, where n_1 is the number of persons who have already adopted in the *total* system. Thus his total transition rate is $\alpha + \gamma n_1$ if his partner is a have-not, and $\alpha + \beta + \gamma n_1$ if his partner is a have.

It is not possible to treat this exactly because n_1 is a random variable whose state we do not know at any time. However, we know that the expected value of n_1 is:

$$E(n_1) = \frac{n}{2}(p_1 + 2p_2). \tag{13}$$

Consequently, we use $E(n_1)$ in place of n_1, and the equations for the group's states are:

$$\frac{dp_0}{dt} = -2[\alpha + \frac{\gamma n}{2}(p_1 + 2p_2)]\, p_0; \tag{14}$$

$$\frac{dp_1}{dt} = 2[\alpha + \frac{\gamma n}{2}(p_1 + 2p_2)]\, p_0 - [\alpha + \beta + \frac{\gamma n}{2}(p_1 + 2p_2)]\, p_1; \tag{15}$$

---

[21] If these data were from a larger sample size, and were uncontaminated by doctors with more than one office partner, it would be worthwhile estimating α and β. However, to do so it would be necessary to know the proportion of *groups* with "no haves," as well as the proportion of "haves" (shown in Figure 3).

$$\frac{dp_2}{dt} = [\alpha + \beta + \frac{\gamma n}{2} (p_1 + 2p_2)] \, p_1. \tag{16}$$

One equation may be quickly eliminated, since $p_0 + p_1 + p_2 = 1$. However, they remain a pair of nonlinear differential equations, which cannot be solved in closed form but must be subjected to parametric analysis. Parameter studies have been carried out with a digital computer, and examples of results are shown in Figures 3, 4, 5, and 6. Figure 3 shows, for a structure with groups of size 3, the effect of increasing γn 3 (that is, either increasing the contacts between groups, γ, or increasing the total number of groups, $n/3$, while keeping constant the frequency of contacts between groups). The curves of cumulative number of haves approach a logistic curve as this between-group effect increases, but also, the overall rate increases sharply. Figure 4 shows, for groups of size 3, and 300 total persons (100 three-person groups), the effect on adoption when the total number of contacts with an out-group member to an in-group member increases from 1/10,000 to 1. Figure 5 shows, for a single ratio of in-group to out-group contacts, the effect of an increasing amount of stimulus from the constant source. Figure 6 shows the effect of increasing the group size from 1 to 5, while holding constant the constant-source stimulus and the contact between group members (with no between-group contact).

FIGURE 3

EFFECT OF INCREASING CONTACTS BETWEEN GROUPS
OR INCREASING TOTAL NUMBER OF GROUPS
(Frequency of Contacts between Groups Constant,
Structure with Groups of Size 3)

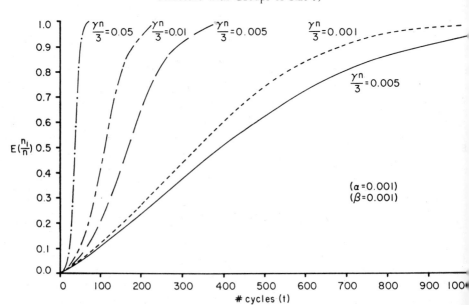

FIGURE 4

EFFECT ON ADOPTION WHEN TOTAL NUMBER OF CONTACTS
WITH AN OUT-GROUP MEMBER TO AN IN-GROUP MEMBER INCREASES FROM $\frac{1}{10,000}$ TO 1
(Groups of Size 3, 100 Groups)

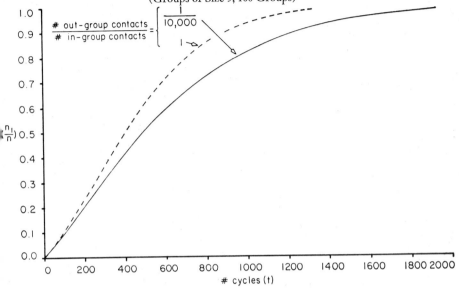

FIGURE 5

EFFECT OF AN INCREASING AMOUNT OF STIMULUS FROM CONSTANT SOURCE
FOR A SINGLE RATIO OF IN-GROUP TO OUT-GROUP CONTACTS

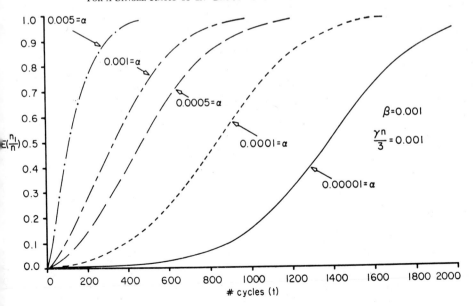

FIGURE 6

EFFECT OF INCREASING GROUP SIZE FROM 1 TO 5,
WHEN HOLDING CONSTANT STIMULUS AND CONTACT BETWEEN GROUP MEMBERS
(No Between-Group Contact)

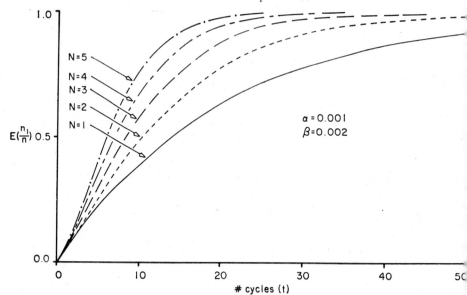

Incomplete Social Structures: Partially Interpenetrating Groups

A totally different approach to the problem is provided by the existence of large groups in society that have limited contact with one another. For example, studies of association patterns show that persons associate primarily with others of the same religion, or of the same economic class. Sociometric data and observational data often yield patterns like those shown in Table 1 (in this case, among boys in a high school). As the table indicates, most boys name as associates others in their own grade.

TABLE 1

		To:			
		Freshmen	*Sophomores*	*Juniors*	*Seniors*
	Freshmen	216	15	4	1
	Sophomores	11	230	16	5
From	*Juniors*	2	16	134	33
	Seniors	1	4	15	126

Thus in such a system, if an item (e.g., a clothing fad) began to diffuse in one grade, it might spread very quickly through that grade but might not "catch on" in other grades for some time. This is, in fact, what often happens in schools; and it is this kind of phenomenon that may be examined by the approach described below.

For simplicity, we consider two groups, A and B, which are partially interpenetrating, but which associate more within than between. The data which would give the amount of this interpenetration are shown in Table 2, where n_a is the number of people in group A, and n_b the number in group B.

TABLE 2

ASSOCIATION WITHIN AND BETWEEN GROUPS A AND B

	A	B	
A	n_{aa}	n_{ab}	$n_{a.}$
B	n_{ba}	n_{bb}	$n_{b.}$
	$n_{.a}$	$n_{.b}$	n

If this were a table showing actual pairwise associations at a slice in time, then it would necessarily be symmetric in the off-diagonal cells. That is, $n_{ba} = n_{ab}$: or the number of As associating with Bs equals the number of Bs associating with As. Often, the data are not entirely symmetric, being based on interviews with each person. However, we shall assume symmetry here, for the very concept of association implies it.

Now let us look at the deterministic diffusion equation for group A, assuming that its unconverted members were in contact only with As. Following the basic equation (1), we get:

$$\frac{dx_a}{dt} = k_1 x_a (1 - x_a), \tag{17}$$

where x_a is the proportion of As converted, and k_1 is a coefficient of conversion proportional to the frequency of contact.

Similarly for the Bs:

$$\frac{dx_b}{dt} = k_2 x_b (1 - x_b), \tag{18}$$

where the quantities are defined analogously to those in Equation 17. But now, if the fraction $(1 - x_a)$ of unconverted As are in contact with converted Bs, as well as with As, this adds to the rate of change, x_a, as follows:

$$\frac{dx_a}{dt} = k_{11} x_a (1 - x_a) + k_{12} x_b (1 - x_a), \tag{19}$$

where, because the interpenetration is only partial, $k_{12} < k_{11}$.

Similarly for the rate of new converts in group B:

$$\frac{dx_b}{dt} = k_{21} x_a (1 - x_b) + k_{22} x_b (1 - x_b). \tag{20}$$

It is important to recognize the implicit assumptions about contacts in these equations. It is assumed that each person in group A is alike in his probability of contacting a B and another A; each has identical probabilities of contacting an A (proportional to k_{11}), and each has identical (and smaller) probabilities of contacting a B (proportional to k_{12}). There is no subset of As who associate with the Bs and are isolated from the other As. If there were, then Equation 19 could not describe the process. For example, the converted Bs, whose effect appears in the last term, would not work on all the unconverted As $(1 - x_a)$, but only upon that fraction of As who associate with them and are unconverted.

Now to return to Table 2. The probabilities upon which k_{11}, k_{12}, k_{21} and k_{22} are based can be estimated from such data. We must, of course, make the above assumption that there is no difference in association patterns between the As who happened at this time to be associating with Bs, and all the other As.

The estimates of the probabilities of contact, p_{ij} using data represented by Table 2, are:

$$p_{ab} = \frac{n_{ab}}{n_{a.}}; \tag{21}$$

$$p_{aa} = 1 - p_{ab}; \tag{22}$$

$$p_{ba} = \frac{n_{ba}}{n_{b.}}; \tag{23}$$

$$p_{bb} = 1 - p_{ba}. \tag{24}$$

Under the condition of symmetry, $n_{ba} = n_{ab}$, so that:

$$p_{ba} = \frac{n_{ba}}{n_{b.}} = \frac{n_{ab}}{n_{b.}} = \frac{n_{a.}}{n_{b.}} \frac{n_{ab}}{n_{a.}} = \frac{n_a}{n_b} p_{ab}, \tag{25}$$

and

$$p_{bb} = 1 - \frac{n_a}{n_b} p_{ab}. \tag{26}$$

These data, then, provide estimates of the relative sizes of the $k_{ij}s$ (up to transformation by a scale constant, k):

$$k_{11} = k(1 - p_{ab}),$$
$$k_{12} = kp_{ab},$$
$$k_{21} = k\frac{n_a}{n_b} p_{ab},$$
$$k_{22} = k\left(1 - \frac{n_a}{n_b} p_{ab}\right).$$

With these substitutions, equations 19 and 20 become:

$$\frac{dx_a}{dt} = k[(1 - p_{ab}) x_a + p_{ab}x_b] (1 - x_a) ; \tag{27}$$

$$\frac{dx_b}{dt} = k\left[\frac{n_a}{n_b}p_{ab}x_a + \left(1 - \frac{n_a}{n_b}p_{ab}x_b\right)\right] (1 - x_b). \tag{28}$$

These equations describe deterministically the process of diffusion when there is partial interpenetration between two subgroups. The degree of interpenetration is determined by the parameter p_{ab}, derived from such association data as are shown in Table 1 and represented in Table 2.

Equations 27 and 28 are a pair of nonlinear differential equations that cannot be integrated to find explicit values of $x_a(t)$ and $x_b(t)$. However, they are amenable to parameter studies on a computer to investigate effects of different values of p_{ab} and of the relative group sizes, n_a/n_b. First, however, a classical investigation of the points of singularity in the (x_a, x_b) plane, and the behavior of the system in the region of these points, will allow some qualitative deductions.

This investigation shows four singular points, of which only two are in the quadrant where x_a and x_b are positive. These singular points are at $(0,0)$ and $(1,1)$. At $(0,0)$, the system is unstable, and at $(1,1)$ it is stable (as intuitive considerations would already have told us). The general behavior of a point (x_a, x_b) describing the path of the system through time is roughly shown by the trajectories in Figure 7.

FIGURE 7

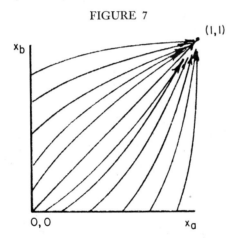

Both groups move toward the stable equilibrium where the item has diffused to all members. If the system starts out with many in A having it, and none in B [for example, at $(.5,0)$], then the group in which it started initially gains faster, only later slowing down as it nears its upper limit of 1.0.

There are two variations of interest in the qualitative examination of this system: variations in degree of interpenetration (p_{ab}), and variations in relative group size (n_a/n_b). What happens as the groups are more and more isolated from one another (e.g., as $p_{ab} \rightarrow 0$)? The diagram of the trajectories becomes like that of Figure 8. The trajectories become much more concave relative to the 45° line. That is, if something starts in group A, it will grow there very rapidly, until it is nearly universal, before it catches on in group B.

FIGURE 8

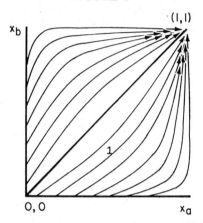

Such a case is shown by the trajectory labelled (1). This means also that a stochastic disturbance near the origin would have a much greater effect—when p_{ab} is very low—than in the preceding case, when p_{ab} is relatively high. A stochastic disturbance might easily throw the system off the 45° line onto a trajectory, such as (1), where it would diffuse through A before affecting B very much.

The effect of changes in the relative group size occurs only in the presence of some separation of the group (that is, when p_{ab} is less than chance).[22] When there is some separation of the groups, the effect of a large discrepancy in size of groups A and B is shown in Figure 9. There is asymmetry in the speed with which groups catch the item from one another. If it begins in the small group (group B in Figure 9), or if a stochastic

FIGURE 9

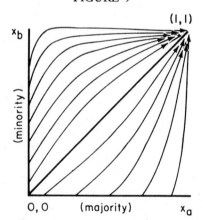

_____

[22] Or when p_{ab} is greater than chance, although that situation of association with unlikes is not considered here. It will be mentioned below.

disturbance starts it off there, then it will diffuse through this group before it goes far in the larger one. But if it begins in the larger group, it will catch on very quickly in the smaller group, so that the groups rapidly become more nearly equal in the proportion of haves.

It is useful to add a word about a different case: when there is greater diffusion-laden contact between the two groups than within the same groups. This might occur between the sexes, for example, where there was more contact between sexes than there was within each sex. In such a situation, where there is much greater association among unlikes than expected by chance, the trajectories would look like Figure 10a (for equal-size groups). In this situation, any initial imbalance between the two groups is quickly righted, and they become nearly equal in their proportions of haves. If the groups are of unequal size, the trajectories show an asymmetry, as in Figure 10b. Here, if the item begins in the smaller group (group B), almost all the initial diffusion is into the larger group, thus equalizing the groups. If it begins in the larger group, there is less equalization, as Figure 10b indicates.

FIGURE 10

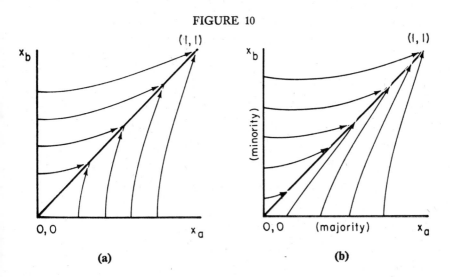

(a)   (b)

Finally, one other situation may be mentioned. So far, the assumption has been that the *total* frequency of association was the same in both groups. But in some cases, especially where association is with unlikes, there may be much greater total frequency of contact in one group than in the other. A good example is sexual contact among adolescents, and the diffusion of venereal disease. The number of boys who have sexual relations in adolescence is much greater than the number of girls, and consequently the average frequency of intercourse for girls is much higher. Considering only those who are promiscuous (i.e., free intermixing among the pool of potential partners), a table of frequency of contact might look like this:

	A	B	
A	0	50	300 total As (e.g., boys)
B	50	0	100 total Bs (e.g., girls)

In such a case, what would the trajectory of diffusion be if the item entered in one or the other group? Such a case is shown in Figure 11. It exhibits symmetry, as if the groups were of equal size, and would quickly move near the 45° line, where the proportion of haves was nearly the same in both groups.

FIGURE 11

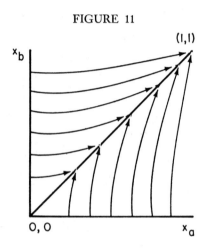

A further step in this same direction involves expanding the number of groups beyond two. Analogous to equations (27) and (28) can be written the general equation for diffusion in group i in a system of m partially interpenetrating groups:

$$\frac{dx_i}{dt} = k \sum_{j=1}^{m} p_{ij} x_j (1 - x_i) \tag{29}$$

where $p_{ij} = n_{ij}/n_i$, and n_{ij} ($= n_{ji}$) is the number of associations between groups i and j in any slice of time.

Once the problem is opened up in this way, numerous additional questions of interest arise. For example, what is the lag in diffusion from group 1 to group 3, where there is little or no association between 1 and 3, but association of each group with an intermediary, 2? This is the situation among the high school boys whose association patterns are shown in Table 1. Freshmen have almost no association with seniors, and there is not much between freshmen and juniors or between sophomores and seniors. Between adjacent grades there is more association.

FIGURE 12

Diffusion Rates when Item Adoption Starts in Freshman Class
(3 Freshmen Adopt Item)

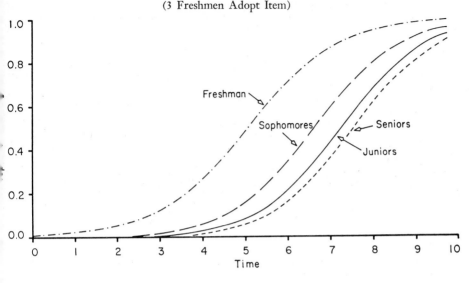

Using equation 29 and taking the average of n_{ij} and n_{ji} as the frequency of association between each pair of grades (and letting $p_{ij} = 1 - \sum_{i \neq i} p_{ij}$), the data of Table 1 were used to calculate the relative rates of diffusion in each grade when the item being diffused began among the freshmen (starting with three freshmen having adopted the item). The results are shown

FIGURE 13

Diffusion Rates when Item Adoption Starts in Junior Class
(3 Juniors Adopt Item)

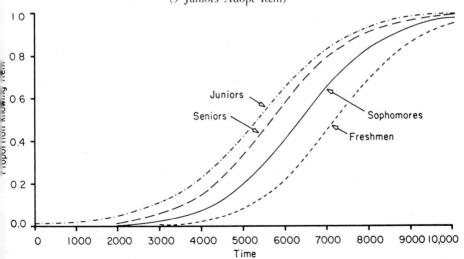

in Figure 12. Figure 13 shows the relative rates of diffusion when the item began with three juniors.

Conclusion

The problem of diffusion in incomplete social structures presents considerable difficulty for the development of formal diffusion models. The two approaches presented here approximate some of the structural irregularities exhibited by actual social systems, and allow an examination of their consequences for diffusion. The models have, of course, made only a start on the general problem.

There are other approaches that offer considerable interest. One is to approximate the varying "social distance" of persons by models of diffusion on a line, in a plane, and in higher-dimensional spaces. Models of this type would assume persons distributed uniformly over the given space, and examine the rate of spread over the space. Some work has been carried out in this direction for medical epidemics (see Bailey, 1957, p. 32), but no great progress has been made.

16

Information Input Overload: Features of Growth in Communications-Oriented Institutions *

Richard L. Meier †

WE NOW LIVE in a place and at a time in which increasing numbers of workers belong to the white collar and professional groups. The chief product of these workers is one or another form of communication. The extraordinarily rapid growth in the flow of messages over the past few decades, paralleling the rise of these occupational groups, has created many new and unanticipated problems. Increasing attention is being paid to those unwanted situations caused by the expansion of scientific and technical documentation and the growth of the mass media. Our own studies were undertaken primarily to enable us to construct a coherent description of changes in large social organizations that may be attributed to *growing* external demand for their services and products. More specifically, we have been interested in public utilities which are unable to adjust the price of their service in accordance with demand, and are forced to resort to other economizing behavior appropriate to an environment that is rich in communications and feedback systems.

The demands for service may take the form of a flood of inquiries, requests, or orders; and these demands may be transmitted in person or via mail, telephone, or other media. The basic argument holds that established organizations (i.e., institutions) have a variety of policies open which, when combined into a strategy, enable them to adjust to increasing demands for service. Stress appears whenever an organization fails to complete transactions for which it is responsible as rapidly or as accurately as is felt desir-

* I wish to acknowledge the assistance of George Zollschan in the historical evaluation, Bruce Hackett and Margaret Boland in the analysis of the questionnaires, and Joanne Denko, M.D., for the study of library use behavior. Support was provided by Project Michigan funds and by the Mental Health Research Institute. Much of the stimulus for the study came from a multidisciplinary workshop on Information Input Overload, organized by James G. Miller. This paper, which appeared in slightly different form in *Libri* (Vol. 13, 1963, pp. 1–44), also draws on the content of Report No. 10 of the Mental Health Research Institute (March, 1961) and on a presentation at the meetings of the American Association for the Advancement of Science (Denver, December 26, 1961).

† University of Michigan.

able by the profession that dominates the institution. In a healthy organization the response to the stress is flexible and innovative until operations have been pushed to levels beyond such capacity. The various policies deemed practicable to the organization are those that tend to shift costs from itself to its clients or suppliers in the immediate environment. Once adopted and put into effect, each policy will have a characteristic impact upon internal social structure as well as upon the relations with clients and suppliers.

Once the long-run operating capacity has been reached and exceeded, the supply of various resources, previously never considered to be scarce, appears inadequate and complete exhaustion threatens. If the institution is large and reasonably coherent, the stress at the executive level then builds up very rapidly. The alarm diffuses down into the middle levels and a state of general crisis pervades the administrative hierarchy. Then, in the "overload" situation, as the prospects of catching up with the backlogs and arrearages become dismal, it is decided that performance standards for services or product quality for goods must be reduced. At this stage, much of the newly induced stress is transmitted to people at the bottom levels. The institution may either disintegrate under the pressure, or it may borrow ideas or invent rules as a basis for ignoring a large share of the demands made upon it (often referred to by administrators as a "narrowing of the field" or "trimming the agenda").

The model that has been employed for this assessment of overload is one that is often applied to communications channels in operations research, management science, and related areas of investigation; but it is quite uncommon in economics, sociology, anthropology and political science—the disciplines that traditionally have been concerned with the study of social organization. The present preoccupation with structural-functional theory (in the latter fields) has not been very helpful in identifying generally applicable measures for understanding the growth and decline of organization. Such theories have emphasized qualitative restructuring and reformulation of function in response to external stimuli, internal conflicts, changes in relative replacement rates in the environment or in the ranks of the organization, but they have been least illuminating when growth was involved.

The following features must be present before our own model can be applied:

a) The respective flow rates of distinguishable types of messages impinging upon the organization can be measured;

b) The filtering and coding procedures maintained at the boundaries of the organization and applied to incoming messages are discoverable;

c) The interaction with memory, documented knowledge and other accumulated resources within the organization can be traced;

d) The capacity for responding to messages (which introduces a convenient index for defining "load") can be estimated;

e) The respective flow rates of the types of outputs can be measured; and
f) The rules that determine what constitutes an error in performance by the institution are detectable.

In order to fulfill these requirements many different techniques of estimation and measurement may need to be employed before sufficient data have been acquired for identifying social adjustments to communications stresses. The methodology, therefore, must be rather eclectic.

Despite the stringency of the requirements built into this model, it still should apply to most public service institutions which do not have complete freedom in setting the price tag for the services rendered. Also, the increasing pace for communications transmission is presently experienced in virtually all *urban* environments. As a consequence of the trend, therefore, an increasing number of institutions is likely to be pushed beyond their respective information handling capacities. The theory that grows out of the use of the model should have widespread practical applications, but it should also make more explicit the manner in which modern communications theory—as it has developed in the physical sciences and engineering—may be wedded to the techniques for the analysis of social systems.

Recently, March, Simon, and Guetzkow [1] have assembled an inventory of the relatively well-supported features of the modern theory of social organizations. They note that the function of communications in a social structure is that of linking individuals and/or groups for purposes of (*a*) coordinating respective role-oriented activities, (*b*) supplying data for the application of strategies in the execution of programs, (*c*) supplying information on the outcomes of action, (*d*) stimulating and evoking action through instruction, leadership, preset alarm signals, etc., and (*e*) gratification of the private curiosities and social propensities of the participants.

It is significant that the volume of communication within an organization is minimal and perfunctory once a great deal of experience has been obtained about the tasks at hand by all parties filling the roles. Most messages would then be employed to maintain friendship groups and acquaintance relationships. However, when the phenomena described or alluded to in the communications are less well defined by the terms employed in the messages (as is likely when innovations are being introduced or when the members of the organization are less experienced), the work-related message flow is noticeably greater. In larger organizations the communication function is clearly reflected in the division of work, and a large number of specialized roles are devoted to various features of it. Sociologists hitherto have not been very much concerned about the differentiation of channels for communications that are maintained by organizations, except at the level of description or of pathology.

The most explicit and comprehensive body of data about the workings

---

[1] James G. March and Herbert A. Simon (in collaboration with Harold Guetzkow), *Organizations* (New York: John Wiley & Sons, Inc., 1958).

of any social organization can be obtained by sampling the flow of messages and reviewing records at the points of receipt or transmission. However, in order to be unambiguous, such an analysis of the circulation of messages requires a detailed evaluation of sources, symbol content, meaning, transmission techniques, perception, decoding, interpretation of pattern, the sources of noise and distortion, and the formulation of response. The complete analytical task involves far more than content analysis, which is itself so arduous and time consuming when dealing with organizations of significant size that it is adopted as a last resort. As computerized techniques come into existence, however, the communications focus for the study of social organization should become one of the most fruitful available.[2] It is possible that sociological investigators will generate overall measures of social communications rate and the accumulation of recorded knowledge analogous to gross national product and gross capital formation in economics, but the proper conventions and definitions have yet to be established. At this time we must be content with representations of structure of social organization, depicting their changes over time as messages flow in it and through it. This structure elaborates and subdivides in the course of growth in communications volume, while atrophy of important parts is most evident during periods of decline.

The new technology of communications is responsible for the accelerated growth in recent times. Natural resources—energy, water, foodstuffs, minerals, and flat land—are becoming increasingly scarce, so that marginal costs tend to rise. The expense of labor is increasing even more rapidly, but the marginal cost of both the storage and transmission of information is declining. The technology of communications is, and promises to remain for at least a decade or two, much more productive than competing technologies because the huge multipliers inherent in it have yet to be fully exploited. One man may communicate simultaneously with tens of millions, or annihilate the time lags that previously hindered coordinated movements over thousands of miles of space, or collect tens of millions of items into a single sum or index within a matter of hours.

Each successive stage of automation seems to require the storage and the processing of an extra order of magnitude (e.g., ten times), and more information, handled mostly by means of equipment. But significant increases are also registered in the human and institutional environment. Message transmission has substituted for the more expensive inputs, especially transportation. The number of trips per address in North American society has now almost stabilized, but the number of telephone calls, pieces of mail, television programs, etc., is steadily increasing. Thus, face-to-face

[2] Richard L. Meier, "The Measurement of Social Change," *Proceedings of the Western Joint Computer Conference*, 1959, pp. 327–31; "Measuring Social and Cultural Change in Urban Regions," *Journal of the American Institute of Planners* (November, 1959) Vol. 25, pp. 180–90.

public contacts remain almost constant in their frequency but they are extended more and more by telephone calls, memoranda, recordings, etc., all of which demand their share of a limited time budget and interrupt or foreshorten personal interaction. At some point, within a generation or two, the growth in social communications (estimated at 3–7 percent per year per capita in various metropolitan areas) must slacken because humans have limited perception, learning rates, and memory.[3]

What will these communications-oriented institutions be like when they are required to process two times, five times, or even ten times the number of inquiries, requests for service, demands for attention, etc., as at present?

FIRST EXAMPLE: A STOCK EXCHANGE

Commerce-oriented urban institutions have in general, retained enough control over their own operations so that periods of continually increasing demand—when operating capacity is being approached (or even temporarily exceeded)—are met by charging higher prices for services or products. Price increases serve not only to stem upsurging demand, but they generate internal surpluses which can be reinvested in capital equipment and in recruiting extra labor, thereby increasing the overall capacity of the institution. Publicly regulated utilities and various public services are not able to adjust so readily to growing demand. Even some commercial institutions are subject to many kinds of gentlemen's agreements making adaptation to dramatically increased demand a stressful experience.

When exploring the urban environment for suitable cases for closer study, stock exchanges were seriously considered. They have the advantages that the standard "transaction" requires a relatively constant number of communications, the rules of procedure are quite explicit, much of the operations is open to the public, and newspapers carry daily reports on their activity. However, the major exchanges normally handle only 30–60 percent of the capacity that could be mobilized quickly in the face of any unusual spurt in activity. The chances that the secular trend in transactions, combined with the normal variations in buying and selling, would test the capacity of the institution for as much as a week were assumed to be quite small, and waiting for such occasions did not seem worthwhile. Therefore the investigating team concentrated its attention elsewhere. Shortly after they had done so, however, the unexpected occurred.

As is well known, New York has two dominant securities exchanges that

---

[3] Almost all innovations in organization today that reduce the amount of human effort or the amount of raw material required per unit of output seem to involve an increase in message transmission, data processing, or the accumulation of records. Messages in various forms are substituting at the margin for other inputs. Cf. R. L. Meier, "Information, Resources and Economic Growth," *Conference on Natural Resources and Economic Growth,* Social Science Research Council, April, 1960. (Proceedings edited by J. J. Spengler and published by the Johns Hopkins University Press.)

carry on trading about a block apart. The junior organization, the American Stock Exchange, is a direct descendant of the colorful New York Curb Exchange; it has retained in its present corporate structure a few vestiges of the free-wheeling-and-dealing of early days. It specializes in the stock issues of new and developing firms, so that the issues on its list have lower prices and wider price ranges. The required regular reports on corporate operations are not as complete as those on the senior exchange, a feature that attracts listing on the part of some closely held but highly reputable firms. This also means that the exchange can be used more conveniently by price manipulators, who are adept at spreading "inside dope" rumors and cashing in on the resultant price swings. The average transaction rate was about 30–40 percent of the designed capacity of the exchange at the time its operations were first reviewed. Accordingly, many of the positions on the floor and in the staffs of the brokerage houses were not kept filled, but the brokers and the American Stock Exchange Clearing Corporation (which supervised the accounts and the transfer of stock certificates) maintained a state of readiness so that flurries in trading could be handled with very little delay or variation in the quality of the service rendered.

About the middle of January, 1959, a speculative fever caught hold of the stock markets that soon proved itself to be the strongest since 1929. Speculators concentrated on the American Stock Exchange because it registered a larger relative price variation. These preferences caused the American Stock Exchange, always a poor second in trading rate to the New York Stock Exchange (recording only about a third of the volume of the latter) to quadruple its transaction rate. "Furor on the Amex," headlined *Forbes Magazine* (February 1, 1959) shortly after the splurge began.

The first sign of trouble arose in the internal operations. The "clearing" of the trades had previously been accomplished within four days, but during February this period stretched out to two weeks. Extra clerks and accountants had to be hired, but the supply was far from adequate, and, in desperation, inadequately trained persons were added. On March 17 the clearing system broke down altogether. A week later 80,000–100,000 "pieces of paper," worth many millions of dollars, were in the backlog waiting to be processed. Priorities had been established, apparently, so that accounts with non-member brokers were straightened out, but the remainder were left in such a complete snarl that the exchange had to call for outside assistance ("Big Board Gives Helping Hand," noted the *New York Times* on March 26). The New York Stock Exchange Clearing Corporation was asked to take over all the routine operations of its neighbor on Broad Street, and authorities asserted that "things would be back to normal by the end of the week."

The government tried to help and took action that would otherwise have been resisted by members of the American Stock Exchange. "Securities

Exchange Commission Opens War on Manipulators" is the way *Business Week* summed it up (April 11). The *Wall Street Journal* had until this time underplayed the story, noting the official statements under small leads, but—by April 14—it apparently had dug into the background and it put a finger on a crucial feature of the episode: "Errors Mount as Stock Sales Flood Brokers, Exchanges." It pointed out that brokers on the trading floor occasionally made a slip so that records of the seller and buyer did not jibe. The slips were then marked DK ("don't know") and sent back to the brokers to be threshed out. In the previous few weeks the DKs had been piling up, thus explaining the story's subhead: "Securities Firms Spur Hirings."

When institutions fail to meet well-established standards and contractual guaranties, morale drops, turmoil mounts, and investigations are made to discover how to prevent catastrophe from recurring. *Business Week* reviewed the situation a month after the breakdown: "Paperwork Troubles Bog Down American Stock Exchange; Harassed Brokers Turn to Computers" (April 18). They reported that the American Stock Exchange Clearing Corporation was still trying to get back into operation, and gossip was going the rounds that it would never again open up completely. "Corps of accountants and extra help were trying to untangle the mess."

The largest brokerage houses had ordered large computers, while the smaller houses were setting up a joint installation; but it would take years to put these systems into full operation. A feeling of guilt, resulting from failure to perform according to public expectations, was associated with the affair. It was evidenced by the careful exclusion of the press, followed by terse "explanations" which tried to minimize the breakdown, but of course all this did little more than excite curiosity.

Trading activity, however, resumed a more normal state at last, and the American Stock Exchange still does business at the old address and in much the same manner as before. Morale was restored in part by an unusual Christmas bonus (*New York Times*, December 5). The consequences of a thoroughgoing systems and procedures review appeared in the form of announcements of reorganization. A new ticker network was readied (*ibid.*, January 1, 1960), and later a method of reducing the DKs generated during hectic moments—at the same time that the quality of service was improved —was devised. The *Times* headlined: "American Board Orders High Speed Quote System," and explained in the story that followed that "this would contrast to the present procedure which does not have the flexibility to allow the history of the activity of a stock action to be incorporated or the ability to speed up during peak periods when the demand for information increases" (*ibid.*, January 11, 1961).

In retrospect, it appears that the customer's men in the brokerage firms, and even the floor traders, were less affected by the experience of overload than those at work in the back rooms where the congestion became most evident. All the computerized systems, which no doubt required a complete overhaul of procedures, were addressed to the internal problems. The personal touch with the outside world is retained while the core of the operations is reduced to electronic data processing.

SECOND EXAMPLE: A LIBRARY

Library Growth and Development

A large library for research and higher education is a remarkably complex institution that services highly diverse requests for information while concurrently handling a large volume of relatively routine demands. Such libraries are being subjected to a rapidly increasing influx of printed materials, and they are forced to improvise social organization to deal with the accumulations of recorded knowledge entrusted to their stewardship. The precedents for such organization in government and business, and in those instances where relevant features exist at all, are fragmentary and superficial. Therefore libraries, particularly those that attempt to be comprehensive in their coverage, must be pacemakers on the urban scene: they invent institutional forms that are particularly appropriate to an information-rich environment. This approach is contrasted to industrial and military procedures for coping with the needs for more message handling capacity and information storage, where problems are most often resolved by the introduction of new "hardware."

Large libraries, although multi-million dollar operations, typically do not have research and development departments but tend to borrow and adapt innovations from the outside. Changes in approach and procedure usually are implemented piecemeal. Thus library organizations may be expected to be similar to public utilities and government administrative bureaucracies, but because they are so strongly communications-oriented, libraries should more resemble the future of such entities than the past.

The relative dimensions of communications in and out of a large university library (that, on most scales, ranks among the top ten in North America) is shown in Figure 1. The bulk of the identifiable transactions are associated with *acquisitions* and *circulation*. Our attention will be concentrated particularly on the relationship of these rates to changes in internal structure.

The development of this library was rather typical of the land-grant universities that came into being in the latter part of the nineteenth century. There are no regular records of the library before 1875, a time when the need for systematic acquisition of books was first expressed. We may surmise from scattered sources that before then a collection of books existed which had been assembled from the bequests of deceased professors, clergy-

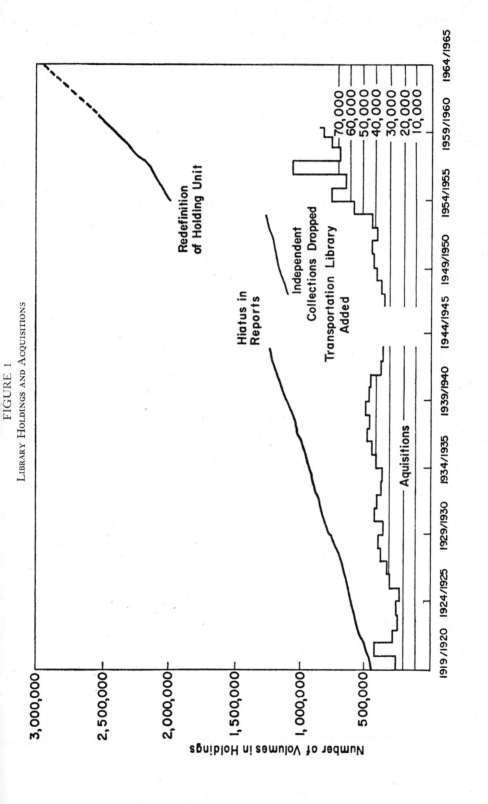

FIGURE 1

LIBRARY HOLDINGS AND ACQUISITIONS

men, and other leading citizens. One of the first card catalogs in the United States had been installed around 1860. A separate law library was established in 1859. By 1877 the holdings amounted to 25,000 volumes and were increasing at the rate of 10 percent per year; and, in 1883, the first building was completed. An acquisition rate of 10,000–13,000 volumes per year was achieved in the latter part of the nineteenth century, and additions to the first building were required within 15 years.

The acquisition rate was stepped up in the pre-World War I period, and special trips were made to Europe immediately thereafter in order to fill gaps in the collection. An average acquisition rate of 25,000 volumes per year was achieved at that time, and the figure has since moved irregularly to perhaps 70,000 volumes per year.

Historical reports give repeated evidence that the chief librarian, (later director) has had considerable influence on the rate of growth of the collection, even though he wields formal power primarily within the library organization itself. The reasons for this influence are well understood by administrators of leading universities. They realize that an outstanding man in the profession can be attracted to their institutions only by granting him freedom of action in those areas which seem most central professionally.

The new appointee normally employs the various resources granted to him in such a manner as to extend the range and coverage of the collection (the most common indices of quality). He augments this with efforts to improve the physical plant and equipment. Since overflowing stacks act as a strong damper on attempts to improve the quality of a collection, each new chief librarian, regardless of his ultimate goals, finds he must spark expansion of ordinary storage capacity. The budget authorization to acquire more space is followed immediately by a renewed burst of book-buying, many of the order slips being drawn directly from backlogs. As the regime of a chief librarian lengthens, his program often is attenuated by continuous conflicts with budgetary authorities (and sometimes with his own staff) so that the rate of growth tends to level off. Storage capacity is ever more closely approached.

Like most institutions, this library evolved from the most amorphous beginnings. It defined its function in the light of the public it served and the standards of performance elaborated by a profession that was simultaneously springing up. Originally no more than a bookpile through which one searched almost at random for titles and categories of content that were of interest, it proceeded to evolve structure. Classics and History were given separate reading rooms in 1883; and the reserving of books for courses began in 1889. A bindery was acquired in 1896, a professional Catalog Department came into existence in 1900, and shortly thereafter the acquisition process became a special function. The last operation, after a bewildering series of reorganizations, culminated in a Selection Depart-

FIGURE 2

The Library Represented as a Communications System

INPUTS

STRUCTURE

OUTPUTS

Cataloged items
acquired: 90,000 per year

Publisher's announcements
and dealer's catalogs scanned:
1.0 – 1.2 million titles

Catalog cards: 140,000

Ingress of clients:
3,000,000 entries

Reference inquiries:
50,000

Loan requests: 1,000,000 titles

Photo-reproduction requests

New, partly trained personnel 120 persons

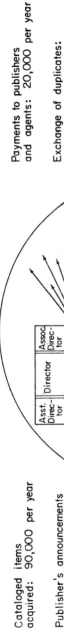

25
Divisional
Libraries

College C

College B

College A

Amer. History

Storage Annex

Bus. Admin.

Law

Asst. Direc-tor | Director | Assoc Direc-tor

Selection Dept. | Chief Divisional Libr.

Order Department

Catalog Department

Circulation Dept.

Reference & Maps

Special Collections, Gift & Exchange

Photo Reproduction

Payments to publishers
and agents: 20,000 per year

Exchange of duplicates:
10,000 items

Contributions to union catalog:
30,000 cards

Bibliographies, reports, etc.

Reference information

Reading opportunities at
tables and in carrels:
2,000,000 visits

Charged publications:
700,000 titles

Photo service: $ 10,000

Experienced personnel: 100

ment which determined what should be bought, an Order Department which procured the books from publishers, and an Exchange and Gift Department which took advantage of special opportunities here and elsewhere for obtaining the more obscure material.

The first separate branch library, Engineering, was set up in 1905, Natural Science and Chemistry followed in 1916, and the Medical library in 1924. By 1940 there were thirteen sites outside the General Library building, eleven of them split off from the main collection and two obtained by amalgamation. A rare book collection came into being in 1917, and a special historical adjunct was founded in 1923. After World War II it proliferated rapidly into the structure shown in Figure 2.

It is worth noting that this spatial decentralization of the library proceeded despite the strenuous objections of the librarians themselves. Between 1920 and 1950 the profession placed particular emphasis upon maintaining the order in the collection and improving its completeness in essential areas of coverage. It was perfectly obvious to librarians that fractionalization would interfere because, first, a limited book budget would be spent acquiring duplicate copies of many books and, second, the catalog could not be kept up to date conveniently. The dates of establishment of branch libraries by the splitting off process coincide with bitter complaints about near-capacity conditions in the stacks of the General Library. Thus the continuous growth of the overall collection interacted with a demand from the faculty for convenience in getting at the most useful printed materials. The outcome was a spatial decentralization that brought the books closer to the offices and laboratories of the staff of the University, and into space supplied by the respective schools and colleges. The librarians could not afford to resist the pressures from the faculty because the inexorable accumulation of books within limited quarters meant that they risked being swamped within a few years at most.

Growth and decentralization brought about extension and revision of the organization chart. At the turn of the century the chief librarian was assisted by a small crew, but by 1920 the payroll had 60 salaried positions and the level of "department head" was established. Later, the academic status of librarians was formally recognized and, subsequently, further distinctions were made between the academic staff and other salaried persons. "Middle management" was installed in the 1950s.

The present hierarchy contains eight discernible strata within almost 400 full-time position equivalents, but there is a great deal of interleaving and interpenetration of status levels which is attributable mostly to the existence of a Library Science department with a flow of graduate students taking apprenticeship training but to some extent also providing the high level of skill required to fill certain specialized nonprofessional posts. The lowest level contains temporary part-time student employees and some full-time disabled persons working on subclerical tasks.

These various features of internal structure—including the departments, the branches, the special services, and the multistratum social hierarchy—were organizational responses to demands for much greater message handling. When increasing requests for an ever wider range of titles intensified the pressure upon the library, the first institutional reaction was to expand the acquisitions function, thus increasing the supply of books. These efforts were followed by an expansion of management, since coordination of services became more than a full-time job, and, finally, to the use of mechanical equipment for routine operations. The last stage is only now beginning to take effect and, as volume increases, should become increasingly evident. An increased intake of books, combined with a more complex shelving and records problem, required a boost in cataloging activity that is percentagewise even greater. Since cataloging is not susceptible to mechanization, it is becoming an increasingly important feature of the social organization.

The Accumulation Processes

The selection of incoming messages requires the construction of an elaborate filtering system that distinguishes between what is relevant and warrants some institutional action, and that which should be disregarded. Certain expedients and practices are stimulated, and the practices are refined over time into decision rules. Libraries have evolved far more elaborate sets of rules than most other institutions, primarily because their information handling task is so much greater. Nevertheless much of the acquisitions procedures remains at the level of art, as contrasted with an evolving science of documentation.

The *opportunities* for acquiring new materials suitable for libraries arrive as lists of titles in bibliographic serials, the "books received" columns of professional journals, dealers' catalogs, publishers' blurbs, and offers for exchange. Much more is published, however, than can be accommodated by the funds, effort, and space available; therefore many of the decision rules apply to the selection of the relatively more desirable titles, frequently on the basis of subtle or inconsequential clues.

The utilities that are advanced by application of these decision rules are readily apparent; they have to do with the expressed needs for teaching, the relevance for on-going research, the expressed intellectual interests of faculty members, the value for reference work, the expected obsolescence rate of the information provided, the anticipated interests of historically-oriented scholars, etc. However, these valuations are normally expressed in a qualitative and ambiguous fashion that is hardly suited for making millions of decisions per year. The rules therefore are forced into a relatively explicit form which contains elements that reflect contemporary attitudes in the bibliographic professions, the particular history of that department or section, and (very likely) a personal style for making decisions. Wherever such rules exist, the choices can be readily remembered, and, as a consequence, are often matched against subsequent operating experience.

In this library the first stages of selection go on at 25–30 different specialized locations. Therefore each must have a fairly clear idea of the categories of content for which it is primarily responsible and of the zones where its interests are shared with others. Similarly, the allocation of funds for book buying, and taking account of their shortage or surplus, must enter into the selection decision. There will also be rules for timing, form-filling, etc., which are aimed at improving the efficiency of operations at later stages. The step-by-step selection processes for medicine, chemistry, and library science (all decentralized) were reviewed in detail, as well as the operations of the centralized Selection Department (responsible for humanities and most social science).

Medicine and chemistry were chose because they represented the "polar extremes" in the selection process. In medicine, a professional librarian searched the *Journal of the American Medical Association* (the richest source of potentially useful titles), accession lists distributed by the National Institute of Health, and several scientific journals and dealers' catalogs. The yield of searches initiated prior to ordering amounted to about 10 percent of the items scanned, with at least an equal number that excited some interest as being possibly worthwhile. In medicine, errors of omission on the part of the selector are not too important because the crucial materials are published in serials, and the compendia are not likely to be out of print a year or two after publication.[4]

In chemistry, an active faculty committee received lists marked by the librarian and made most of the final selections. Therefore, the rules employed were:

1. Avoid texts (foreign and domestic) unless high quality is indicated.[5]
2. Use the *expressed* interests of faculty members as guides.

---

[4] Typical decision rules employed in selection of medical materials:
  1. Mental illness is covered thoroughly by Social Science, and epidemiology by Public Health; therefore rule out to prevent duplication;
  2. Nevertheless order any such book related to known research projects (e.g., radiation biology) irrespective of duplication;
  3. Avoid foreign texts unless recommended by faculty;
  4. Obtain research monographs from North America, Britain, Germany, Scandinavia, and France as promptly as possible;
  5. Proceed with caution on Spanish and Italian materials; they may be obtained more cheaply on exchange;
  6. Postpone purchase from publisher with uneven quality in the list of prior publications;
  7. Postpone purchase of expensive collector's sets;
  8. Order medical history regardless of language;
  9. Absolutely no poetry, satire, etc.
Library Science made even finer differentiations in the course of selection.
[5] This rule may seem unreasonable on the part of the librarian and the committee, but they know from experience that texts are stolen from the shelves. The best texts are kept "on reserve," a rather expensive method of storage.

Librarians point out that this last procedure usually exerts an upward pressure on the book budget for that category of content, but it leads to some imbalance in the coverage of the collection when viewed retrospectively.

A review of selection procedures was undertaken three years after the initial survey in order to discover the direction of change. The medical library was under the management of a new dean, a new librarian, and a new, very active faculty committee. It had also obtained a much larger book budget. As a result, the selection process more nearly resembled that described for Chemistry. Chemistry itself had a new librarian and a much enlarged book budget. This increase had the effect of increasing the range of the librarian in searching for appropriate titles, and it reduced the difficulties of the faculty committee in making choices.

The "suggested order" slips from points all over the campus are funnelled into the Selection Department, whose specialists check them for the presence of sufficient information for ordering, as well as for repetition. They may also query the proposed shelf location of the item, or its quality. They simultaneously attempt to fill in interstices that may be neglected by temporary gaps in the faculty, reorganizations of departments, etc. Altogether, 46 percent of the suggested order slips were returned for further information or for reconsideration by the originator. As a result of these interchanges, orders for 30,000–40,000 books per year were placed, but the rate three years later was more than a third greater. These processes of selection are responsible for the heaviest acquisition, but an equal flow is obtained via special arrangements for serials, exotic languages, gifts, and exchanges.

The detailed studies of selection at representative sites can be expanded into estimates that apply for the full organization:

The total number of titles scanned	1000–1200	thousand/year
The number of different titles seen	240–280	" "
The number of titles seen only once	60–100	" "
The total number of titles offered in world	350	" "
The number of books decided upon favorably	70–90	" "
The number of different titles obtained	55–70	" "

The lists of prospective titles are scanned somewhere in the vicinity of the boundary of the library organization. A few faculty members who serve in specialized areas occupy a somewhat ambiguous position with respect to the boundary, but the final stages of selection are under full control of the library. The choice process is described diagrammatically in Figure 3, elaborating the anatomy of the filtering function as it occurs at the periphery.

A citation comes into existence when a publisher decides to mass produce and market some material he has obtained from an author, editor, composer, producer, or elsewhere. The publisher normally has experience in promot-

FIGURE 3

THE "FILTER MODEL" FOR SELECTION IN A LARGE RESEARCH LIBRARY

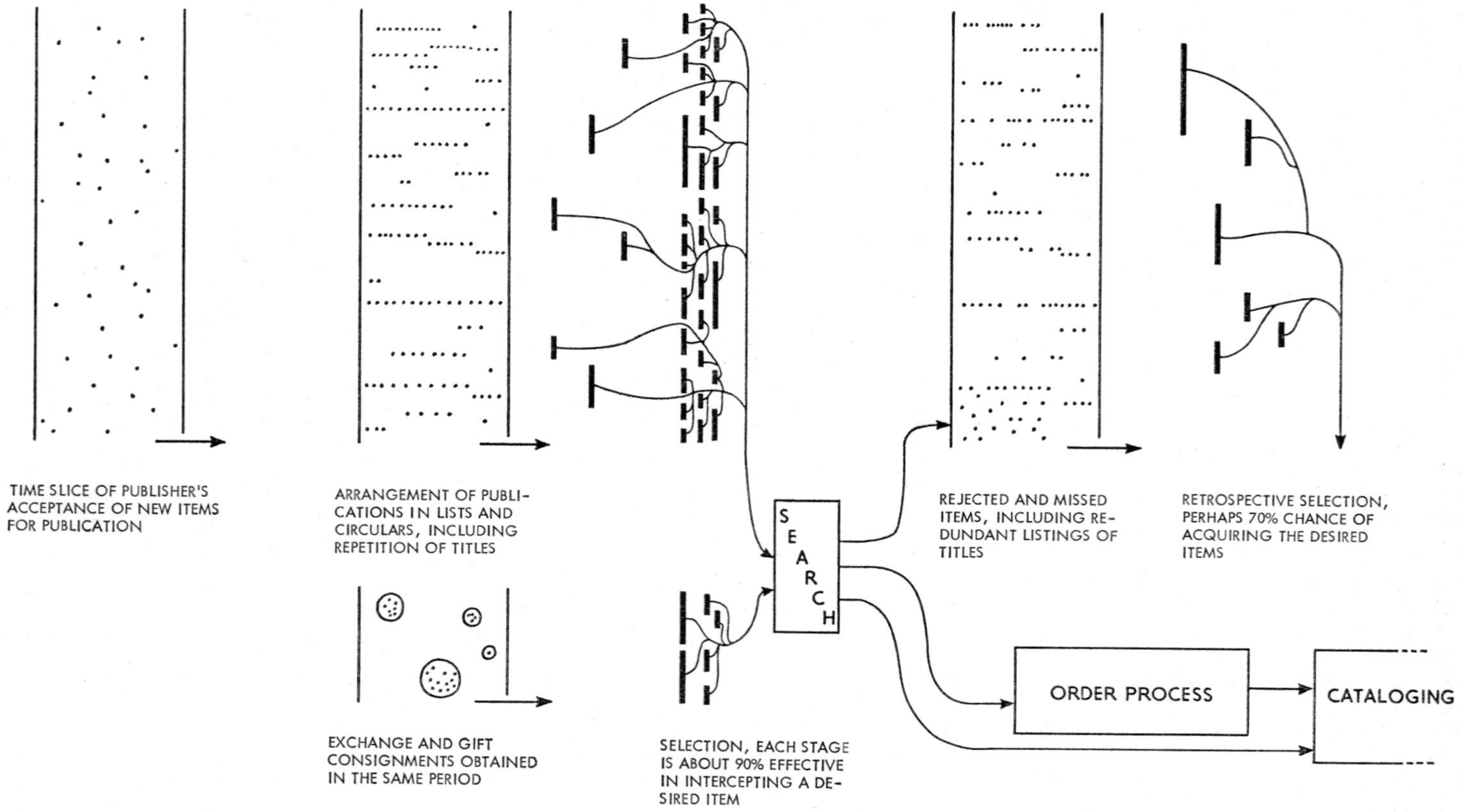

TIME SLICE OF PUBLISHER'S ACCEPTANCE OF NEW ITEMS FOR PUBLICATION

ARRANGEMENT OF PUBLICATIONS IN LISTS AND CIRCULARS, INCLUDING REPETITION OF TITLES

EXCHANGE AND GIFT CONSIGNMENTS OBTAINED IN THE SAME PERIOD

SELECTION, EACH STAGE IS ABOUT 90% EFFECTIVE IN INTERCEPTING A DESIRED ITEM

REJECTED AND MISSED ITEMS, INCLUDING REDUNDANT LISTINGS OF TITLES

RETROSPECTIVE SELECTION, PERHAPS 70% CHANCE OF ACQUIRING THE DESIRED ITEMS

SEARCH

ORDER PROCESS

CATALOGING

ing the sale or distribution of his publications. He broadcasts citations and descriptions of the item in channels scanned by libraries and also directs a flow of messages to the specialized publics that are expected to be interested in the item after it has been printed. Thus, often in concert with other publishers, he will advertise in appropriate alphabetized lists, so that at the first step a partial sorting and ordering is imposed upon what would otherwise be almost a random emission of titles. Librarians and other scholars take advantage of these organizing efforts, so that to this extent their interests coincide with those of the publishers.

However, in another direction, the interests of publisher and librarian conflict, and this conflict is responsible for many of the decision rules built into acquisitions procedures. The publisher, in seeking to maximize the sale of his product, will continue to broadcast descriptions of it until sales do not warrant the promotion costs. A library wishes to acquire no more copies than are needed. Therefore, an alert library will initiate its order after the first announcement and must reject the citation each time it appears thereafter, even if scanned at a place on the boundary of the library organization quite distant from the first contact.

Libraries have found that the clerical costs involved in returning most items acquired through mistake exceed the value of the item itself, so they have, as a general rule, abandoned attempts at making the publisher take back unwanted items. As a consequence of this situation, publishers are continually testing the efficiency of the rejection mechanisms that the libraries have built into their selection procedures. The steady state that has been reached in this quasi-game implies that the lists of titles scanned are 90–95 percent redundant on the average, although the most fruitful lists—normally given the highest priority—are only 70–80 percent redundant. The first selection step converts this flow into a stream of "suggested orders," which is perhaps 40 percent redundant, and the final selection process reduces this to 1–2 percent after searches of the standing order file, the catalog, and backlogs have been conducted.

As the quantity of published material increases, and as the means for advertising it multiply, the effort put into selection is expected to increase proportionately. At present, selection is estimated to cost about $2 per title acquired, to which must be added another $2 for the clerical costs of the ordering process, and perhaps $6 to $10 for cataloging. These sums may be compared to an average of $6 per item paid to the publisher. The inverse of selection—the withdrawal of extra copies and worn-out volumes from circulation in order to make space for some of the new input—is now becoming a serious additional expense.

As book use in the environment increases, only moderate pressure is placed on the selection process. Details about the changing patterns in circulation (the most visible component of book use) are conveyed to the selectors by word of mouth from those working at the desk. The uses of books and catalogs within the library are expedited by the reference librarians, whose experiences are relayed informally. At most of the branch libraries the functions of circulation, reference, and initial selection are supervised by a single professional, so that the amount of intraorganizational communication required is minimal. Shakeups in informal structure will therefore result in gaps in the collection.

The Circulation of Library Materials

Library organizations are designed to provide public access to published materials wherever the accumulation of the latter has reached a point where professional assistance is required. Libraries prepare catalogs and develop reference services, along with other aids for finding whatever is wanted, but each must fall short of a perfect system for predicting requests from the public it serves. Moreover, a library can do very little in the short run toward preventing one client from temporarily preempting a copy needed by another.[6] Therefore, the amount of service actually provided by a library is substantially less than the demands made upon it.

A university library is also an organization accustomed to handling an impressive turnover of small loans. Librarians, forced to keep individual records of these loans, have devised virtually automatic procedures for discovering when the loans are overdue; and they apply sanctions in order to gain possession of materials in the possession of delinquent borrowers. The loan records therefore are the most systematic data shared by libraries. These circulation statistics are used as indicators of overall volume of use and are particularly sensitive to the cyclical changes in the amount of use of library materials. Libraries are normally compared by the circulation they generate because this figure, despite its crudeness, is the best available indicator of book-use activity. Thus any quantitative appraisal of library operations must be strongly linked to circulation statistics. *A unit of circulation represents, by convention, one title that has been charged out of the system for use off the premises.*

A typical test of the loan performance of a library (with stacks closed to a majority of the users) is presented in Table 1. For a representative period, the valid slips filled out and presented at the circulation desk of an unspecialized, million-volume collection were counted and the performance was evaluated. At this time more than 40 percent of the books could not be obtained within 25 minutes, and about a quarter could not be obtained

---

[6] The obvious alternative of preparing a quick, temporary photocopy is, in most instances, forbidden by copyright law. Major publishers of journals, such as the American Chemical Society, have indicated their intention to prosecute flagrant violations because no satisfactory alternative to the sale of subscriptions has been found for the support of scientific publications.

within an hour (the modal length of stay in a university library). Of those that could not be readily obtained, more than half were already in use, about a sixth were in storage and could be picked up the next day, while a twentieth could not be located at all (this category includes stolen copies, misplaced volumes, and books on the way to their proper locations by roundabout processes). As circulation rate increases relative to the number of active copies in the collection, the proportion of slips reported "not on shelf" tends to increase.

TABLE 1

SERVICE AT CORRIDOR DESK OF GENERAL LIBRARY
February 18 to March 2, 1957

Requests received 4614			
Delivered immediately (10–25 min.) 2686		58.2%	
Not on shelf 1928		41.8	
On reserve	461	23.9%	
In circulation	623	32.3	
In storage (16–24 hrs. delay)	240	12.3	
Not located immediately	604	31.3	
Search requested	441		
Accounted for	363		82.3%

How much communication does a unit of circulation normally represent? In this library system it was convenient to separate the estimates of faculty use from student use because the latter had fewer privileges. Faculty use of library, as indicated by circulation figures, was relatively constant between mid-September and mid-July, whereas student loans reached peaks before major holidays and one or two weeks prior to the end of the semester.

A study of faculty use of library materials and facilities in the whole system was undertaken during a typical week in May. In a population of 3,420 qualified recipients, a sample of 745 was employed and a return of 453 (61 percent) was obtained. By various tests, the returned question-

TABLE 2

FACULTY USE OF LIBRARY MATERIALS FOR ONE WEEK

Reported Use of Materials	Use per Circulation Unit
Books .... 11,600 item-use-days	5.6 item-use-days
Journals 9,700	4.7
Abstracts, indexes, & bibliographical references 2,600	1.3
Encyclopedias, handbooks, etc. 1,500	0.7
Government publications . 1,500	0.7
Total .... 26,900 item-use-days	13.0 item-use-days

naires seemed quite representative of the population served, the most underrepresented sector being that of the medical staff engaged in activities other than teaching (49 percent returned). The faculty as a whole (librarians excluded) was estimated, on the basis of these reports, to have obtained 26,900 *item-use-days*[7] of service during a period when 2,066 books were circulated to it, an average of 13.0 per circulation unit (see Table 2).

In the breathing spell shortly after this survey was made, the circulation procedures were reorganized so that every user was expected to find his own book in the stacks after looking up its call number in the card catalog. This change saved time once the client became familiar with the layout of the stacks; it also enabled him to find substitutes for the title he was seeking. Because of this, strictly comparable data can no longer be collected. It is worth noting, however, that the reorganization resulted in an accelerating increase in circulation to faculty members. It also reduced the effort required of the library staff to manage a given circulation rate.

The circulation to students in this library system has been three to four times greater than that to faculty members, but it is distributed over a much smaller number of titles. Student demand exhibits brief periods of peak intensity for specific titles that can be met only by having several copies of the same title on hand, a provision that requires considerable foresight at the institutional level (the mechanism of which was alluded to in the previous section). It is impossible to meet the needs in this manner alone, so that various book rationing devices are employed. The maximum borrowing period can be reduced to "one week" or "overnight" categories, or the books can be placed "on reserve." The so-called "open reserve," which permits students to select their own books from the shelves, is superseded when the demand becomes particularly pressing, or when the

---

[7] The *item-use-day* is a convenient unit devised during the course of this study for measuring the quantity of service rendered by a complex library. It is based upon the library's definition of a separate *item*, which may be a book, a copy of a journal, newspaper, map, microfilm, pamphlet, manuscript, phonographic recording, or reference work, each of which is cataloged, or at least inventoried.

Use is defined by the client of the library, being inherent in the meaning he gives when answering the questions "What library materials did you use yesterday? At the library itself? At the office or laboratory? At home?" We find that neither students nor faculty feel that they have "used" an item if they pulled it off the shelf and looked at the table of contents but if a useful fact or statistic had been obtained, or as much as five minutes was spent reading a selection, the threshold of the conception of use has been reached.

The definition of *day* is a practical one. It refers to the period between rising and retiring, so that the use of a volume during an interval intercepted by the stroke of midnight is not split into two item-use days. A book reported to be used three times in two days while it was charged out would therefore be recorded as *two* item-use-days.

The full implications of this unit for library system analysis are taken up in my article, "Efficiency Criteria for Large Libraries," *Library Quarterly*, Vol. 31, 1961, pp. 215–34.

volumes themselves have been discovered to be irreplaceable, by the "closed reserve" procedure which holds the copies behind the circulation desk for half-day or two-hour use.[8]

Since the circulation service to students was more highly differentiated in its response to student needs (just as acquisition procedures were especially responsive to expressed faculty needs), the research instruments designed for elucidating faculty use of library materials would not reveal many of the significant features of student use of library services. Quite different approaches to the assessment of institutional performance seemed to be in order. They were strongly influenced by special opportunities for data collection provided by the operations employed by the institution.

The growth of the student body after World War II almost overwhelmed the available library facilities. The pressures of the "veterans' bulge" in enrollments, which were still small as compared to the expected impact of the first cohorts of the "baby boom" a decade later, gave highest priority to an undergraduate library. A totally new facility was designed which incorporated a very large share of the experience already acquired for serving students both in this organization and elsewhere. This new facility was coming into use at the time that this study of the overall library organization was initiated. It stimulated the collection of a much wider range of operating statistics than ever before.

The new building, with its new collection of books, caused an estimated 50 percent increase in undergraduate reading within months after its opening, as well as a substantial enhancement in reading by graduate students. Although the number of entries into the building per semester quickly stabilized at 700,000–800,000 (as recorded by a turnstile), the circulation rate grew steadily by 20 percent or more per year. The first indication that the building had reached capacity—the unavailability of seats at peak periods, forcing students to search for substitute places to work—has not been permitted to hold back the growing demand for the use of books. The techniques devised by the librarians to increase the capacity of their facility, the responses of their "clients" (the students), and readjustments worked out by the library staff are likely to be "re-invented" in other communications-rich environments.

Behavior in an Information-Rich Environment

University students as a class are subjected to unremitting demands by their superiors. The ideas and concepts they pick up from the publications in the library are expected to ease this pressure temporarily. This part of

---

[8] The most rapidly circulating book during the period in which student circulation was scrutinized in detail was Hollingshead's *Elmtown's Youth*. The twenty copies (two "missing") were generating almost 100 item-use-days of service per day.

the study intended to discover what behavior students evolved in connection with their use of library resources.

The design features of the new facility must be outlined if this behavior is to be comprehended. The general decor most resembled that of a major merchandising unit in a modern shopping center. The internal environment was intended to maximize esthetic satisfaction at the same time that it expedited the use of books, a policy that rejected both the puritanical and aristocratic approaches to higher education. The facility therefore had excellent lighting and air conditioning, ash trays, a coffee and malt center, typing rooms, an audio-room with private earphones, uncluttered bookshelves, a catalog broken down by subjects as well as authors, and a small art gallery that served as a convenient rendezvous (whose informality was emphasized by colorful contrasts of all plane and perpendicular surfaces, the presence of easy chairs, a few divans, and some low tables).

There were five floors, but only about half the space was allocated to the undergraduate library, the remainder serving education, engineering, and transportation. Shelves were widely spaced and easily accessible from all tables. Books, once read, were supposed to be left on the table. An attendant was on hand to retrieve and reshelve them. Therefore, the order of the collection was kept at a very high level and few disappointments were imposed by lags in the process of restoring books to their proper locations.

The building was kept open 100 hours per week during the term. On an average day (6,000 entries) the seats in the building were filled 40 percent of the time, while on a peak day (exceeding 9,000 entries) seat occupancy rose to 60 percent. Since the peaking of demand is an important aspect in the operation of any public service, special counts of exit rate were undertaken in conjunction with the turnstile data. Daily peaks in library-using population were observed at 10:10 A.M., 3:50 P.M., and about 8:00 P.M., and the building was almost empty at 6:15 P.M. The normal peaks for charging out books were reached about 5:00 P.M. and 10:00 P.M. On peak days the demand for seats was unsatisfied for two to three hours.

After capacity was reached the first time, some students began to come early in the day, "claimed" a seat by leaving their notebooks on it, and returned from time to time between classes. Once this pattern became marked, and some students were forced to stand or sit on the stairs while seats were unused, the librarians countered with a specially worded slip that was inserted into the texts or notebooks when they were pushed to the center of the table or impounded. Scarce titles were monopolized by certain houses or cliques, whereupon the library was forced to reinstitute the closed reserve.

The general comfort and convenience initially attracted a large population that used the building solely as a study hall and meeting place, but the segment using books preempted an increasing share of the seats by arriving earlier and searching more assiduously. The evidence for this was the steady increase in book use within the library (particularly, reshelving by library attendants) both in absolute and per visit terms. As adjustments in living arrangements (mealtimes, rides, etc.) became possible, the "valleys" in library use began to disappear.

Student behavior was analyzed by participant observation during peak periods and found to fall within 23 varieties of acts. The acts were so defined that they may often overlap, permitting a person to be doing two or even three things at once. In the measurement of the allocation of time to these acts, it was convenient to divide a typical visit to the library into three stages: (*a*) entering and getting settled, (*b*) working at a place in the library, and (*c*) typical sequences at the charging desk, usually on the way out of the building (Table 3). More than 98 percent of all student behavior in the library could be accounted for in this manner. Coded diagrams were prepared which followed behavior minute-by-minute. In this manner it was discovered that 65–70 percent of student time was spent clearly at work, 10–13 percent was spent sleeping or staring off into space, about 10 percent in getting settled, and the remainder in socializing and miscellaneous activities. The last two categories were markedly dependent upon the population density in the library.

TABLE 3

EPISODES OF BEHAVIOR IN USE OF LIBRARY

A	Obtaining aid from a librarian	K	Smoking (often occurred in conjunction with work)
B	Use of card catalog		
C	Removing wraps	L	Going to rest room
D	Preparations for leaving	M	Rummaging in briefcase or purse
E	Use of closed reserve books	N	Locating ash tray
F	Socializing with friend (includes casual greeting as well as longer talks)	O	Using drinking fountain
		P	Transit time within library
		Q	Consuming refreshments
G	Charge desk (only when books are being actually charged out)	R	Obtaining seat
		S	Searching for books on shelves
H	Sleeping	T	Returning checked-out book
I	Writing charge slips	U	Reading (including note-taking)
J	Staring into space	V	Other work
		W	Using cigarette machine

Reports by students themselves of their behavior in the building were obtained through a short questionnaire administered on an active day during mid-term. Of a total of 790 distributed (a 9.5 percent sample), 520 were returned (71 percent). Among the students remaining in the building more than 15 minutes, the response rate was 86 percent. No evidence of bias could be detected among nonresponders staying more than 15 minutes (their main characteristics were believed to be lateness for class, forgetfulness, antipathy to questionnaires, etc.). Although opportunity was granted for private, unsigned comment, the statements in all instances but two were signed.

Validation of the questionnaires was obtained through comparing students' reports of their own notebooks, texts, etc., used in the library, with counts at the exit control point where briefcase and large handbags were regularly inspected. The students reported 1.8 such items used, while exit control reported 2.0 to 2.2 carried—a very good fit since it was impossible to standardize the student counts. Another validation was attempted by comparing student reports on the charging out of books with library statistics, but the students' definitions of the term clearly included the use of closed-reserve books since the charge slips were virtually identical. When this adjustment was made, the student reports of book charges were still 15 percent higher than had been recorded by the library. The discrepancy is in the right direction since the library probably prevented the circulation of some open-reserve books after the completed questionnaire had been returned.

The socializing pattern was of particular interest. The question finally employed after two pretests was "How many people did you meet that you nodded or spoke to?" There were 1.3 reported contacts per person per hour in the morning, 2.6 in the afternoon, and 3.1 in the evening. The group that reported being in the building less than 15 minutes had a much greater level of socializing: 3.3 contacts per hour in the morning, 6.6 in the afternoon, and 6.8 in the evening. From these data one must conclude that a large share of the brief trips into the building were prearranged contacts.

The noise and disturbance that accompanies socializing, even in an acoustically treated environment, was recognized by the students themselves as the most undesirable feature of the facility. Among the suggestions for improvement that were volunteered, the control of talking led by far. Yet the students that emphatically decry socializing engage in it themselves to about the same extent as others. About 5 percent of the time was spent in this manner in the morning, 19 percent in the afternoon, and 12 percent in the evening.

The most unexpected finding resulted from a comparison of student reports—on the use of library materials *within* the building—with the library's own reports. Student use for this day, as calculated from the questionnaires, was computed to be 8741 item-use-days. Library statistics suggested a maximum of 4,409, after special estimates were made of newspaper use (186) and the use of reference tables (396), which are normally not counted by librarians.

It was also assumed that each book circulated was used before it was charged out. Students could hardly be accused of deliberately misleading the investigators on this point when, on other questions, their answers could be corroborated within a margin of 10–15 percent. Subsequent inquiry showed that each book taken off the shelf was used by two people, on the average, before it was returned, and closed-reserve books were used almost three times, despite regulations to the contrary. *The socializing, that was so disparaged, appeared to be vital for achieving a high level of book use at peak periods.* Indeed, the standard student ploy upon entering a crowded library was to seek out someone in the class rather than look for the required reading on the appropriate shelf, because in that manner it was more probable that information as to the actual location of the volume could be obtained. Collective use of books was observed to be not uncommon.

In many library facilities, the time required for obtaining a title increases markedly with the load. Such studies were conducted experimentally in this building with 600 representative titles recorded on cards, and divided into typical tasks, one to eight titles per task, with each step being clocked by students to the nearest 10 seconds. It was found that the normal time for seeking a title was 6 to 7 minutes, of which 30–35 percent of the time was spent at the catalog, 25–30 percent in search, 15–20 percent in charging, 10–20 percent for reference questions, and 5 percent in socializing. None of these times was sensitive to the level of load experienced by the library. The fraction of titles not available, however, ranged from 1 percent on a light day in summer to 16 percent on a heavy day in spring, so that a moderately sensitive relationship between load and performance was available. The time spent *per title obtained* increased by 20 percent when the library operated at 80–85 percent of estimated capacity, as compared to 10–20 percent of capacity.

The analysis of student behavior within the building suggested that students rapidly devised individual and group policies that increased book use to a level perhaps 30–40 percent greater than the amount that the librarians had estimated to be present on the basis of operating statistics. If the demand for books increases further, however, the shortage of seats would force students to resort to greater borrowing. This tendency has already been exhibited in the large, nearby general library where a 10 percent per capita increase per year was stimulated (accelerating to 20–30 percent as the undergraduate library approaches capacity a third of the time instead of a tenth). Increased circulation implies greater expenditure in purchasing and cataloging, and in later withdrawing from circulation many additional copies of popular titles, as well as collecting information calculated to yield better predictions regarding the utility of any given title.

Students' choices were not limited to required reading for courses, since 37–44 percent of the books circulated from the student library appeared on none of the lists submitted by professors, thus suggesting that probably more than half of the reading done by students went beyond specific assignments. Qualitatively, it was observed that a large proportion of the reading in the library fell into the category of browsing or working on special projects, except for the period immediately preceding examinations. Eclectic demands upon a library are more easily satisfied by a book selection department than research-oriented demands because there are (at most) very few satisfactory substitute titles for the latter.

Resource Constraints

As with most public services, and in contradistinction to the stock exchange, a library is not financially self-supporting. The fines it exacts upon delinquents pay only for costs of collection. The faculty is a privileged group in the university, therefore very little in the way of sanctions and penalties can be imposed upon it. The library is expected to live on a carefully pruned budget that is drawn up in concert with the administration. Therefore, the institutional behavior in response to increasing demands for service is strongly influenced by the provisions written into the budget. The basic planning of the institution is worked out in the process of preparing annual budget requests. The library differs very little in this respect from a government bureau.

An analysis of the costs and benefits associated with library use suggests that quite noticeable diseconomies have arisen since World War II and have not yet been corrected in the course of the budgeting process. They are revealed by comparison of the costs of providing published materials as against the effort required to gain access to them.

For example, the faculty survey mentioned earlier revealed that the collection exhibiting the greatest use was that of the central library (containing about a million volumes). The calculated number of trips to this library by the faculty, over the course of a typical week in 1958, was 2,938. The time cost by the shortest route from office, laboratory or clinic was estimated at 679 hours. The circulation to faculty was 440 items. Thus the time cost per trip was 0.23 hours, and the time cost per book circulated (representing 13 item-use-days of service) was slightly more than 1.5 hours. If we assess faculty time as being worth salary plus fringe benefits (say $6 per hour) the cost of obtaining a book reaches $9 before there is any opportunity to read it or to gain any by-product advantages from library visits.

In contrast, about a third of the library budget is allocated to activities associated in some way with circulation, so that the variable cost to the library for providing the book and all the by-product services may be set at 60 to 80 cents. The costs to the faculty in terms of time delays are very much less for departmental libraries (varying between 0.25 and 0.65 hr.

per title circulated), so the popularity of convenient collections designed
to meet the needs of a single department is quite justified. It would also be
quite proper for the library to initiate new services designed to improve
the convenience to clientele engaged in teaching and research. However,
such services would inevitably lead to increased usage of the collection
and would intensify the pressures upon the remainder of the library staff,
so that many upward adjustments in acquisitions and cataloging would
have to be made. If the library raised expenditures upon circulation services
to a point where it matched costs to faculty (at, say, around $3 per title
circulated as against a half hour of time expended to obtain it), the library
budget would have to be doubled or trebled.

A drastic reduction in costs to clientele was actually achieved by the
creation of the student library. If the alternate value of student time is con-
servatively set at $2 per hour (the proper rate is what would be earned as
a going wage outside of a university town), the "opportunity cost" to the
student for obtaining the volume desired, once he had reached the library,
was reduced from a figure greater than $1 to between 25 and 40 cents. The
cost to the library is more difficult to estimate because amortization of
building, furnishings, and book stock is relatively large (but unspecified in
the annual budget). It is estimated, however, that the total cost per title
circulated must be in the 20- to 40-cent range.

During the course of these studies, the library administration was en-
couraged by its faculty council to draw up a five-year program for expansion of services to graduate students (doing research) and to the faculty.
Arrearages, where present, were to be eliminated. Such a program implied
increasing the book budget by 120 percent, the operating budget by 100
percent, and the number of regular positions by 95 percent. At least one
additional structure was required. The program has good prospects for
being put into effect, but shortages of personnel and the university's slowness to act on new capital budget items (if they are not self-financing) may
result in delays. Any delay will introduce new and more substantial arrearages because faculty and graduate student circulation is now rising steeply
at around 20 percent per year per capita, and a major expansion of the
graduate and professional schools must begin at about the end of this five-
year program because of the greatly increased size of cohorts in the population served by the university. The library organization still has some
prospects for meeting an enlarged demand, but it is becoming less con-
fident. It realizes also that other research libraries around the world will
be struggling to expand during the same period and that the supply of
specialized personnel will be extremely short.

In a university library, as in the stock exchange, short flurries of transactions can be handled without threat to the system. However, continued
operation at a higher-than-normal level causes heavy backlogs to appear

at various points in the internal processing. The jobs in the back rooms in the library, mainly ordering and cataloging, are highly technical, and months are required before new personnel can reach normal levels of productivity. Library tasks contain less routine than most organizations, and only a few features seem to be subject to mechanization. Thus, a mounting demand for books may cause:

1. Continuous adjustment in the circulation departments, especially the addition of student help;
2. An increase in titles and copies selected for addition to the collection, with no important increase in effort required;
3. Some delays in the processing of invoices after the books arrive;
4. Much greater lags in the cataloging of the materials that are more difficult to classify; and
5. Very serious coordination problems between various departments in the organization due to the need for finding items, important to the users, that are stuck somewhere in the internal backlogs.

RESPONSES TO COMMUNICATIONS STRESS

The social changes that may be expected to occur as a function of the increasing communications load upon an institution can now be specified for the general case. Each response, or policy, is described as a pure type, but in the above institutions the measures actually taken are blends or mixtures. This is inevitable, because at any given moment, when a decision must be made regarding alternative directions for action, some mixed strategy is likely to be superior to a pure strategy.

Let us begin with a pristine institution in an urban environment. An urban environment is required because we shall be positing a growing organization with an even more rapidly expanding circle of clients, but, even together, they remain small as compared to total communications activity. We shall also postulate that the institution is prevented by law or custom from adjusting the sale price of its service and is therefore prevented from using the market mechanism directly as a means of adjustment.

With this statement of underlying assumptions we have only to hypothesize an irregular influx of messages with a strongly upward secular trend. These messages are assumed to be typical in every way of those the institution was designed to handle so that a transaction could be completed without creating difficulties and without delays inside the organization. Thus, opportunities that call for giving service—or actual requests for service—appear in increasing numbers, and are, at first, handled routinely as fast as they appear. The processing time is short, and most departments or roles are standing ready in anticipation of work which appears to come in ever-increasing bursts and flurries until one exceeds the immediate operating capacity.

Policy One: Queuing Inputs at Peak Periods

The incoming requests may be stored, or lined up, in order of arrival at some point in the vicinity of the boundary of the institution. Some department working on the intake side would devise provisions for a waiting line with a "gate" or turnstile which would store the queue outside the main body of the organization and let in items as fast as they could be processed. When the flurry was over, the organization would resume "business as usual," retaining only the decision rules for establishing a queue when it should become advisable.

Discussion: This policy tends to bring about a small increase in cost to the clientele, since users no longer can count on obtaining immediate service and must adjust to more variable delivery times. Unit costs within the institution itself actually diminish substantially because there is less waiting. However, if the queue continues to grow in size—the burst of requests lasting longer than expected—adverse publicity appears. Political pressures may be brought upon the institution. Therefore additional new measures must be taken.

Policy Two: Setting Priorities in Queue

Different degrees of importance may be attached to items in a waiting line. The organization must estimate the value of each item according to the effect its processing would have upon those resources of its own that may be scarce (cash supply, labor, special skills, space, or public regard), giving precedence to those items valued most highly.

Discussion: In any queue in the library, a request by a faculty member would have precedence over that of a graduate student or an undergraduate. In the stock market, a buy or sell order would be accepted over a request for a bid-asked quotation. The net effect would be to reduce costs to the institution for a given processing pace. More often than not, the future welfare of the institution would be linked so closely to that of its clients that the setting of priorities in the queues would also result in savings to the clients taken as a group.

Policy Three: Destruction of Lowest Priorities

As a queue continues to build up in size, it becomes apparent that the lowest priority requests for service will probably *never* receive attention. While they remain in the queue they must be periodically subjected to study to determine whether their priority should be changed. The re-examination appears to be wasted effort for consistently low priority items. It saves time and trouble to destroy the messages that fall into this category immediately upon arrival. This is the "wastebasket policy" for communications.

Discussion: A few libraries early in this century felt it was their duty to preserve everything printed, since it was grist for the historian. This policy seemed to be highly responsible, but the task was overwhelming. Librarians quickly came to designate a class of fliers, community reports, tracts, advertisements, and the like as *ephemera* that were not worth preserving unless a systematic collection were to be made. All organizations quickly develop such rules regarding what incoming mail deserves a reply, and they usually extend these rules to other kinds of communications as they become more pressed.

Policy Four: Adapting to Redundancy with Active Files

Some transactions are noted to be far more common than others. Organizations often find it possible to save time in processing by spending some capital creating an active file which contains the materials needed to expedite the most frequent requests. After such a file is formed, it is common for highest priority and most-valued items to be processed through this file because they remain most visible and the likelihood of error is reduced.

Discussion: The phenomenon of reserve books in a library falls into this category. When activity becomes truly intense, an "even-more-active file" may be created. The "closed reserve" in the student library served this function. New record keeping equipment offers an increasing variety of opportunities to institutions for taking advantage of this policy.

Policy Five: Creating Branch Facilities

A review of the sources of incoming requests for service will reveal that the outside environment is not homogeneous. There are more clients in some locales than others. If a branch facility is established in the vicinity of a large cluster of probable users, it is likely to improve the service and significantly reduce the size of the queues at the main facility.

Discussion: There are many reasons for the decentralization of an institution, but the congestion of message inputs can be a very potent one. It is difficult to imagine a more decentralized organization than the contemporary university library. There are even more branches in several large brokerage houses, and their branches are distributed over far more territory. The branch serves to translate the request into an internal code which can be handled more conveniently at the headquarters, and the lowest priority requests can be screened out immediately. The institution often gains new resources when undertaking such a policy because it is in a position to bargain with special interest groups. The unit costs to these groups can be very considerably reduced, so that they are willing to grant inducements which expedite the formation of a branch.

Policy Six: Encourage Middlemen

When queues and arrearages are inevitable and growing, conditions are ripe for incurring increasing unit costs. Often niches for entrepreneurs are created, which enable them to develop special services for several combined institutions at a cost less than that experienced by each individually.

Entry of such entrepreneurs is especially likely when a new technology can be brought into operation.

Discussion: The library acquisitions problems led to the encouragement of two middlemen, heavily dependent upon the library, and marginal support was provided to several other specialist firms. Also, in order to ease the pressure on active titles, the student library on several occasions publicized the availability of pocket editions in the nearby book stores in the hope that discouraged students would acquire their own copies. In the stock exchange example, three large computation centers have recently set up shop in downtown Manhattan to assist the stock exchanges and the brokerage firms. The general problem is one of creating additional processing capacity, preferably on a temporary or variable "as needed" basis, without completely revamping the organization.

Policy Seven: Create a Mobile Reserve

The internal backlogs of the various divisions and departments seldom remain balanced. After one or another section has been nearly overwhelmed, thus threatening the viability of the whole organization, the management may decide that a mobile reserve should be brought into being. Each of the members of this reserve should have a broad enough range of skills to help in the departments that are likely to be under pressure to keep up. During the lulls, they would work on lesser priority projects or on long-range problems.

Discussion: The mobile reserve is a well-known military concept, but the simile has seldom been used in communications-oriented institutions; when the reserve principle is utilized, it seems to have *ad hoc* origins which suggest that few comparisons with military strategy were ever introduced to justify it. Often such reserves get committed and cannot be released again as reserves. A new group must then be created. In the library studied, the flow of library science apprentices served this function to a considerable degree, but additional reshuffling was required in at least two instances. In one instance, a "research and development unit" that had been formed was committed; later, a small group of "service librarians" was established. The consequences of the policy are widely distributed and not easy to establish empirically. Overhead costs may be raised somewhat for the institution at the same time that the service is made more dependable for the clients.

Policy Eight: Evolve Explicit Performance Standards

Statistical analyses would show quite clearly that the institution could save time and trouble if it simplified its procedures and recognized that certain rates of error were admissible. The application of singleminded attention to every request is wasteful of scarce resources. When a few are allowed to remain unattended, or omitted from processing without scandal or the attachment of blame, the overall capacity can be substantially increased. Often these measures for standardization and reform are designed with the assistance of a consultant.

MATHEMATICAL EXPLORATIONS IN BEHAVIORAL SCIENCE

Discussion: Such a rationalization of decision rules often implies a restatement of the responsibility of the institution for service to the client. It requires some prior expenditures for surveys which demonstrate that no undue risks are involved, that the status of the institution among its peers is not affected, and that the dependability of its service remains at least as good as the collateral services required by clients. The library was quite early forced to set up an indicator of the quality of its housekeeping in the form of "missing titles, unaccounted for." Because larger sums were involved in each transaction, the stock exchange could allow a much smaller share of requests to remain unattended. It is apparent that the maximum tolerable proportion omitted in any category is heavily dependent upon the priority assigned in the queue.

Policy Nine: Reduce Standards of Performance

The pressure has, by this point, become virtually intolerable. Something must give; and, ordinarily, the rules maintaining the standards of performance are officially relaxed or countermanded. This policy recognizes *de jure* what has already been apparent *de facto* for the lower priority requests.

Discussion: Morale, which holds up remarkably well until this stage is reached (mainly because the changes in service stimulate interest and challenge the members of the organizations), drops precipitously when standards are compromised. Absenteeism, sickness rate, and labor turnover (all of them partial indicators of the state of morale) may be expected to show sizable increases. The frequency of errors in operation has shown signs of stabilizing, or has crept upward slightly in preceding stages, but now, despite attempts at reducing the pressures from the heavy load of communications, it tends to mount very quickly if the queue is maintained or increased. The errors tend to cost the clients much more than the organization after the standards are reduced. Thus this policy represents a shift in the costs of making transactions to the other organizations and individuals in the environment. Virtually all divisions of the institution by now show signs of harrassment.

Policy Ten: The Search for the "Magic Formula"

When almost all hope of emerging from the predicament has been lost, the clutching of straws is a behavior that is almost universally followed. Key staff may be taken off the "firing line" and brought together for emergency conferences and quick studies. The growth of queues and arrearages is accelerated by this action, but the institution is by now quite desperate.

Discussion: The privileges and rights of clients are given only perfunctory recognition because the whole organizational superstructure, along with the careers of its directorate, is threatened. In historic times, patrons with abundant resources were sought or the attention and aid of top executives in government was implored, but currently, in communications-oriented institutions, the solution to these problems is almost always sought in the form of mechanization and instrumentation. That this faith in the power of technology is well-founded is still too soon to say, even for the stock exchanges. Thus far, the new technology proposed for libraries seems to be much too imperfect and expensive to permit it to resolve the difficulties of catalogers and circulation librarians.

Policy Eleven: Customer Self-Service

One rather radical formula that is seldom seriously considered is the redrawing of the boundary that separates the client from the service institution. However, the example of self-service in marketing has made the policy appear as if it were only another form of technology. Boundaries and sovereignty over functions are usually defended to the death of the institution.

Discussion: In the past, libraries have jealously guarded their treasures, and, particularly in the world outside the United States, have evolved a series of controls at the boundary which are calculated to prevent theft and destruction. Stack privileges were once very restricted, but the self-service concept has become so engrained in American thinking that a major reorganization of the circulation department of a library almost always incorporates noticeable changes in this direction. The stock exchanges have admitted the curious public to mezzanines overlooking the trading floor as a means of breaking down the public bias toward "Wall Street" and of contributing to the education of potential investors, but this is a very minor adjustment compared to encouraging lower classmen to find their own books in the stacks.

Policy Twelve: Escape

The policymakers and responsible personnel, if they have found no solution to their difficulties from increasing demand for services, are likely to consider resignation. The situation has become intolerable and irremediable, at least within the scope of the knowledge and experience they brought to the institution or acquired within it. The actual form this policy may take is that of permitting a takeover, bankruptcy, or mass resignation.

Discussion: This is, on the surface, a surprising kind of failure. The service provided by the organization was so popular that it was overwhelmed by the burgeoning demand. Yet it is not uncommon. Management consultants are aware of the risks of rapid growth for corporations that are in a position to set prices for their services or products. Thus it is not unexpected that institutions without this freedom are still more susceptible to breakdown.

Policy Thirteen: Work to Rule

If escape is impossible for legal, ethical, or other reasons, there is a strong tendency to limit responsibilities to the amount of load that can be handled by rigid, ritualistic application of working rules. The institution no longer tries to meet the challenge of the task or to correct the mistakes that have been made. Errors tend to be ignored or denied, and clients are expected to find alternate sources or substitutes on their own initiative.

Discussion: When this policy is accepted, the decision rules become characteristic of a capricious, silly, dogmatic bureaucracy that has lost its internal consistency. The priority assignments, in particular, become archaic and meaningless. These patterns are not uncommon, but investigation of the history of such organizations suggests that each may have been overstressed at some time and never really recovered. But the reasons offered to explain the lack of flexibility are various (e.g., personality of the founder, special sources of support, lack of space for maneuver, etc.) and no conclusions can be drawn which connect the kind of stress with the pathology that results.

Policy Fourteen: Salvage of Component Units

Dissolution of middle-size or large institutions is seldom complete. It seems likely, in the cases reviewed here, that some reorganizer would reassemble branches, departments, and independent enterprises and create a new institution based upon a different operating formula. Often fragmentation occurs, so that half a dozen organizations may be operating where there was only one before.

Discussion: It is not difficult to imagine library systems breaking down and being redistributed to various client groups if the systems are not granted sufficient resources with which to survive, but the number of examples of libraries that can be found is nevertheless quite small. Most instances of breakdown and salvage have been observed in departments of larger bureaucracies. Even then the policies undertaken prior to breakdown—usually recapitulated in the successor organizations with only a few important modifications—will include almost all of those recounted above. One such example was observed in Puerto Rico when a small Bureau of Vehicle Registry was overwhelmed by the rapid growth in the ownership of private automobiles brought on by successful economic development programs. In that instance the personnel were transferred or furloughed, and a consultant was brought in with a new, much larger team of workers to clean up the backlog and establish new and more flexible procedures with twice the weekly capacity for handling requests for licenses.

In a similar instance a publications section of a large professional society expanded publications three to four times after World War II, by various devices and with no increase in the number of professional editors. But the future produced only increasingly intolerable pressures; the editors resigned simultaneously and thereby created a publications crisis for the society that could not be eliminated, even with many times greater expenditures for re-equipment and staff than had been spent in half a decade.

Inadvertent overloads are likely to become more frequent as the pace of communications is accelerated. When per capita income increases, urban residents use more services (indeed, in North America a predominant share of the increase now seems to be allocated to such services), and the interdependencies between institutions are also enhanced. References to the increasing spread between prices of raw materials and the sale price of finished goods (with accompanying services) are directed to these same trends, since the spread goes for middlemen's services. The process of functional integration, which represents progress toward more organized social behavior, requires greater frequency of interaction between social units than would be needed to maintain the same metropolitan complex at equilibrium.

COMMUNICATIONS LOAD AND STRUCTURE

The relation between communications load and the appearance of indicators of stress, such as increases in error frequency and interdepartmental friction, is not simple. Communications load is best measured as the rate of receipt of requests for service or other forms of satisfying response, such as cogent explanations as to why the service cannot be provided. It represents the initiation rate for social transactions effected by the institution. The output or transaction completion rate is the generator of rewards for the institution over the long run. When the output rate fails to keep up with the initiation rate, some queues and backlogs develop. If all other factors remain equal, the resultant performance of the institution begins to deviate more and more from the ideal as load increases, until a peak in output rate is reached. As certain resources and internal stock-on-hand are expended, the output becomes less with increasing load. Output rate may drop precipitously, as in the above instances of breakdown, or it may seek a level which is "good enough." The *capacity* of the organization for completing transactions will lie somewhere between the peak performance that could not be maintained and the level chosen for "satisficing" (Herbert A. Simon's term for "doing just well enough to get by"). In this framework, the capacity of an institution for completing a flow of transactions is equivalent to the *channel capacity* of a communications system for coding and decoding messages.[9]

The stress is generally greatest at rates where the peak is reached, and perhaps a little beyond, because the need to abandon previously established norms is not at that stage obvious enough to gain consensus among the members (illustrated in Figure 4). The stress results from conflict in views of how behavior should be changed in a situation where decisions cannot be very long postponed. Often the conflict also exists between the norms internalized within the same individual, so that organizational stress is readily transmuted into personal distress. Thus the appearance of increased absentee rates and personnel turnover is a logical consequence of the

---

[9] It is now evident that these concepts, with some changes in terminology, are applicable to organized systems in general and not solely to social institutions. Thus individual cells, organisms, and small groups are constructed to interact in a discrete fashion. Care must be taken, however, to define the varieties of transactions that can be completed.

J. G. Miller in his "Input Overload and Psychopathology" (*American Journal of Psychiatry*, Vol. 116 [August, 1960], pp. 695–704) identifies eight different adjustments in the response of individuals, and fewer for simpler systems, such as neurons. More can be distinguished in a social institution perhaps because the investigator is, in this case, observing detailed phenomena from many vantage points both inside and outside the organization. Miller has placed such response within the context of general behavior theory. Also see J. G. Miller, "Sensory Overloading," in B. E. Flaherty (ed.), *Psychophysiological Aspects of Space Flight* (New York: University of Columbia Press, 1961), pp. 216–24.

FIGURE 4

COMMUNICATIONS OVERLOAD IN ORGANIZED SYSTEMS

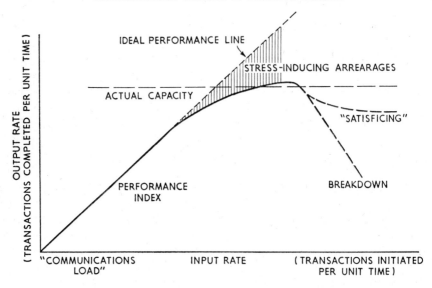

pressure to change behavioral norms. Stress in this case begins with the failure of an institution to perform as well as expectations, and it is then transmitted to groups and individuals within the institution if the load is intensified. Similarly, a larger fraction of the clientele is discommoded (costs are transferred to them), and irritation—and later even signs of stress—may be detected in the milieu.

Once a pristine, communications-oriented institution has been tested by bringing operations up to or beyond the capacity for completing transactions, the experience has inevitable *structural* consequences. The outcome results from the varying strategies that had been employed by the institution, each of them combining and recombining some of the policies elaborated above. Therefore the effects of both policy mix and changes in strategy must be taken into account in any detailed explanation of subsequent structure. However, since the policies were identified sequentially, so that they were appropriate to increasing communications load, the general implications of a severe test can be deduced.

The spatial consequences are perhaps the simplest to describe, although they are far from clear-cut. The well-tested organization has lost the simply defined territorial boundaries with which it had originally been endowed. When interaction rate is very high, the shortcuts and aids that expedite the flow of messages, such as priority assessment and active files, create an infrastructure in the vicinity of the boundary. The need to make and remake policy within the institution, and to ascertain that it had the expected local outcomes, leads to an accentuated headquarters unit, usually surrounded by a "home facility" that provides continuous support.

It has also brought into being a series of outliers, branches, traveling units, missions, satellites, etc., extending deep into the interacting social environment. The organization is likely to have an address of some kind in the vicinity of any group of clients that has become dependent upon it, and these subsidiary units are likely to have differentiated functions. Similarly, very little space is left in the home facility, or elsewhere, that the organization is not sharing with others in one way or another. An area may be reserved for back-room work, particularly if some transactions must be kept at the confidential or secret level, and another area serves as offices for top management and staff; but the remainder is open to mixed use by clients, service organizations, etc. The institution also creates a territory in the environment over which its influence—as compared to others providing the same class of services—is dominant, and a zone that is much broader in scope where a significant minority of the population may prefer its services to those that are nearer at hand.

The overall dimensions of the organization after a severe test should be considerably greater. More persons would be intimately involved in its operations; the resources it allocates on a regular basis should have substantially increased relative to its environment because of its improved bargaining position. On the other hand, the initial capital equipment would be run-down, patched, reorganized, and perhaps partially reconstructed. A great deal of deferred maintenance may be expected to have accumulated. Therefore, the overall capital worth of the physical equipment may have declined, and the capital worth per employee or member almost certainly will have diminished. However, a larger share of expenditures will be made for services of various kinds, from other agencies, and these agencies may often be able to justify strongly capital-intensive installations on the basis of the increased demand and the expectation that the trends will continue in this direction over the long term.

We must also expect that the institution under scrutiny will have converted much of its original capital into a network of interdependencies in the social system which are more valuable to it in relieving stress due to overload and other sources. These obligations take the form of social credits which can be drawn upon in times of necessity, but they are not marketable. When employing this social capital, a communications-oriented institution may easily achieve levels of operation 20–50 percent in excess of designed physical capacity for considerable periods of time.

Status structures within the organization will be strongly affected by a test lasting many months or even years. The intense rates of interaction, the need for making many decisions quickly, and the frequent introduction of new kinds of decisions that are brought on as a result of organizational adjustments are factors which, when taken together, lead to an organization with ambiguous and interleaving status levels. Functional effectiveness and general competence, of course, become more highly valued. The persons categorized as "deadwood," and those who were inadvertently confused or overstressed in the course of the test, are often relegated to low-pressure housekeeping tasks, an activity that might easily develop its own status ladder. Even the formal organization chart is blurred by temporary appointments and *ad hoc* arrangements.

An institution may also be visualized as an agency that transforms certain inputs and resources—in this case, primarily messages, records, and skills—into outputs that complete the transactions it makes with outside parties. A structure of the organization can be recapitulated as a tree of decision rules, or, more often, as a combination of such trees superimposed and linked with each other. A carefully planned new institution would have an internal flow of messages that closely resembles an assembly line, with the main flows being processed in short, easy stages. Queries, rejects, and back-tracking would be minimal. As the load on the institution approaches its capacity, the repertory of decision rules in active use at each station— (the inactive rules have by then been forgotten or specifically countermanded) is greatly lengthened to take care of contingencies that now are expected to arise more frequently per unit of time than ever before, although the absolute frequency (measured as a fraction of situations reacted to) was no greater than before. Through the extra rules, an elaborate system of feedbacks would be created. Each stage in organizational strategy during the course of the expansion of message handling would require the spelling out of a new layer of regulations.

The nature of the striking changes in value structure operative in the institution can be inferred, in part, from the new rules that were promulgated, and, to an even greater extent, from the rules being proposed by the rank and file. An acceleration in the pace of communications and a coincident increase in the frequency of decisions lead to an awareness of new criteria for evaluation. The ambiguities and conflicts inherent in the earlier value structure are revealed at the same time that resources, which were previously in abundance, suddenly became scarce. Special measures for the conservation of these resources need to be worked out when the institution is operating close to capacity and there is little time available for studying the problems. Almost always, the availability of certain professional skills (the professions are viewed in this context as specialized capabilities for dealing with complex or abstract communication) will come to be particularly prized. Often these underlying changes in valuation will interact with discussions of "higher values" that are always reverberating through the milieu, and new insights as to the proper ends toward which the institution should direct itself may gain acceptance.

Each aspect of organizational structure, including those that have already been introduced, may be represented by a network of relationships (i.e., positions and relations) that are maintained over time. A familiar example of this technique is to be found in sociometric diagrams. As transaction capacity is approached, the foregoing arguments—translated into their impact upon relations between positions—suggest that all such diagrams should show

a) A greater *variety* of relations between positions,

b) A larger *number* of relations maintained by the central, or nodal, positions,

c) Many more relations *between* established positions within the institution and the milieu within which it operates (the external relations will be most highly concentrated in decentralized branches),

d) Mobilization of almost all isolated positions relatively unconnected with the main body, and

e) Creation of many more alternative paths by which one position might influence another.

Policy Eleven (the reduction of standards of performance) implies the relinquishing of some internal relations, while Policy Twelve (escape) requires the loss of positions, however they are defined, or fragmentation of the network. Policy Thirteen (working to rule) involves a major reduction in relations with clients as well as an internal consolidation. Policy Fourteen (salvage) implies the reestablishment of relations between a fragment and some other organization, or the formation of totally new relations that promise to make the fragment self-sustaining.

These methods of viewing the structural effects of overload are limited to institutions and their immediate environments. Estimation of the cumulative effect of local overloads upon certain specialized urban areas will require quite different techniques. The threat is imminent enough, however to demand a systematic study of urban organization with the view toward facilitating the defenses of institutions (including, for example, appropriate means for the taxation of communications). The implications of communications stress for various professions, many of them scientific and technical; for health, recreation needs, and family life would also merit investigation. Such information would make possible plans that reduce the costs of inadvertent overload.

POSTSCRIPT

This paper was introduced to the conference, together with reports of inexorably growing rates of social communications. It was demonstrated that the accumulation of knowledge and the acceleration of the pace of public interaction was necessary to counteract the effects of the depletion of natural resources. Therefore "communications stress" was an exceedingly important phenomenon to take into account in planning for future advanced societies, including most of the United States and the metropolitan centers of Europe. Although I concentrated upon strictly institutional responses in the paper, it is impossible not to note some of the corollary developments. Both the quantifiable and essentially qualitative features have been assessed in my monograph *A Communications Theory of Urban Growth* (M.I.T. Press, 1962). However, some insights deriving from the sociology of institutions, which were irrelevant to that argument, may be more pertinent here.

The fundamental question might be worded as follows: How would one construct a public service organization which has a high tolerance for overload situations and is otherwise efficient?

The intuitive answer that derives from these studies suggests:

1. Employ individuals with a high capacity for communication (strongly correlated with educational achievement);

2. Make standby arrangements with other organizations for storage and transmission of information that exist in the immediate surroundings, so that they can be recruited for routine tasks on short notice;

3. Allocate a larger than normal amount of time and effort to a variety of interesting, but nonessential, projects, so that a plethora of informal channels of communication come into being which offer opportunities for shortcuts in processing procedures;

4. Study all man-machine interaction situations very carefully, and make sure that the very great information handling capacity incorporated within much of the new equipment cannot place intolerable pressures upon the individual or group working with the output;

5. Create a series of realistic expectations of changes within the organization that are consequences of communications stress (e.g., the increased frequency of erroneous processing) so that normal releases, such as humor, can be activated;

6. Establish new conventions respecting privacy, so that individuals and groups can retreat behind these barriers and are less likely to be hurt by organizational stresses (and, simultaneously, provide more sensitive indicators of localized stress).

One major future asset will be the improving level of communications skills of the top deciles of the students now attending universities. These students are acquiring a wider range of technical languages than ever before, are more adept at the use of simple abstract models; many can now reduce undesirable routines to computer programs. They are also continuing their education for several years longer than was the case a generation earlier. As a consequence it should be possible to assemble much more adaptive headquarters staff than ever before. The tolerable loading of input requests should increase by a significant amount due to this factor alone.

Similarly, the information handling capacities and the information storage in the physical environment continue to expand steadily. It is not unlike the situation where the fertility of the soil builds up under conditions of good agricultural practice, and provides a cushion for short-run, high-volume production of a crop in great demand. High-capacity, high-efficiency organizations are much more dependent upon well-stocked surroundings at all levels of operation because they have reduced the marginal cost of communications with the surroundings to a very low level and can shave overhead costs without loss of adaptability.

A final observation: The many apparently random channels of communication built up between positions in an ultramodern organization (random, that is, to the external observer, but quite patterned for the participants) require a great deal of intellectual playfulness to keep them open and useful. More and more, the line that has been drawn between serious work and fun will become blurred, and occasionally even obliterated. These media for expression also represent an opportunity for synthesizing new patterns for which esthetic standards can evolve. Thus the strong rift that has hitherto separated most public service institutions from the novel (and often popular) arts is likely to be repeatedly bridged. We should expect that the slack in an organization, which must exist to allow it to cope with peak demands, will be increasingly converted into intellectual games of all kinds.

Thus the simple-minded extrapolation into the future of the growth of social communications is confounded. We need not anticipate an increasing number of overload situations as an inevitable outcome of rapid communications growth. There appear to exist promising new structures for organizations which employ higher-grade human components in such a manner as to evade this expression of the "iron law" of diminishing returns.

Some Sociological Aspects of Message Load: "Information Input Overload and Features of Growth in Communications-Oriented Institutions"*

17

LINDSEY CHURCHILL [†]

DR. MEIER has written an excellent paper, orienting sociologists like myself to the important problem of message load in organizations. By considering message load from an economic point of view, Meier's basic thesis is an interesting one: Message load is increasing greatly in urban areas and is harassing urban dwellers and urban organizations more and more. In his Postscript, Meier considers steps toward developing organizations with increased tolerance for overload.

Meier feels that sociologists have not devoted sufficient time to the problems of growth and decline of organizations. His approach to the problem is to create measures of growth based on the flow of messages in an organization. But messages are a product of organizational procedures for producing and handling them. Therefore, measures derived from the flow of messages will be fruitful to the extent that the procedures of which messages are a product are cleverly captured in them. In this discussion, some aspects of organizational procedures for handling messages are studied.

Meier's Theory

The theory of how an organization responds to increasing message load is stated in several ways throughout Meier's paper. The 14 policies in the section, Responses to Communications Stress, are treated here as a specific version of his theory.

---

* The author wishes to express his thanks to Harold Garfinkel, Oscar Grusky, and Harvey Sacks for their comments on earlier drafts of this discussion of Richard L. Meier's paper.
† University of California, Los Angeles.

It is assumed that an urban organization that cannot regulate the price of its goods and services is faced with a constantly increasing demand for its goods and services. The organization's time-ordered responses to the demand are stated as a sequence of 14 policies, repeated here for convenience in reference.

1. Queuing inputs at peak periods
2. Setting priorities in the queue
3. Destruction of lowest priorities
4. Adapting to redundancy with active files
5. Creating branch facilities
6. Encourage middlemen
7. Create a mobile reserve
8. Evolve explicit performance standards
9. Reduce standards of performance
10. The search for the 'magic formula'
11. Customer self-service
12. Escape
13. Work to rule
14. Salvage of component units

To arrive at this theory, it is assumed that Meier imagined the sequence of responses that the typical organization meeting the criteria would make to increasing message load. In all likelihood, the list of responses is not meant to be complete or necessary in every case. Rather, the list appears to be illustrative of what can happen, given the general hypothesis that increasing message load creates more and more stress for an organization of the given kind. The illustrative quality occurs because the typical organization may not closely represent many of the organizations under study. If organizations are not similar in response to message load, then the experience of any one, even the most typical, need not closely represent the experiences of others.

Strategies that Allow Organizations to Escape Meier's Prediction

The most significant inference to be drawn from Meier's theory is that every organization must reach the Policy 14 stage when message load gets sufficiently high. Therefore, every organization meeting the criteria must have whatever makes them recognizable as unique organizations, their essential structure, destroyed. However, there appear to be some organizations meeting the criteria that can escape this fate.[1] Some organizations with resources smaller in amount than necessary to deal with the demand are socially allowed to service part of the demand immediately and to ignore the remainder. Five examples are given to illustrate different *ignoring strategies*.

Consider a judicial court in an urban area. This kind of organization has no pricing mechanism (except in the indirect sense that it may be expensive to bring cases to it at all), and at the present time faces increasing case load. It seems improbable that the court will disintegrate under an increasing case load because court officials can delay cases into the indefinite future.

---

[1] Meier discusses this question in the Postscript to his paper. The reader is referred there for a comparison with the present analysis.

Since justice is socially seen as a timeless state of affairs, at least at an abstract level of analysis it doesn't make too much difference when justice occurs. Further, justice is expected to be administered with utmost meticulousness. When substantial personal and judicial issues are involved, these two properties of justice enjoin the staff of the court from hurrying through cases just to handle more cases per unit of time.[2]

Another organization that can escape the pressure of increasing demand is a hospital. As with the court, poor treatment of cases is socially intolerable. The hospital staff has two ignoring strategies that it can use.

1. The hospital staff can use the strategy of delay in a limited way. Since many cases do not need immediate care, demand can be scheduled over some period of time.

2. The hospital staff can divert excess demand to other hospitals, for two reasons. First, there is the convenient fiction that quality of care is equal everywhere in the medical profession. Secondly, the hospital does not have a monopoly over medical care, as do the courts, Meier's example of the stock exchange, or Meier's example of the library.[3] Therefore, the hospital staff cannot be required to service all the cases that are presented for care, under ordinary circumstances.

A third ignoring strategy can be seen at an Air Defense post where planes are tracked on a radar screen. Boguslaw and Porter [4] report the simulation of such situations. In cases where first one, then two, then a few, then a great many blips appear on the screen, the scanner is forced to stop reporting an exact count of blips and to report an approximate number instead. This strategy allows the scanner to convey some kind of information about the developing display.

However, it is the importance of the Air Defense post to national security that prevents its disintegration under increasing message load. If the blips are appearing on the screen in greater and greater number, then the Air Defense post must make do with its present organization. The more blips that appear on the screen, the more important it is for the organization to give notice about them, even if that notice is only approximate.

Boguslaw and Porter consider another example, that of firemen fighting a brush fire.[5] Suppose that the fire gets away from the firemen in one

---

[2] Concern with court backlogs is, however, widespread in judicial circles.

[3] It has been pointed out to me by Harvey Sacks that the concept of monopoly in these cases must be used carefully. By "monopoly" is meant that the members of the court, the stock exchange, and the library are the sole suppliers of certain goods and services, *at least locally*, and cannot refer some of their customers elsewhere. But the number of customers who want specific stocks, or books, may be small. Many investors want only to invest wisely, not caring about specific stocks. Many library users want only to learn about some topic, not caring about a specific author. In both these cases, organization members may use the strategy of *substitution* within the limits of an equivalent class of stocks, or authors, as defined by the customer.

[4] R. Boguslaw, and E. H. Porter, "Team Function and Training," Systems Development Corporation, Santa Monica, Calif. (SP–278; June 5, 1961), p. 17.

[5] *Op. cit.*, p. 17.

sector. Rather than commit their resources to a losing battle at that point, they are socially permitted to let the fire burn unmolested. It is more important for the organization to continue in existence than to risk destruction by having organization members fight a losing battle with one part of the fire.

A fifth strategy is seen in the operation of the ticket office of a successful Broadway musical comedy. The producers of the musical have the right to regulate the prices of seats, and thus do not appear to meet Meier's criteria. But the producers of the typical musical normally set prices prior to the opening of the show and maintain them no matter what the demand.[6] In this sense the organization meets Meier's criteria because its members voluntarily reject the strategy of regulating demand through pricing.

The ticket seller has a fixed number of tickets to sell for the present evening's performance. Thus he has an upper bound on the amount of demand he must service per day. Demand for future performances can be stored, if in letter form, or turned away at the ticket window with the hope that the customer will return at a later time.

The social rules governing queue behavior at the ticket window also help the ticket seller from being inundated by demand. The ticket seller must keep selling tickets as quickly as he can during the period the window is open. The customers must not demand service faster than he can supply it. The police can be called upon by the ticket seller to enforce his right not to be rushed if customers get unduly impatient.

Disposing of excess demand is not a problem for the ticket seller, either. A "sold out" sign disposes of persons coming to the ticket window. Refunds of mail demands can occur at a slower pace than they came in because the ticket seller has no particular social obligation to return the money instantly.

The spacing out of the organization's service, performance by performance, allows organization members some freedom in filling demand. Further, the luxury aspect of the service means that no serious repercussions will occur (other than loss of profit) if some segment of demand goes unserviced.

So far, several organizations have been studied that might be able to escape Meier's fate. Two organizations are now considered where Meier's theory appears to describe their history under increasing message load.

The executives of a newly formed commercial bank decided not to require service charges on checking accounts. The number of new accounts in the bank increased dramatically. The demand was so overwhelming that the bank staff became unable to keep up with each day's accounting, even though many new employees were added. Finally, federal officials closed

---

[6] Scalpers, of course, evade this constraint by extralegal means.

the bank to allow the staff to catch up with the bookkeeping.[7] In Meier's theory the bank had reached at least the Policy 10 stage, and, without government intervention, might have reached the Policy 14 stage.

The bank is not able to use the ignoring strategies discussed above for the following reasons:

1. The bank staff cannot delay processing demand because (a) the basis for its tremendous business can easily be removed if other banks adopt the same practice. Since the bank's monopoly is precarious, it must grant equal service with other banks; (b) delaying service would snarl the transfer of funds from one person to another. In fact, the closing of the bank has done just that. Local merchants are either forced to hold checks offered by their customers on that bank until the bank reopens, or to refuse service to persons who offer checks on the bank. In the first case the merchants tie up their own funds, and in the second case they alienate customers.

It should be noted, however, that commercial banks indirectly delay demand by refusing to accept business that doesn't occur within rather narrowly defined banking hours.

2. Bank members cannot divert demand to other banks, because they don't dare. The regular customer counts on and needs regular, not occasional, service. To divert him to another bank on any particular occasion runs the risk that he might transfer all his banking business to another bank. The bank would lose the profit not only from his immediate transaction, but from all future transactions that he might make. (The question of diverting new accounts is considered under (5) below.)

3. The bank staff cannot approximate demand in any way because each transaction must be precisely carried out.

4. There is no escape for the bank staff from some segment of demand— as there is for firemen fighting a brush fire—since that produces the same problems as diverting demand.

5. The bank staff doesn't typically regard the bank as similar to a theatre with a fixed number of seats. Yet it may be true that, at any particular time, the bank can effectively service only a fixed number of accounts. The bank might survive overload by refusing all new accounts after a fixed number has been reached.

Two reasons can be suggested why the bank didn't adopt this strategy: (a) refusing new business is distasteful to any organization whose goal is profit making, and (b) the average amount of money available per day for investment is not yet large enough for the bank to make a profit. Too many small accounts may be the source of the trouble. Here, the bank staff cannot screen prospective customers to select only those who will open big accounts.

The second example reconsiders the hospital discussed earlier where

---

[7] See the *New York Times* (Western Edition), Nov. 12, 1963, p. 11; and *Los Angeles Times*, Nov. 17, 1963, section A, p. 8.

ordinary, routine social conditions were assumed in effect. Here, nonroutine social conditions, such as during and following a widespread disaster, are assumed. Imagine that, in the center of the disaster area, a tremendous number of injured persons are brought to the local hospital for treatment. Under these conditions, medical care could deteriorate dangerously. However, the hospital staff would not be allowed to employ any of the ignoring strategies discussed earlier. Delay of treatment would not be permitted, because these cases would need immediate attention. The staff could not divert cases elsewhere since a widespread disaster would overload all hospitals in the given area, making diversion unavailable, at least to other hospitals in the center of the disaster area. A strategy using the idea of approximation, as in the Air Defense post, is not possible since each case must be treated individually. Escape from part of the demand is not allowable, nor is pleading a fixed number of cases allowable.

Under these conditions the hospital staff might reorganize medical care drastically to give intensive care to certain cases only or at least *some* kind of care to all injured persons, perhaps giving away some if its own usual functions to nonmedical organizations. If the emergency were of long enough duration medical care might be reorganized so that the old hospital system would be no longer recognizable, corresponding to the final stage—salvage of component units—in Meier's theory. But such extreme situations are rare. The hospital would typically weather the nonnormal conditions as best it could, and return to its normal operation afterwards.

In contrasting organizations that appear to escape Meier's fate with organizations that do not, the following points become clear:

The Relevance of Time.   The way time is arranged in the situation is the most important factor in determining whether or not an organization will escape Meier's fate.

1. If an organization is to escape disintegration, its members must be able to disengage service from the demand for service. The organization members must be able to avoid having to respond one-for-one to demand as fast as that demand is presented. As illustrated above, some organizations are socially permitted to use strategies that accomplish this separation.

2. If the demand must be dealt with as it occurs, then slowly increasing message load is clearly less dangerous for the organization than sharply increasing demand. Slowly increasing demand gives the organization members more time for reorganization than does sharply increasing demand.

But however demand objectively occurs, it is organization members' anticipation of what *future* demand will be like that determines how they will respond to the present message load. Organization members may believe in slowly increasing demand, but perhaps not in sharply increasing demand. They may regard sharply increasing demand as a temporary spurt rather than as a permanent state of affairs. The situation can be disastrous if organization members anticipate a temporary spurt when demand in fact continues to increase sharply for a long period of time. By anticipating a decrease soon, the organization members may try to weather the demand without considering reorganization. Yet radical reorganization may need to take place immediately to give the organization any hope of mastering the problem.

The Relevance of Nonnormal Social Conditions.   Meier's theory seems more appropriate for organizations experiencing nonnormal social conditions, in the following ways:

1. A sharp increase in demand is indicative of nonnormal social conditions itself. There must be some kind of social change occurring to produce sharply increased demand. The disaster created nonnormal conditions for the hospital. The bank created its own nonnormal condition by using an unusual strategy to attract business.

2. Unusual social conditions may rule out the use of ignoring strategies. There are always some social conditions where the operation of a rule is negated. One implicit limitation of the strategy of diversion, ordinarily used by a hospital, is that appropriate care be available elsewhere. Under disaster conditions every hospital may be overflowing, so that one condition for diversion no longer exists. The strategy of delay is based on the implicit limitation for the hospital that treatment in the future is as satisfactory as treatment in the present for the patient. But, under disaster conditions, a much larger percentage of the demand may be injury cases that must be treated immediately.

The Relevance of the Kind of Service.   The importance of the organization's services will affect how well it can escape Meier's fate.

1. The organization's services may be considered *socially necessary*. Medical service fits in this category. Under normal social conditions the necessity of the services will permit organizations giving the service to use ignoring strategies. But under nonnormal social conditions the necessity for the service, coupled with the removal of social permission to employ ignoring strategies, makes Meier's theory more plausible.

2. A second group of organizations gives *socially important but not necessary* services. Telephone service fits in this category. Telephone service is rarely necessary since variously acceptable alternative methods of communication exist. Organizations of this kind may be able to employ ignoring strategies all the time, particularly if the organization has a monopoly on the service. The importance of the service prevents the organization from disintegrating, and the lack of necessity of the service keeps it from being forced to deal with an overload immediately.

3. A third group consists of organizations whose goods and services are *not socially important or necessary*, for example, a toy manufacturing company. Though the example is not in the field of public utilities, it still may meet Meier's criteria. The toy manufacturer may not wish to raise his prices to reduce demand because he fears that his competitors will

undersell him and take over too large a share of his business. He has no
social permission to employ an ignoring strategy because he offers nothing
of general social importance. Thus, he may be forced to try to fill all demand immediately, even though he may recognize the demand overload
problem. Organizations in this category may be vulnerable to Meier's
prediction.

The Relevance of Lack of Knowledge. The organization staff may be
operating with less knowledge of strategy than is available. It is possible
for an organization to suffer Meier's fate even when strategies exist that,
if applied at one point in time, would have allowed the organization to
escape the consequences of demand overload. It is, of course, not sufficient
for some organization member to know what to do. That strategy must
get put into practice through all of the barriers to innovation in the organization. The role of the management consultant is clearly important in
this regard.

Lack of knowledge may not be the only hindering factor. The organization members may refuse to employ a strategy because the use of the
strategy requires the adoption of unacceptable ways of regarding themselves or their organization. The problem of allowable changes in organization structure is an important theoretical problem that can only be
mentioned here. This kind of hindrance may have occurred in the bank
discussed previously. Refusal to stop accepting new accounts may have
occurred because that strategy is against bankers' fundamental conception
of themselves and their banking organizations.

Message Load and Its Impact on the Organization

Meier considers message load as an impersonal economic force. In this
section message load is treated as the product of negotiations between
customers and organization members. Negotiation is intended broadly here.
The negotiation may consist of the customer's assessment of his chances of
getting service when he wants it. No organization member may ever be
aware of this potential customer if his assessment causes him to avoid contacting the organization.

From the Customer's Point of View. The amount of message load is not
necessarily independent of the organization on which it impinges. Demand
for service will adapt itself, in part, to the degree to which the organization
can handle it. If an organization has no monopoly over its service, customers
can go elsewhere. And if service gets progressively poorer under increasing
demand, as Meier suggests, more and more customers will go elsewhere.
Even members of organizations with a monopoly find that customers adapt
to them in part. For example, inefficiency in a government bureau that
monopolizes automobile licensing soon becomes known and even exaggerated. Customers may call for appointments rather than walk in, whether

or not the organization customarily sets up appointments. Customers may allow the organization to put them off because they expect slow service. Customers may come in at less popular times, so that demand is distributed more evenly during the day and week. In fact, customers often act as if the organization staff were doing them a favor by granting service.

The lack of independence between demand and service can also be seen in queuing strategies.

1. Consider the policy of setting priorities in the queue. The rule of "first-come-first-serve" is what Americans expect, and it is difficult for an organization staff to set priorities among customers except on that basis. If the staff tries to establish queues on other bases, new customers will automatically assume the operation of "first-come-first-serve" and will proliferate messages until the rules have been explained to them and accepted by them. In this way the organization may unwittingly add to the problem it is trying to control.

However, different kinds of requests for service can be queued without invoking "first-come-first-serve," e.g., dinner trade over dessert-and-coffee trade in a restaurant, or "buy" or "sell" order over request for bid-asked quotation in a stock exchange.[8] Again, the queuing procedure will operate more smoothly if customers agree that their kinds of requests for service should fall into the same rank order that the organization has used in the definition of the queue.

2. Consider the policy of destroying the lowest priority categories in the queue. Meier discusses the case where organization members destroy low priority categories in the queue. But customers with low priority may remove themselves from the queue, either permanently or temporarily, because they are not motivated to wait out their turn in the queue. There is probably some "self-destruction" of demand going on in the queue at all times.

The fact that customers can interact with organization members gives the latter additional strategies to deal with the message load. Customers can be asked to wait their turn; they can be "apologized to" for slow service; they can be asked to return at a later time; etc. Organization members implicitly utilize their knowledge of "human nature" in these ways in dealing with their particular customers.

From the Organization Member's Point of View. Two general issues are considered here:

1. *Presented demand versus recognized demand.* Meier implicitly assumes that presented demand is recognized demand. However, it is hard to say what organization members will make of demand for service. Each message represents a collection of potential responses for an organization member, some of which he will make depending on the practical situation at the moment. Included in the collection, of course, is the possibility of

---

[8] The second example is Meier's.

not responding at all. It is impossible to tell how many responses a given message will generate at a particular time, if any.

For example, consider the letter: "Please send me your free brochure on X." First, the message must be recognized by the organization member as a request for service. The brochure may be out of stock, generating internal messages to replenish the stock. But perhaps a policy decision has to be made about the advisability of sending out that brochure any longer. Perhaps something should be charged for it. Perhaps the person requesting the brochure is in a special relation to the organization, so that his motives have to be assessed in asking for the brochure. Perhaps the organization no longer sells X but wants to refer the person to another organization that does. In short, the message enters a particular practical situation of the organization, and its content will be assessed appropriately to that situation.

But if the demand is sharply increasing, organization members will at least perceive the enormity of the message processing task that faces them. It seems reasonable to assume that anxiety will be created in organization members, a panic quality, easily leading to frustration and hostility. Meier implies these qualities in his discussion of "the search for the 'magic formula,'" "escape," and "work to rule." Once these emotional factors enter the message flow, they add greatly to its overburdening because many messages now carry additional meanings, and upsetting meanings, to those perceiving them, inducing anxiety, frustration, and hostility in return.

Related cases occur when organization members have few rules of thumb, and few theories, about the general character of the sources of the demand. Brush fires and blips on radar screens, discussed earlier, fall in this category. Another example occurs in the movie, *The Birds,* where flocks of birds suddenly and inexplicably attack human beings. Often, nonhuman or nonnormal human sources of demand have these qualities. The independent, often unpredictable character of this kind of demand creates anxiety, even terror, in organization members if it is problematic that sufficient resources are available for dealing with the demand. Organization members know only that at some time they must deal with a vaguely specified quantity of demand that is not amenable to negotiation and whose general character is only obscurely known.

2. *Error rates.* In assessing the impact of increasing message load, Meier's Policy 8: "Evolve explicit performance standards," seems to be the pivotal one. The recognition that certain rates of error have become inevitable, and will necessarily become higher, may be a hard one for organization members to accept. Getting organization members to render legitimate a higher error rate, no matter how sharply demand is increasing, may be extremely difficult, for several reasons. First, the staff must now be persuaded that the high level of demand is not a sudden spurt of peak demand that will decrease, but a new, higher, average demand load. Secondly, errors are usually regarded as improper, an inessential feature of an organization's

procedures, and therefore eliminable through careful work. Thirdly, the organization staff, having passed through Meier's Policies 1 through 7, has now exhausted its repertoire of strategies that can easily be fitted in with the way the organization operates.

Still, the problem of overload hasn't been solved. Meier proposes that organization members must now begin to question whether or not they can continue to operate as in the past. For the first time, the essential structure of the organization must be questioned, whereas up to now only a series of nonessential changes have been tried. Organization members are being asked to consider changes that ordinarily they would not allow.

Old-line organizations probably induce a more firmly rooted conception of the organization in members than is the case for relatively new and fluid organizations. It is likely that in such old-line organizations a consultant would have the greatest amount of trouble convincing important organization members that increased error rates may—under certain conditions—be an inevitable price of eventual survival.

Summary

In this discussion some aspects of Meier's theory have been elaborated. It appears that some organizations meeting his criteria can escape the prediction of disintegration because they are socially protected from having to process excess demand per unit time. The relevance of time, nonnormal social conditions, type of service that the organization gives, and lack of knowledge of strategies were considered in searching for kinds of organizations that cannot escape Meier's prediction. In the last section, some sociological aspects of message load were regarded from the point of view of a negotiation between customer and organization member within given practical circumstances.

PART VI

The Behavior of Large
Social Aggregates: Parks,
Cities, and Society

How physical is social man?
Did Newton speak for him,
And Tycho's telescope
        track
        human
Shenanigans at Uraniburg?

How firm and straight the bridge
        from me to you?
May I soon touch an arid star,
And tie my heart's love
        to Gravity?

Could be,
        Could be . . . .

                                        F.M.

The Concept of "Mass" in the Sociological Version of Gravitation*

18

WILLIAM R. CATTON, JR.†

DESPITE certain recently noted convergences [1] and despite certain claims for the predominance at the present time of one or another style of sociological thinking and research,[2] there remains discernible in modern sociology a division of long standing. On the one hand, there are sociologists who want to use the assumptions and procedures of natural science as a path toward laws of social behavior; on the other hand, are those who want to rely on insight, contextual interpretation, and informal but meticulous description as a means of *understanding* social phenomena.[3] Each type of sociologist "holds fast to his prejudices and proclivities. Each

* A grant from the Agnes H. Anderson Research Fund partially supported the collection of data for this study. The assistance of Mr. Gary Barbour in performing many computations is also gratefully acknowledged. The courtesy of a number of persons in the National Park Service in providing access to files was especially appreciated. Of particular assistance were Chief Rangers at several national parks and Mr. Rendel B. Alldredge, Chief of Statistics Analysis.

† University of Washington, Seattle, Wash.

[1] See John C. McKinney, "Methodological Convergence of Mead, Lundberg, and Parsons," *American Journal of Sociology*, Vol. 59, No. 6, May, 1954, pp. 565–74; George A. Lundberg, "Letter to the Editor," *American Journal of Sociology*, Vol. 60, No. 2, September, 1954, pp. 182–84; George A. Lundberg, "Some Convergences in Sociological Theory," *American Journal of Sociology*, Vol. 62, No. 1, July, 1956, pp. 21–27.

In one sense, convergence of disparate schools is an implication of the presidential address by Kingsley Davis, "The Myth of Functional Analysis as a Special Method in Sociology and Anthropology," *American Sociological Review*, Vol. 24, No. 6, December, 1959, pp. 757–72.

[2] See George A. Lundberg, "The Natural Science Trend in Sociology," *American Journal of Sociology*, Vol. 61, No. 3, November, 1955, pp. 191–212; Roscoe C. Hinkle, Jr., and Gisela J. Hinkle, *The Development of Modern Sociology* (New York: Random House, 1954) p. 56; Walter Buckley, "Structural-Functional Analysis in Modern Sociology," Chapter 8 in Howard Becker and Alvin Boskoff (eds.), *Modern Sociological Theory* (New York: Dryden, 1957), pp. 248–49.

[3] Llewellyn Gross, "Theory Construction in Sociology: A Methodological Inquiry," Chapter 17 in Llewellyn Gross (ed.), *Symposium on Sociological Theory* (Evanston, Ill.: Row, Peterson & Co., 1959), p. 532.

For an expression of the view that there is a fundamental distinction between the type of causality involved in physical events and the type applicable to social behavior, see Robert M. MacIver, *Social Causation* (Boston: Ginn & Co., 1942), p. 299.

is sure that he is working in the right direction and believes he has good reasons for disparaging the other's achievements." [4]

Few sociologists would deny that our discipline lags far behind the physical sciences in the accomplishment of precise description and explanation of the phenomena we study. But it is neither necessary to accept the lag as permanent nor merely to dream that if only our research budgets were commensurate then our results would achieve parity with the "established" sciences. There is another attitude we can take. We can urge the "natural science" sociologist and the *verstehende* sociologist to seek seriously to combine their talents. "With so little substantial knowledge," we may wonder, as Llewellyn Gross does, "why haven't more sociologists attempted to combine the perspectives and resources of both approaches?" Such a course, he contends, is the only way out of "the deep-rooted division that now separates natural scientists from some social scientists and sociologists from one another." [5]

It is the purpose of this paper to demonstrate the possibility of such a synthesis and to suggest some of its advantages and implications.

Objections to Physicalism

While the present attempt is by no means the first to try to bridge or bypass the apparently wide gulf separating the "natural science" sociologist from the *verstehende* sociologist, it will be seen to have some new and unique features.[6] It will undoubtedly encounter objections from many of those who have in the past objected to "physicalistic" sociology. Sorokin, for one, has taken the position that "most of the defects of modern psychosocial science are due to a clumsy imitation of the physical sciences." [7] Although it is not altogether clear whether his *main* objection is to the imitation or to its clumsiness, he maintains that the devotees of " 'natural science

---

[4] Gross, *op. cit.*, p. 532.

[5] *Ibid.*, pp. 532–33.

[6] It certainly differs from MacIver's *Social Causation*, which Page has appraised as attainment of "the golden mean between the position of many neopositivists, who identify social causation with natural causation, and the skeptical view, recently voiced by Sorokin among others, that denies the applicability of the concept of *cause* to social phenomena." Charles H. Page, "Robert M. MacIver," in Nicholas F. Timasheff, *Sociological Theory: Its Nature and Growth* (rev. ed.; New York: Random House, 1957), p. 254. Nor is it, obviously, similar to the symbolic interactionism of Mead, described by McKinney as a "more moderate type of behaviorism" which he credits with partially closing the gap between "radical behaviorism" and "subjectivism." John C. McKinney, "Methodology, Procedures, and Techniques in Sociology," Chapter 7 in Becker and Boskoff, *op. cit.* (footnote 2), p. 207.

It will appear more physicalistic, too, than the attempt by Gross himself to build a theory of "successively higher orders of conditional sentences" on the basis of the empirical generalizations in Sutherland's *White Collar Crime*; Gross, *op. cit.*, pp. 541–59.

[7] Pitirim A. Sorokin, *Fads and Foibles in Modern Sociology and Related Sciences* (Chicago: Henry Regnery, 1956), p. 174.

sociology'... are usually deficient in their knowledge of physical science." [8]

Emulation of the method of the natural sciences, and especially the use of "physicalistic" concepts, meet with adamant opposition. According to Sorokin, "None of the established natural sciences has reached its maturity by merely imitating another science." [9] C. Wright Mills, too, opposes the idea that a science can, by taking epistemological thought, increase its stature. Historically, epistemology comes after the fact.[10] Even Gross, sympathetic to the natural science aspirations of sociology, says "It is a well-known fact . . . that natural scientists construct and test theories and obtain highly useful results without benefit of methodological analyses as the philosopher of science interprets these words." [11]

When a sociologist borrows models from physics to describe and explain social behavior, he is likely to be accused of coveting the prestige of the physical scientist.[12] Nevertheless, he has a legitimate reason for at least giving careful consideration to the steps which brought the older sciences to their present level of admired achievement. Newtonian physics is, as Martindale observes, the paradigm of scientific knowledge. Newton's ability to explain the movements of the solar system by mathematical deduction from his three laws of motion, along with his subsequent principle of universal gravitation, "fused the two major elements of science—rational proof and experimental-observational evidence." [13] This accomplishment merits attention in relation to the differences between the social physics viewpoint and the *verstehende* approach, for it had the effect at the end of the 17th century of establishing the natural science framework in a realm which had previously been thought exempt; it demonstrated the applicability of terrestrial laws of mechanics to "heavenly" bodies.[14]

Today, those who would still exempt social phenomena from "physicalistic" laws argue that "radical operationism" is too specific, and that sociology requires *general* concepts. Efforts to conduct sociological re-

---

[8] *Ibid.* See also, Gross, *op. cit.*, p. 531; Herbert Feigl, "Unity of Science and Unitary Science," in Herbert Feigl and May Brodbeck (eds.), *Readings in the Philosophy of Science* (New York: Appleton-Century-Crofts, 1953), pp. 352–53; Gideon Sjoberg, "Operationalism and Social Research," Chapter 19 in Gross, *op. cit.*, p. 622; Gustav Bergmann and Kenneth W. Spence, "The Logic of Psychophysical Measurement," in Feigl and Brodbeck, *op. cit.*, pp. 118–19.

[9] Sorokin, *op. cit.*, p. 175.

[10] C. Wright Mills, *The Sociological Imagination* (New York: Oxford University Press, 1959), p. 58. A similar position was stated by Charles Horton Cooley, "Sumner and Methodology," *Sociology and Social Research*, Vol. 12, No. 4, March-April, 1928, pp. 303–6.

[11] Gross, *op. cit.*, p. 539.

[12] See, for example, Sjoberg, *op. cit.*, p 611.

[13] Don Martindale, *The Nature and Types of Sociological Theory* (Boston: Houghton Mifflin, 1960), p. 24.

[14] On the transition from a physics based on the assumption that terrestrial and celestial phenomena were fundamentally different to one based on recognition of the earth as a celestial body moving in space, see I. Bernard Cohen, *The Birth of a New Physics* (Garden City, N.Y.: Doubleday, Anchor Books, 1960).

search within a natural science framework are said to become in practice a form of "raw empiricism." [15] In reply, Stuart Dodd, one of the staunchest exponents of "social physics," has insistently stated his aspiration to "build up a body of laws of social mechanics as dependable as those of physical mechanics," and he has asserted that his models are not dependent on the particular kind of behavior used in his attempts to test them, nor on the particularities of the local situation in which such tests have been conducted.[16]

To *aspire* to formulate dependable laws, and then to *assert* their generality does not, however, necessarily mean that these goals have been achieved. To discover why "social physics" has remained a "crude imitation," and to discover how it might be fruitfully wed to the sociology of insights and interpretations, let us consider the Newtonian paradigm more closely.

What Newton Did

Newton's first law of motion stated that a body remains at rest, or in uniform linear motion, unless accelerated by a force. This amounts to a qualitative definition of force as that which *accelerates* motion, and a crucial innovation in scientific thought. Earlier animistic thinking had regarded a force as that which *maintains* motion.[17]

His second law quantifies the concept of force by asserting that the net external force acting on a body of a given mass is directly proportional to, and in the same direction as, the acceleration. Or, turned around, it amounts to a definition of "mass" as the inertial property of matter, measured by the ratio between a force applied and an acceleration obtained.

Thus Newton began with the concept of force, and used it to define mass; as we shall see presently, the "social physicists" have tried to do it the other way around—beginning with an analogue of mass and using it to define "social force"—and this has made a fundamental difference.

Newton's third law reads: "To every action there is always opposed an equal reaction: or the mutual actions of two bodies upon each other are always equal, and directed to contrary parts." (This should give aid and comfort to sociologists, for it defines an "action" as simply a one-sided view

[15] See, for example, McKinney, "Methodology, Procedures, and Techniques in Sociology," *op. cit.*, p. 208; and Sjoberg, *op. cit.*, pp. 620, 623.

[16] Stuart C. Dodd, "The Counteractance Model," *American Journal of Sociology*, Vol. 63, No. 3, November, 1957, p. 284.

[17] Galileo *almost* achieved the inertia concept, but his imagination was not quite capable of conceiving a straight line extending to infinity, along which a body might move forever. His contributions to dynamics included the principles of uniformly accelerated motion, and the analysis of velocities into component velocities. On this foundation Newton erected the principle of inertia. See Cohen, *op. cit.*, pp. 95, 113–28, 159–66.

of what is actually an *interaction*.) Guided by this third law, Newton was able to derive his principle of universal gravitation, a quantitative description of the interaction of physical bodies in space, whereby they exhibit a *mutual* attraction directly proportional to the product of their masses and inversely proportional to the squared distance between them.

It was with this principle that Newton extended laws of earthly mechanics to the behavior of heavenly bodies. As always, however, his intellectual accomplishments depended on those of his predecessors. The idea that the planetary motions resulted from solar gravity was consistent with his "laws of motion," but it would hardly have occurred to him had it not also been consistent with the empirical generalizations he inherited from Kepler. Kepler had shown that the planets revolved in elliptical orbits around the sun; he had calculated the relation between a planet's velocity in any portion of its orbit, and its distance from the sun in that portion; and he had fitted a remarkably simple formula to the relation between the orbital periods of revolution and the orbital radii of the several planets. This is where Newton began.

Galileo's earlier research on the mechanics of projectiles and falling bodies had not only provided the basis for Newton's formulation of his "laws of motion" (basic postulates) but had also made the concept of centrifugal force familiar. *If* earthly laws applied to heavenly bodies, it was obvious (from Newton's first law) that planets moving in roughly circular orbits must be subject to a centrifugal force tending to pull them out of orbit. Since they remained in orbit, however, it was also obvious that some sort of "centripetal" force must exactly counterbalance this force.

The radii of the various orbits were known fairly accurately, and the period of revolution for each planet was also known, so the centripetal *acceleration* of each planet could be easily calculated. By Newton's second law, the centripetal *force* acting on each planet would be the product of this acceleration times the *mass* of the planet, an unknown quantity. But by the third law, the "pull" exerted on each planet toward the center of its orbit (i.e., the sun) would be exactly equal to the "pull" exerted on the sun by each planet respectively. Since the mass of the sun would be a factor in that "pull," and since the mass of the sun was constant, the *relative* masses of the planets could be calculated.

Thus, in effect, Newton's schema for "explaining" planetary motions (1) began with the observed velocities and distances and the known shape of the orbits. From this (2) he calculated the relative magnitudes of the centrifugal and counterbalancing centripetal forces that *must* be acting on the various planets (on the basis of the second law of motion). And (3) he hypothesized the principle of universal gravitation, and derived each planet's relative mass on the basis of the third law of motion.

The Basic Flaw in "Social Physics"

In contrast, "social physics" has simply *taken* population size to be the sociological analogue of mass, and has gone in the other direction, defining the concept of "social force" in terms of this analogue and deriving magnitudes of social forces accordingly. In physics, force equals mass times acceleration; in "social physics" a "social force" has been defined as the product of a population and an acceleration along any relevant sociological continuum.[18]

It may at first seem to be of no consequence whether the logic proceeds in one direction or the other. Moreover, the equating of "mass" with size of population is deeply entrenched in sociological thought. We speak of "mass movements," of "mass communication," or of life in a "mass society." We teach students the subtle relations between the terms "mass," "crowd," "aggregate" and "public." We take no exception, as sociologists, to the expression "mass production," meaning production of large quantities of identical items by the assembly line method. But this usage utterly misses the meaning of "mass" in the conceptual system of physics. There the term refers not to bigness but to the inertial property of matter: its *capacity to resist acceleration.*

Suppose sociology were to adopt a similar definition of "social mass," and regard it as the inertial property of any sociocultural entity—its capacity (or tendency) to resist change in the rate of change. Much of the work done by so-called social physicists would have to be done over again, but it is the author's opinion that this might pay off handsomely. First of all, by being more consistent with physics in our definitions of the terms we borrow from physics, we may expect to achieve increased conceptual clarity. In physics, a larger mass is more difficult to accelerate (requires greater force) than a smaller one. In sociology, acceleration (changing social rates or social change) is more characteristic of a large urban population than of a small rural population. It is clear, therefore, that the premature equating of "mass" with population size was either not good physics or not good sociology. Secondly, there is at hand a sociological concept which *does* denote the inertial property in sociocultural entities: the concept of "sacredness," abundantly used by Howard Becker to label an idea formulated earlier by Ogburn.[19]

Becker took the position that there is room in sociology for such diverse interests as physicalism and *verstehende*,[20] although he himself has been

---

[18] Stuart C. Dodd, *Dimensions of Society* (New York: Macmillan, 1942), Chapter 11.
[19] See William F. Ogburn, *Social Change* (New York: Viking Press, 1922), Part III, "Cultural Inertia and Conservatism."
[20] Howard Becker, "Vitalizing Sociological Theory," *American Sociological Review,* Vol. 19, No. 4, August, 1954, p. 379.

characterized as adhering to the latter persuasion.[21] He defined a continuum extending from maximum sacredness (resistance to change) to maximum secularism (receptivity to change).

Any society or part thereof that imparts to or elicits from its members evaluations that can be altered, if at all, only in the face of definite emotionalized reluctance is a sacred society—a shorthand term for a society bearing a cultural system making for the reluctance indicated.[22]

He is known for his typological analysis of sacred vs. secular societies, and it has been said that constructed types were, in his work, "end products or goals of research" rather than provisional conceptual tools as they were for Max Weber.[23] But Becker also wrote:

If sacred-secular theory can be fruitfully applied in empirical research, fine; if it cannot be so applied it represents sadly wasted effort.[24]

A Supposedly Gravitational Model

The present paper attempts a fruitful application of the concept of sacredness within a framework of (corrected) social physics. We will fit a gravitational model to data borrowed from a previous study in "social physics," combined with an abundance of new data. We will derive estimates of the "social mass" of several cultural entities and then show that the obtained results can be understood in terms of the *institutionalized* property, sacredness. It will thus be indicated, we believe, that social physics and *verstehende* sociology can enjoy a happy and fruitful marriage.

In an unpublished doctoral dissertation, Joseph Cavanaugh sought to test Stuart Dodd's "interactance hypothesis," which Dodd claimed "is for human groups what the law of gravity is for physical masses. The form of the formula is exactly the same for both," he supposes, "differing only in that the aggregates of interacting particles are molecules in the case of physical gravity and persons in the case of social interactance."[25]

The interactance hypothesis is actually a generalized version of the P_1P_2/D formula of George K. Zipf.[26] John Q. Stewart has argued that this formula is an analogy to gravitational energy: putting D (for distance) in the denominator, it substitutes in the numerator the number of persons, P,

---

[21] See McKinney, "Methodology, Procedures, and Techniques in Sociology," *op. cit.*, p. 196.

[22] Howard Becker, "Current Sacred-Secular Theory and Its Development," Chapter 6 in Becker and Boskoff, *op. cit.*, p. 142.

[23] Don Martindale, "Sociological Theory and the Ideal Type," Chapter 2 in Gross, *op. cit.*, p. 76.

[24] Becker, "Current Sacred-Secular Theory and Its Development," *op. cit.*, p. 184.

[25] See Joseph A. Cavanaugh, "Formulation, Analysis and Testing the Interactance Hypothesis," unpublished Ph.D. dissertation, University of Washington, 1950, p. 124.

[26] George K. Zipf, "The P_1P_2/D Hypothesis: On the Intercity Movement of Persons," *American Sociological Review*, Vol. 11, No. 6, December, 1946, pp. 677–86.

in each of the two interacting populations—in place of mass, M, in the Newtonian gravitational formula.[27]

Part of Cavanaugh's work dealt with interacting cities, for example, the number of long-distance phone calls between pairs of cities in a given time period. He found that the recorded number of calls tends to be, as expected by the interactance hypothesis, approximately proportional to the product of two cities' populations divided by their distance apart.

But he also attempted to test the model against some other data of a quite different character. His dissertation included several tables showing the number of automobiles entering various national parks in the West. According to Cavanaugh's interpretation of the interactance hypothesis, the cars entering Yellowstone National Park, for instance, should be numerically proportional to a state's population divided by its distance from Yellowstone. The first P in the P_1P_2/D formula was dropped, Cavanaugh explained, because the "mass" of the park was constant for all the entities (i.e., states) interacting with it. Later we shall show that this deletion led to a serious misinterpretation of the data, but first a comment is in order on the sociological unconventionality of the P_1P_2/D formula even when both population terms are retained.

Sociological research since Durkheim has tended to begin with some *rate* and has tried to discover the state of the social system which makes the rate what it is.[28] Such social rates are usually stated in per capita (or per 100,000) terms. Suicide, birth, crime, marriage, and divorce rates are familiar examples. By a simple algebraic manipulation, the P_1P_2/D formula can be recast in this more conventional sociological form. This will help us evaluate the oversight committed when Cavanaugh applied the formula to national park travel data.

Instead of:

$$I = P_1P_2/D, \tag{1}$$

where I stands for the number of interacts, P_1 and P_2 the respective populations of two interacting entities, and D the distance between them, we can write:

$$I/P_2 = P_1/D. \tag{2}$$

We thus have a *rate* of interaction related to the population and remoteness of the entity with which a given entity interacts.

---

[27] As quoted in Cavanaugh, *op cit.*, p. 46. See also John Q. Stewart, "A Measure of the Influence of a Population at a Distance," *Sociometry*, Vol. 5, No. 1, February, 1952, pp. 62–71.

[28] See Alex Inkeles, "Personality and Social Structure," Chapter 11 in Robert K. Merton, Leonard Broom, and Leonard S. Cottrell, Jr. (eds.), *Sociology Today* (New York: Basic Books, 1959), p. 254.

In the present study, state-by-state vehicle or visitor frequencies have been converted to visitation *rates* by dividing by state automobile registration figures or state population estimates obtained from various volumes of *Statistical Abstracts of the U.S.*

With the formula thus recast, if we follow Cavanaugh's decision to ignore P_1 because it is constant, we get:

$$1/P_2 = k/D \qquad (3)$$

Converting the number of cars entering Yellowstone from each state into rates by dividing by the "population" of cars registered in the respective states, and plotting these rates against distance, we should expect the scatter to be linear on double log paper. In Figure 1 the data have been plotted in this manner (with similar data from Shenandoah National Park for comparison). It is evident that the Yellowstone scattergram is not linear. Cavanaugh applied the P_1P_2/D formula to three other national parks: Mount Rainier, Yosemite, and Glacier. Although not shown graphically here, the same curvilinearity appears when his data for these three parks are converted into rates and plotted as the Yellowstone data are in Figure 1. Moreover, the *same twenty-five eastern states*, which are represented by white dots in Figure 1, turn out to have a similarly vertical scatter for these other three parks.

FIGURE 1

1948 AUTOMOBILE VISITATION RATES AT
YELLOWSTONE AND SHENANDOAH NATIONAL PARKS
AS A DOUBLE LOG FUNCTION OF DISTANCE
FROM HOME STATE TO PARK

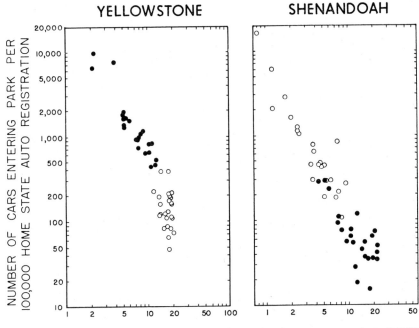

Does this simply mean that visitation rates tend to have a steeper gradient at a greater distance? If so, the same curvilinearity should appear (with the *western* states dropping away too sharply) in the Shenandoah scattergram. This is not the case, however. Except for three states (Utah and North and South Dakota) the entire scattergram is distinctly linear, and these three exceptions are by no means the most remote of all the western states from Shenandoah National Park. This comparison suggests, then, that the country may divide itself into two somewhat distinct cultural areas with respect to national park travel patterns. In the case of eastern states, visitation rates are inversely related to distance only with respect to eastern parks. But with western states the linear inverse distance relation holds for both western *and* eastern parks. The two cultural areas are shown in Figure 2.

FIGURE 2

Division of Continental U.S. into
Two "Cultural Areas," according to
Patterns Found in 1948 National Park Visitation Rates

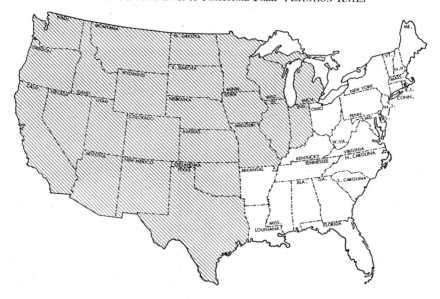

The remainder of this paper will deal exclusively with the western cultural area. This is the region in which the simple inverse distance relation most nearly applies, so it would provide a conservative test of the hypothesis that certain modifications can improve the model.

By *dropping* P_1 from the formula, Cavanaugh failed to put the allegedly gravitational "interactance model" to a severe enough test. He made no comparisons between one park and another; he simply computed separate correlations for each park between the observed number of cars entering from each state and the ratio of state population to distance from park. If the interactance model is truly gravitational in character, then one might expect the different parks to vary in the magnitude of their attractive "mass." The P_1P_2/D formula is construed as gravitational only by regarding population, P, as the social analogue of physical mass, M. Certainly the attractiveness varies from park to park. A more rigorous test of the model would take into account variations in park "mass" as indexed by some measure of "park population." But national parks are not cities. What, then, can be meant by their "population"?

In addition to the figures on numbers of cars and numbers of persons entering each park which were compiled by the National Park Service for many years, counts or estimates are made of the number of days the visitors spent in the park. The annual total of "visitor days" may be taken as a measure of the anomalous "park population" concept. Divided by the number

TABLE 1

WESTERN STATES' AUTOMOBILE VISITATION RATES AT NINE NATIONAL PARKS (1948)

	Crater Lake	Rocky Mountain	Shenandoah	Mesa Verde	Yosemite	Mount Rainier	Glacier	Yellowstone	Lassen Volcanic
Arizona	255.0	715.0	64.4	250.1	737.2	61.3	156.0	935.3	118.2
California	1,170.3	376.1	50.3	76.6	—	113.4	205.3	936.9	—
Colorado	113.6	—	42.8	—	239.6	28.8	167.4	1,826.1	23.7
Idaho	521.1	275.8	36.3	42.7	226.1	82.8	875.3	6,474.1	35.7
Illinois	63.5	1,692.1	230.3	43.7	212.1	30.4	130.8	823.4	10.5
Indiana	40.8	599.6	270.8	22.4	146.2	20.2	60.4	527.8	5.2
Iowa	73.5	2,497.0	77.6	39.8	147.9	35.4	137.4	1,214.2	10.2
Kansas	92.9	3,870.5	65.4	115.3	187.5	34.7	93.6	995.4	15.4
Michigan	37.4	373.0	289.6	24.0	140.4	22.8	83.4	468.5	6.5
Minnesota	63.5	340.0	56.6	23.0	116.9	51.4	310.5	1,095.8	4.6
Missouri	61.8	1,857.1	109.9	49.7	161.5	23.4	67.7	641.8	9.9
Montana	190.0	178.3	35.7	30.2	179.0	96.7	—	9,929.4	20.6
Nebraska	105.5	6,019.4	54.5	63.1	155.6	41.6	137.2	1,542.5	12.9
Nevada	817.7	426.8	74.0	114.1	1,675.5	78.2	291.6	1,652.3	1,003.6
New Mexico	111.5	776.5	56.1	665.8	347.2	15.8	105.2	724.4	31.6
N. Dakota	75.6	194.7	18.4	12.9	106.3	66.3	637.6	1,683.1	10.4
Oklahoma	57.2	1,323.6	79.5	92.3	196.3	19.3	55.5	641.9	12.4
Oregon	—	162.3	34.6	28.1	340.9	376.6	447.0	1,445.1	211.1
S. Dakota	71.0	512.5	28.0	17.2	86.6	32.8	157.0	1,365.4	8.1
Texas	43.4	1,064.2	121.8	81.7	155.5	18.2	42.0	431.2	7.5
Utah	148.9	771.9	15.2	334.9	288.7	49.2	543.3	7,711.3	43.2
Washington	1,433.4	148.1	41.8	35.9	325.8	—	938.6	1,948.2	98.7
Wisconsin	45.7	463.2	92.4	23.2	139.4	27.4	145.9	814.1	6.8
Wyoming	121.3	3,817.7	37.6	128.6	199.0	31.5	394.3	—	25.5

TABLE 2

DISTANCES (IN 100 MILES) BETWEEN 24 WESTERN STATES AND 13 NATIONAL PARKS

	Crater Lake	Rocky Mountain	Shenandoah	Mesa Verde	Yosemite	Mount Rainier	Glacier	Yellowstone	Lassen Volcanic	Grand Canyon	Hot Springs	Sequoia and Kings Canyon	Mammoth Cave
Arizona ...	8.4	5.5	18.8	3.1	5.2	10.5	10.4	7.5	7.0	—	10.8	4.4	14.3
California ..	4.6	7.9	22.2	6.3	—	7.3	8.9	7.2	—	4.5	14.9	—	18.2
Colorado ..	9.2	—	14.7	—	7.7	10.1	8.3	5.0	8.4	4.2	7.7	7.3	10.4
Idaho	4.1	5.5	19.2	6.0	5.7	3.9	3.2	2.1	4.7	5.8	13.7	6.0	15.6
Illinois	17.1	8.8	5.9	10.5	16.4	16.9	13.5	11.4	16.9	12.8	4.5	16.1	2.5
Indiana	18.5	10.2	4.3	12.0	17.8	18.2	15.0	12.9	18.3	14.2	5.3	17.4	2.0
Iowa	14.6	6.4	8.2	8.5	14.1	14.2	11.0	8.9	14.4	10.9	5.3	13.9	5.0
Kansas	12.9	4.3	10.7	5.5	11.7	13.3	10.7	7.8	12.3	7.8	4.0	11.2	6.6
Michigan ..	18.4	10.8	5.2	13.0	18.4	17.7	14.1	12.6	18.4	15.3	8.3	18.2	5.0
Minnesota .	13.8	7.2	9.3	9.7	14.1	12.9	9.5	8.1	14.0	11.7	8.2	14.2	7.4
Missouri ...	15.8	7.2	7.6	8.8	14.7	15.9	13.0	10.3	15.3	10.9	2.9	14.2	3.4
Montana ...	6.8	5.3	17.0	7.1	8.2	5.8	—	2.2	7.2	8.0	12.4	8.9	14.0
Nebraska ..	11.5	3.2	11.3	5.5	10.9	11.5	8.6	6.0	11.2	7.7	6.2	10.8	7.8
Nevada	3.9	6.0	20.3	4.8	2.2	5.9	6.9	5.1	2.9	3.5	13.3	2.1	16.3
New Mexico ..	10.7	4.4	15.5	2.5	7.9	12.1	10.9	7.8	9.5	4.0	7.3	7.2	11.1
N. Dakota..	11.1	5.8	12.7	8.3	11.9	10.0	6.3	5.4	11.3	10.1	9.8	12.0	10.1
Oklahoma .	14.1	5.5	10.7	6.1	12.2	14.8	12.3	9.3	13.2	8.2	2.8	11.9	6.2
Oregon	—	8.1	22.1	8.0	4.8	2.6	4.6	5.1	2.8	7.3	16.1	5.7	18.5
S. Dakota...	11.0	4.1	12.0	6.8	11.1	10.5	7.2	5.2	11.1	8.6	8.0	11.1	8.9
Texas	15.0	7.3	12.7	6.8	12.8	16.1	14.3	11.3	14.0	8.4	4.5	11.7	8.2
Utah	6.0	3.3	17.8	2.4	4.6	7.6	6.8	3.9	5.3	2.4	11.0	4.2	13.8
Washington	3.4	9.1	22.0	9.5	7.0	—	3.1	5.1	5.1	9.2	16.9	8.0	18.7
Wisconsin .	16.1	8.8	7.3	10.9	16.1	15.4	11.8	10.3	16.2	13.0	7.3	16.0	5.5
Wyoming .	7.4	2.3	15.5	4.2	7.3	7.4	5.3	—	7.2	5.6	9.9	7.4	11.8

of days in the year, it would indicate the average daily visitor population, though of course it is not likely to be evenly distributed through the year. To the extent that the ranger staff and other employed personnel in the park would tend to be proportional to the visitor load, this "visitor days" figure would also be an approximate index of the actual *resident* population of the park.

Fitting the Model to Data

Using such figures, let us then put to a more rigorous test the supposedly gravitational P_1P_2/D model. Data from five additional parks have been

TABLE 3

1948 NATIONAL PARK "MASS" ESTIMATES

Park "Population" (Annual Total of Visitor days)	Estimates of Park "Mass" by 3 Versions of the Model			
	$\dfrac{\sum\limits_{i=1}^{m}\sum\limits_{j=1}^{n} R_{ij}}{\sum\limits_{j=1}^{n}(P_j \sum\limits_{i=1}^{m} D_{ij})}P_j$	$\dfrac{\sum\limits_{i=1}^{m} R_{ij}}{\sum\limits_{i=1}^{m}(1/D_{ij})}$	M_p/a	$\dfrac{\sum\limits_{i=1}^{m} R_{ij}}{\sum\limits_{i=1}^{m}\sqrt{1/D_{ij}^3}}$
Crater Lake 345,717	1,324.2 (4.3)*	2,119.7 (7.7)	30,355,692.2 (3.1)	5,509.6
Rocky Mountain 1,208,455	4,628.8 (14.9)	6,810.8 (24.7)	225,078,006.8 (23.2)	15,002.6
Shenandoah 987,074	3,780.8 (12.2)	897.6 (3.3)	7,247,940.8 (0.7)	2,692.2
Mesa Verde 93,045	356.4 (1.1)	592.6 (2.1)	1,712,695.7 (0.2)	1,308.7
Yosemite 2,202,450	8,436.1 (27.2)	2,276.6 (8.3)	33,078,602.0 (3.4)	5,751.4
Mount Rainier 620,403	2,376.3 (7.7)	523.2 (1.9)	1,859,132.2 (0.2)	1,363.5
Glacier 463,330	1,774.7 (5.7)	2,073.4 (7.5)	27,512,123.0 (2.8)	5,245.2
Yellowstone 1,965,653	7,529.1 (24.3)	11,699.8 (42.4)	639,093,568.1 (66.0)	25,280.3
Lassen Volcanic 212,491	813.9 (2.6)	602.5 (2.2)	2,138,906.2 (0.2)	1,462.5

* Figures in parentheses express the "mass" of a given park as a percent of the nine-park total for easy comparison.

gathered to supplement Cavanaugh's data. Automobile visitation rates are given for all nine of these national parks in Table 1. Distances to each of these nine parks (and five others) were measured in scale miles on a conic projection map from arcs bisecting the areas of each of the twenty-four states in the western cultural area. These are shown in Table 2.

Annual totals of "visitor days" for each park in 1948 are given in the first column of Table 3. In the second column of that table, numbers proportional to these are given which will reproduce an m by n matrix of "expected visitation rates," whose mean equals the mean of the observed rates. Thus:

$$R_e = X D_p, \tag{4}$$

where R_e is a matrix of expected rates, X is a matrix of inverse distances between m states and n parks, and D_p is an nth order diagonal matrix whose non-zero entries are proportional to the "visitor days" figures for the n parks.

According to the interactance hypothesis, these expected rates should be in high agreement with the observed rates given in Table 1.

The actual coefficient of agreement [29] is .783, which could be taken as "confirmation," but it leaves room for considerable improvement in the model. In considering this result the weakness of "social physics," unwed to *verstehende*, becomes apparent. Manifestly, it is not a *population* at each of these national parks which exerts an attractive force on the populations of the several states. While a high proportion of park visits are made by family groups, and some fraction of the visitors may even journey to the park with the intention of meeting (and perhaps camping with) other relatives or acquaintances, it could hardly be argued that people already in the park constitute the principal attraction for others on their way to the park.[30] Some park visitors may even be said to go there in spite of the presence of numerous others; crowds detract, rather than attract, when one is seeking a wilderness experience. Unless the sociologist has himself been numbered among the visitors to various national parks he may not be sufficiently sensitive to the values implicit in tables of visitation rates.

Improving the Model

With this in mind, we can perhaps justify introducing a modification into the $P_1 P_2/D$ model. In Equation 3, k is merely a constant of proportionality for a given park between the various state visitation rates and the inverse distances. We could have written:

$$\frac{1/P_2}{1/D} = k. \tag{3a}$$

We may expect the value of k to vary from one park to another, but we can change the model by deliberately relaxing the requirement that k be proportional to "park population."

The third column of Table 3 gives values for k for each park which will

---

[29] For an explanation of the coefficient of agreement, see W. S. Robinson, "The Statistical Measurement of Agreement," *American Sociological Review*, Vol. 22, No. 1, February, 1957, pp. 17–25.

[30] For a discussion of the attractions indicated by population, see Charles T. Stewart, Jr., "Migration as a Function of Population and Distance," *American Sociological Review*, Vol. 25, No. 3, June, 1960, pp. 347–56.

reproduce an m by n matrix of "expected visitation rates" where the mean of the expected rates equals the mean of the observed rates for each park (each column) as well as for the matrix as a whole. Thus:

$$R_e = X D_k, \tag{5}$$

where D_k is an nth order diagonal matrix whose non-zero entries are given by the formula at the top of the third column in Table 3.

This results in a somewhat higher coefficient of agreement, .892. In altering the model to improve the agreement between expected and observed visitation rates, however, we have undermined what might be generously called the "theoretical rationale" provided by the gravitational analogy. Equation 2, derived directly from the original P_1P_2/D formula, purports to be *gravitational* in form because population size is taken as the analogue of mass. But our arbitrary k values in Equations 3, 3a, and 5 are only imperfectly correlated with "visitor days" and cannot be construed as measures of "mass" unless we are going to cease regarding P_2 (in the denominator of the left-hand term of Equations 2 and 3 as a measure of "mass."

In either case, in making the model fit the data better we have made it less clearly analogous with physics. Does this vindicate Sorokin's charge? To answer this we may try a further modification of the model, trying both to improve the agreement between model and data and at the same time bring it into closer parallel with physics.

Consider some implications of the visitation rates. They are, of course, measures of probability: the chances that any given car from state i will have entered park j in the year in question. They may also be taken as measures of *velocity:* the speed at which the population of state i is being acquainted with park j. The higher the rate, the shorter the time it would take for all residents of a given state to be exposed to a given park.

Now Newton's gravitational model won acceptance in large part because it fitted (and "accounted for") previously known patterns of planetary motion. In particular, Newton was able to derive Kepler's empirical generalizations from his model, including Kepler's third "law": that the square of the time it takes a planet to go around its orbit is proportional to the cube of its distance from the sun.[31]

If we now lay aside the P_1P_2/D model as conceptually inapplicable to the national park situation, and take visitation *rates* as an analogue of angular velocities, the hypothesis that the attraction of people toward a national park can be fitted by the gravity model leads to the expectation (by analogy with Kepler) that the square of the visitation rate will be inversely proportional to the cube of the distance. This quantitative hypothesis can be

---

[31] On the relation of Newton's work to that of Kelper and Galileo, see Gerald Holton, *Introduction to Concepts and Theories in Physical Science* (Reading, Mass.: Addison-Wesley, 1952), Chapters 9–11.

simplified by taking its logarithmic form: twice the logarithm of the visitation rate plus three times the logarithm of the distance to the park should equal a constant for the several states. This means that the hypothesis can be visually tested by the very simple expedient of plotting the data on double log paper, on which the pattern should be linear and negative in slope. Moreover, if the double log paper is specially constructed so that each log cycle on the distance scale is one and a half times as large as each log cycle on the visitation rate scale, we should expect a $-45°$ line to fit the data. The test of the model is this: Do scattergrams so plotted exhibit a $-45°$ slope?

In formal terms:

$$R_{ij}^{2}D_{ij}^{3} = k, \qquad (6)$$

where $R_{ij} = I/P_2$ and is the observed visitation rate for state i and park j, and D_{ij} is the map distance between state i and park j. We can define:

$$R_e = YD_{\sqrt[]{\frac{-}{k}}}, \qquad (7)$$

where R_e is an m by n matrix of expected rates, Y is a matrix of m rows and n columns whose entries are $\sqrt{1/D_{ij}^3}$, and $D_{\sqrt{k}}$ is an nth order diagonal matrix whose non-zero entries are given by the formula at the top of the last column of Table 3.

The two scattergrams in Figure 3 provide a comparison between this model and the previous one. The scattergram on the left is plotted on

FIGURE 3

Comparison of Two Models Fitted
to 1948 Automobile Visitation Rates
at Mount Rainier National Park

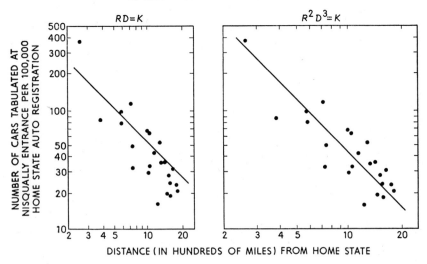

ordinary double log paper, so that the $RD = k$ model is represented by a
$-45°$ slope. It is apparent that the dots fall away too steeply to fit the
expected line. In the right-hand scattergram, however, the distance scale
is "stretched out" by 50 percent so that the $-45°$ slope represents the
$R^2D^3 = k$ model, and it is apparent that the dots more nearly fit the line.
When expected visitation rates are computed according to Equation (7),
they result in a coefficient of agreement with the observed rates that equals
.934, which is a further improvement over the first modified model.

As noted earlier, when Cavanaugh ignored park differences he had to
delete from the interactance formula the term which supposedly stood for
the "mass" exerting an attraction on the forty-eight state populations. Equa-

TABLE 4

WESTERN STATES' VISITATION RATES AT 9 NATIONAL PARK AREAS (1952)

	Grand Canyon	Crater Lake	Hot Springs	Rocky Mountain	Shenandoah	Sequoia and Kings Canyon	Mammoth Cave	Mesa Verde	Yosemite
Arizona	—	150.1	44.5	572.5	74.7	99.4	27.5	235.2	622.3
California	1,270.9	933.0	32.8	375.5	83.8	—	26.5	107.6	—
Colorado	1,081.9	82.8	83.7	—	103.5	129.3	45.4	—	289.6
Idaho	798.6	436.1	12.5	383.7	115.4	129.6	29.1	91.3	308.6
Illinois	516.0	36.3	592.2	1,297.9	337.5	70.4	657.9	55.7	166.4
Indiana	465.0	31.2	139.9	429.8	472.6	51.7	1,197.4	36.2	121.4
Iowa	537.0	59.8	192.5	2,477.3	172.3	62.9	110.3	73.3	148.8
Kansas	699.4	78.8	200.2	4,132.8	183.9	85.7	99.9	196.5	212.6
Michigan	390.5	27.2	83.2	362.4	494.8	44.0	752.4	36.1	124.4
Minnesota	414.5	46.6	137.1	507.0	126.3	46.8	55.4	34.2	116.3
Missouri	502.6	30.1	348.1	1,411.0	174.5	8.3	109.2	61.2	143.0
Montana	544.9	143.4	18.0	396.7	53.8	64.9	21.4	30.4	173.0
Nebraska	564.1	85.9	125.8	5,803.9	147.9	60.0	70.1	114.2	169.8
Nevada	2,074.3	482.5	43.7	599.5	128.4	278.1	50.8	81.4	1,966.1
New Mexico	1,667.3	68.1	58.9	720.9	87.4	142.7	34.7	926.7	400.5
N. Dakota	339.8	44.5	194.7	259.1	70.7	42.2	26.7	14.9	66.3
Oklahoma	604.0	41.2	524.7	1,217.0	130.7	117.7	67.5	128.9	187.1
Oregon	584.4	—	8.8	206.8	85.0	94.7	21.2	48.0	418.5
S. Dakota	327.7	66.6	111.4	648.9	67.0	42.9	21.6	25.2	106.4
Texas	567.4	29.4	345.4	1,048.2	203.4	81.9	73.2	148.1	170.2
Utah	2,573.3	133.8	9.2	580.4	60.6	104.4	16.0	595.1	396.4
Washington	508.5	781.7	10.3	149.5	64.8	76.1	17.5	40.7	295.1
Wisconsin	352.3	35.4	133.6	488.1	190.1	49.7	204.0	40.0	114.5
Wyoming	772.9	96.9	58.6	3,888.1	110.2	93.9	45.1	179.0	200.7

tions 6 and 7, however, enable us to derive estimates of the relative "mass" of each of the nine parks. It can be shown, in the case of the solar system, that:

$$T^2 = \frac{4\pi^2}{GM_s}D^3, \tag{8}$$

where T is the time it takes a planet to go around its orbit, G is the universal gravitational constant, M_s is the mass of the sun, and D is the radius of the

TABLE 5

1952 NATIONAL PARK "MASS" ESTIMATES

Park "Population" (Annual Total of Visitor Days)	Estimates of Park "Mass" by 3 Versions of the Model			
	$\dfrac{\sum\limits_{i=1}^{m}\sum\limits_{j=1}^{n} R_{ij}}{\sum\limits_{j=1}^{n}\left(P_j \sum\limits_{i=1}^{m} D_{ij}\right)} \cdot P_j$	$\dfrac{\sum\limits_{i=1}^{m} R_{ij}}{\sum\limits_{i=1}^{m} (1/D_{ij})}$	M_p/a	$\dfrac{\sum\limits_{i=1}^{m} R_{ij}}{\sum\limits_{i=1}^{m} \sqrt{1/D_{ij}^3}}$
Grand Canyon 1,082,447	2,418.6 (10.4) *	5,327.8 (25.2)	155,940,153.8 (33.4)	12,487.6
Crater Lake 339,955	759.6 (3.3)	1,452.9 (6.9)	14,368,648.4 (3.1)	3,790.6
Hot Springs 1,222,252	2,731.0 (11.7)	999.9 (4.8)	5,568,656.0 (1.1)	2,359.8
Rocky Mountain 1,611,366	3,600.4 (15.5)	6,689.9 (31.6)	217,011,199.7 (46.5)	14,731.3
Shenandoah 1,592,164	3,557.4 (15.3)	1,692.0 (8.0)	25,762,730.5 (5.5)	5,075.7
Sequoia and Kings Canyon .. 1,334,773	2,982.4 (12.8)	681.1 (3.2)	2,721,510.1 (0.6)	1,649.7
Mammoth Cave 504,693	1,127.7 (4.9)	1,036.7 (4.9)	5,857,368.0 (1.3)	2,420.2
Mesa Verde 153,261	342.5 (1.5)	844.6 (4.0)	3,594,436.8 (0.8)	1,895.9
Yosemite 2,561,801	5,724.1 (24.6)	2,418.9 (11.4)	35,475,127.2 (7.6)	5,956.1

* Figures in parentheses express the "mass" of a given park as a percent of the nine-park total for easy comparison.

planet's orbit.[32] In our analogous case, D stands for distance from home state to park, and R, the visitation rate, may be taken as $1/T$. We can then solve for M_p, the "mass" of a given park:

$$M_p = D^3 R^2 \frac{4\pi^2}{G} \; ; \tag{9}$$

or,

$$M_p = D^3 R^2 \, a. \tag{9a}$$

But, by Equation 6 and Equation 9a:

$$k = M_p/a. \tag{10}$$

Thus the relative "masses" of the parks are, by this model, proportional to the square of the figures given in the last column of Table 3. These squared values are shown in the column headed M_p/a.

Another set of visitation rates is given in Table 4. When the original $P_1 P_2/D$ model is fitted to these data by Equation 4, the coefficient of agreement is .710 between expected and observed rates. When the modified model is fitted by Equation 5, the coefficient of agreement increases to .864. And when the $R^2 D^3 = k$ model is fitted by Equation 7, a slight additional increase brings the coefficient of agreement to .898.

In both sets of data—1948 and 1952—it is apparent that "park population" is an inadequate index of the "mass" of a park; and it is also apparent that it is not necessary to abandon physicalistic models in order to increase the agreement between expected and observed visitation rates.

Giving the Model Meaning

Sorokin and others might still object that such a physicalistic concept as "mass" has no sociological meaning. If so, the model would be of doubtful worth despite its capacity for predicting observed visitation rates at various national parks. Let us therefore explicitly consider *why* national park visitation patterns should conform to a gravitational model.

People are *attracted* to national parks.[33] It would be surprising if the strength of this attraction did not vary from park to park. It would be just as surprising if it did not wane with distance from a park. People are attracted toward other destinations besides national parks, however. Can the nature of the national park attraction help to account for the fact that the distance gradient conforms rather closely to a model derived by analogy from physical gravity? As an exercise in *verstehende* sociology, consider

[32] *Ibid.*, p. 183.

[33] In this connection, see the perceptive cover article on Recreation, *Time*, July 14, 1961, pp. 46–53. See also "Vacation Spots off the Beaten Track," *Newsweek*, July 3, 1961, pp. 45–49. It is significant, perhaps, that "best-seller" lists for many weeks included William O. Douglas' *My Wilderness* (Garden City, N.Y.: Doubleday, 1960).

the following statements that have been made to justify visiting national parks.

Bernard De Voto gave this justification:

First of all, silence. In any park, a three-minute walk will permit you to be alone in the primeval, and this single fact is enough to justify the entire National Park System. Moreover, you will enjoy the intimacy of nature as your forefathers knew it. . . . Our civilization excludes steadily increasing numbers of Americans from first-hand knowledge of nature—streams, plants, forests, animals, birds, even the effects of storm—and yet their need of it can never be extinguished.[34]

With reference to a particular area that was later to acquire national park status, Theodore Roosevelt wrote:

In the Grand Canyon, Arizona has a natural wonder which, as far as I know, is in kind absolutely unparalleled throughout the rest of the world. I want to ask you to do one thing in connection with it in your interest and in the interest of the country—keep this great wonder of nature as it now is. . . . I hope you will not have a building of any kind, nor a summer cottage, a hotel, or anything else, to mar the wonderful grandeur, the sublimity, the great loneliness and beauty of the canyon.[35]

Devereux Butcher echoes this sentiment by saying "A national park is not the place for fads and experiments; it should not be intruded upon by eye-catching architectural monstrosities."[36] And a recent director of the National Park Service has written that "the cultural and inspirational products of parks are supplied by the natural or historic scene undamaged, unmodified, and unimpaired. To change the character of a park area in any important way destroys a part of its ability to yield those benefits to the human mind and spirit."[37]

The mere presence of people in one of these areas changes its wilderness character. Large numbers of people, all present at once, would, according to the views quoted, significantly reduce the area's *attractiveness* for each of them. Even the intrusion of buildings or other indicators of human presence can be expected to detract. The size of the crowd present at any given time in a national park should reflect, by this argument, some sort of balance between the attractiveness of the area and the unattractiveness of the crowd attracted. It would follow that the P_1P_2/D model is conceptually inappropriate to the analysis of national park travel data. If the *verstehende* approach suggests that "park population" functions in part as a deterrent to park visitation, it implies that "park population" cannot be an appropriate sociological analogue of mass.

---

[34] Quoted in John Ise, *Our National Park Policy: A Critical History* (Baltimore: Johns Hopkins Press, 1961), p. 4.

[35] Quoted in Devereux Butcher, "Resorts or Wilderness?" *The Atlantic*, Vol. 207, No. 2, February, 1961, p. 48.

[36] *Ibid.*, p. 49.

[37] In National Park Service's *Mission 66 for the National Park System* (Washington, D.C.: U. S. Department of the Interior, January, 1956), p. iii.

National parks are areas of superlative scenery made reasonably accessible and yet *preserved* relatively unchanged. Despite Theodore Roosevelt's wish, there are some buildings on the rim of the Grand Canyon, but not so many, perhaps, as might have sprung up had the area not been designated a national park. Each national park is established by an act of Congress. Nature endows them with scenic qualities, but Congress (an agency of human society) endows them with the quality of *sacredness* by declaring that they shall be preserved relatively unaltered. Outside national park boundaries the landscape is increasingly subjected to man-made changes.

Referring to a "normative reaction to normlessness," Becker discerned a tendency for far-reaching secularization in a society to engender "sacralization." [38] As cultural objects, the national parks may be viewed as products of this cultural process. Their attraction for the American public has grown as that public has become increasingly an urban, mobile, secularized population. The quality of sacredness (the capacity to resist change from an existing steady state) is clearly a close cultural analogue of inertia as a physical property of matter.

It is the argument of this paper, then, that insofar as the essence of the national parks is preservation of certain areas as nearly unchanged as possible (commensurate with public visitation), the institutionalization of the National Park System is an almost ideal-typical instance of sacralization. Furthermore, the "sacredness" of these areas is a major component of their attractive power, and is closely parallel to the inertial property of matter which is called *mass*.

Not all national park travel is in response to this kind of attractive force. "It is doubtless true," a spokesman for the National Park Service has said, "that a great many Americans have not yet grasped the concept of the national parks and that a great many more have only a vague idea of the extent and character of the National Park System. Yet few institutions are more ardently accepted by those who know something about them." [39]

In this connection, there is evidence that the $R^2D^3 = k$ model excels the $RD = k$ model most clearly for just those persons whose travel to a national park is most deliberate. Serendipity played a part in bringing this to light. When data were requested from Yellowstone National Park for the year

---

[38] Becker, "Current Sacred-Secular Theory and Its Development," *op. cit.*, p. 175. See also his presidential address, "Normative Reactions to Normlessness," *American Sociological Review*, Vol. 25, No. 6, December, 1960, pp. 803–10.

[39] National Park Service, *op. cit.*, p. 6.

One writer has observed: "This is so much the age of technology and the machine that machines come to be loved for their own sake rather than for other ends. Instead, for instance, of valuing the automobile because it may take one to a national park, the park comes to be valued because it is a place the automobile may be used to reach. A considerable number of automobilists would like when they get there to do what they do at home or at the country club. An even greater number prefers to drive straight through so that they can use their machine to get somewhere else." Joseph Wood Krutch, *Grand Canyon: Today and All Its Yesterdays* (New York: William Sloane Associates, 1958), p. 259.

1948, it turned out that state-by-state breakdowns of cars entering the park were given separately for each of the five park entrances.

For each entrance in turn, then, it is possible to separate the figures into two categories:

1. States for which this entrance is on "the near side," and
2. States for which this entrance is on "the far side" of the park.

Visitors from the first category of states may or may not be going somewhere else besides Yellowstone before returning home, but visitors from the second category of states almost certainly have already been somewhere else and are visiting Yellowstone en route home. Thus there is probably a higher proportion of persons in the second category for whom the visit to Yellowstone is an *incidental* part of a trip to some other destination.

Figure 4 compares "outward bound" and "homeward bound" visitation rates at each of the five entrances to Yellowstone. In general, the distance gradient is steeper for the "outward bound" visitation rates, and a comparison of coefficients of agreement shows that at four of the five entrances the $R^2D^3 = k$ model fits the "outward bound" visitation rates better than the $RD = k$ model. By contrast, at three of the five entrances the "homeward bound" visitation rates conform more closely to the $RD = k$ model than to the $R^2D^3 = k$ model.

It is the contention of this paper that $R^2D^3 = k$ is a more truly gravitational model than $RD = k$, and Figure 4 thus tends to support the view that "sacredness" (as manifested in the national parks) is an appropriate sociological counterpart of *mass*.

The sociological concept of sacredness appears to be reflected in a number of statements of the purpose of the National Park System. It has been suggested that, depending on "the accuracy and inspirational content" of exhibits explaining them, the geological and other scientific wonders, the historic remains of early man, and the buildings "that once rang to the footsteps of the founding fathers" can have "value in holding America to her best ideals and traditions." [40]

Promotion of national solidarity has been seen as an important function of the national parks:

Where else do so many millions of Americans, under such satisfying circumstances, come face to face with their government? How else can that government better promote the unity of the family than through experiences in which every member shares? Where else but on historic ground can Americans better renew the idealism that prompted the patriots to their deeds of diplomacy and valor? Where else do they have such opportunity to recapture the spirit and something of the qualities of the pioneers? [41]

---

[40] *Ibid.*, p. 33. Cf. Emile Durkheim, *The Elementary Forms of the Religious Life* (Glencoe, Ill.: The Free Press, 1947), where it is argued that a major function of religion's sacred objects is the cohesion of the group.
[41] National Park Service, *op. cit.*, p. 119.

FIGURE 4

Outward Bound and Homeward Bound Visitation Rate Patterns at Yellowstone

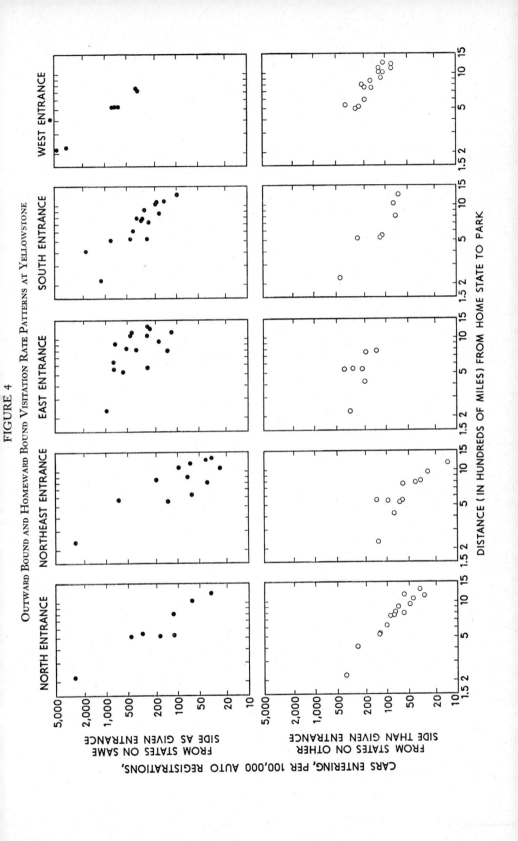

Pressure toward sacralization is expected to grow out of secular activities: "As encroachment upon wild areas by man's activities becomes more severe, the role of the national parks as sanctuaries for wildlife becomes increasingly important." [42]

The major mileposts in the development of present national park policies imply the process of sacralization:

1. The Yellowstone Park Act, 1872, which established the *first national park*, directed the Secretary of the Interior to publish rules and regulations that would "provide for the preservation, from injury or spoliation, of all timber, mineral deposits, natural curiosities, or wonders within said park, and their retention in their natural condition." [43]

2. When the National Park *Service* was established, the Secretary of the Interior instructed its first Director that "the national parks must be maintained in absolutely unimpaired form for the use of future generations as well as those of our own time." [44]

3. Efforts of the National Park Service to educate the public regarding national parks were soon supplemented by a *voluntary organization*, the National Parks Association, which, at its first meeting in May, 1919, announced its purpose: "To defend the National Parks and Monuments fearlessly against assaults of private interests and aggressive commercialism." [45]

4. In anticipation of the fiftieth anniversary of establishment of the National Park Service, the ten-year development program, *Mission 66*, has included among its purposes to "Provide for the protection and preservation of the wilderness areas within the National Park System and encourage their appreciation in ways that will leave them unimpaired." [46]

With park visitation rapidly increasing, the National Park Service has the difficult task of developing facilities in the parks which will minimize the extent to which visitors' activities will damage park features and the extent to which visitors' presence in abundance will detract from park value. Yet the facilities themselves must not detract.

The Growth of Park "Mass"

If the "mass" of a national park is the result of a process of sacralization, we should expect that, with the passage of time, two things would occur: (1) There should be an observable increase in "mass" at successive dates after an area has been designated as a national park, and (2) There should be an increasingly close fit between travel data and the gravitational model. Figure 5 indicates that this has happened in the case of Mount Rainier National Park. Visitation rates are plotted against distance for three different years, at ten-year intervals. The height of the curve increases, representing an increase in "mass," and the dots come to cluster more evenly and more

---

[42] *Ibid.*, p. 46.
[43] John Ise, *op. cit.*, p. 18.
[44] *Ibid.*, p. 194.
[45] *Ibid.*, p. 200.
[46] National Park Service, *op. cit.*, p. 17.

closely about the expected −45° line. The coefficient of agreement between expected and observed visitation rates is actually as large in 1939 as in 1949, although this may not be apparent from the double log scattergram. The $R^2D^3 = k$ model gives the following coefficients of agreement: .844 in 1929, .962 in 1939, and .961 in 1949. The park "mass" rises from 3,078,621 in 1929 to 5,014,912 in 1939, and to 21,336,085 in 1949.

FIGURE 5

MOUNT RAINIER NATIONAL PARK VISITATION RATES
AS DOUBLE LOG FUNCTIONS OF DISTANCE FROM HOME STATE

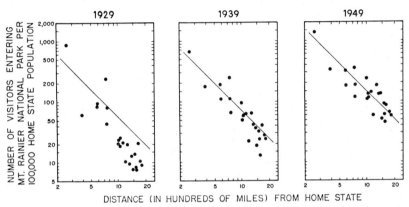

Since the sacredness of a national park area is socially defined, there is no reason to expect this process to be entirely irreversible. Similar longitudinal comparisons were made for three other parks for which sufficient data were available. The overall pattern is generally consistent with the expectation of increasing "mass" and increasing agreement between expected and observed rates, but with some partial exceptions. While Crater Lake's coefficient of agreement increased during each decade from 1930 to 1960, its "mass" declined between 1950 and 1960, after growing during the two previous decades. Rocky Mountain National Park had much greater "mass" in 1952 than in 1936, but both the "mass" and the coefficient of agreement had dropped way down in the war year of 1944. Mesa Verde has shown a continuously accelerating growth in its "mass": from 284,942 in 1930 to 611,524 in 1938, to 1,712,696 in 1948, and to 7,848,963 in 1958, but its coefficient of agreement reached a high of .902 in 1948 and then dropped to .845 in 1958.

It was actually an *apparent* change in the "mass" of Mount Rainier National Park that first suggested the possibility of rethinking the gravitational model along the lines described in this paper. When visitation rates calculated from the data given by Cavanaugh for 1947 and 1948 were compared (with no particular version of the hypothesis in mind), it looked as if Mount Rainier National Park had suffered a "loss of mass" in that interval. It so happens that in October, 1947, a natural catastrophe altered some of the features of the park.[47] The idea that such a change in park features might entail a reduction of "mass" was the serendipitous stimulus for considering the analogy between physical inertia and social sacredness. Upon further investigation it turned out that the apparent "loss of mass" could be fully accounted for by the fact that the 1948 data were for the Nisqually entrance only, whereas the 1947 data had been for the entire park. When an estimate of "mass" was computed from 1947 Nisqually entrance data only, it proved to be comparable to the 1948 figure.

Implications for Further Research

If we have now established that the equation $R^2D^3 = k$, analogous to Kepler's third law of planetary motion, is both conceptually and empirically preferable to $RD = k$, based on the P_1P_2/D formula, what additional re-

---

[47] The relation between physical change wrought by nature and the social attribute of sacredness is implicit in the following, from Freeman Tilden, *The National Parks: What They Mean to You and Me* (New York: Alfred A. Knopf, 1951), pp. 303–5:

"There is something else at Mount Rainier National Park that every visitor should see, and not only see but ask about and then ponder. It is a dramatic example of the inexorable law of nature by which the earth's surface—all that we see and all that we think we see—is constantly undergoing change by upbuilding and demolition. It is also, when understood, a graphic interpretation of the concept of land management that governs the setting aside of national parks for *preservation* 'in their natural condition.'

"In October 1947, after several days of moderately heavy rains, the sky really opened and dropped nearly six inches in a few hours. At the park headquarters at Longmire the ground shivered for many hours as great boulders hurtled down the Nisqually River. But to the west of the Nisqually, in the broad valley of Kautz Creek, a melodrama of the highland wilderness was in the making. High up on the slopes of Mount Rainier a part of the Kautz Glacier was being undermined and broken up by the streams of water that were pouring down upon it from the sides. Loose rock and debris of all kinds began to move down into the stream bed, first creating a dam, then breaking the barrier with deafening roars and sweeping down upon the heavily wooded country below.

"Trees five feet in diameter and hundreds of years old were pounded and sawed till they went down as helplessly as the ferns and other undergrowth. In building Hoover Dam the engineers figured that they had removed eight million cubic yards of earth and rock. In about fifteen hours the waters coming down the upper Kautz Valley moved more than six times as much material as was moved at Hoover Dam in three years with the finest modern machinery!

"After the flood there were all kinds of suggestions for dealing with the situation. Some people recommended that the felled trees be salvaged for lumber, and the scarred area near the highway be nicely landscaped. The standing trees, many of them partly cut through by the abrasive waters, should surely be converted into boards and planks, because they would die anyway!

"Such proposals were no doubt very well meant, but how obvious it is that they could come only from people who have never realized the underlying meaning of the parks! In the life of the wilderness a flood like this one is the merest incident. It has, of course, some local importance to the plants and animals involved. During the ages and eons these petty 'catastrophes' have happened and will happen. The aim of the Park Service is to preserve natural phenomena, wherever humanly possible—not to repair and reconstruct and refashion them. Whatever nature does is right. It is only the dilapidations and changes brought about by human occupation and use that have to be curbed and managed."

search may be in order? One clue can be gained from Figure 6, where the "visitor days" data for the various parks are plotted against the estimates of park "mass" by the $R^2D^3 = k$ model, with visually fitted curves. The scattergrams are distinctly L-shaped; as if there were, in effect, two distinct series of national parks in which "park population" and "mass" bear strikingly different ratios to each other. Nearest the zero point where the two arrays intersect, assignment of dots to one array or the other must be arbitrary. By dividing them up as in Figure 6, however, it is possible to regard Yellowstone, Grand Canyon, Rocky Mountain, Glacier, Crater Lake, Mesa Verde, and Lassen Volcanic as one series. This puts Hot Springs, Shenandoah, and Mammoth Cave, all of which are outside the "cultural area" comprising the twenty-four western states, into the other series, along with two areas in populous (and secular?) California: Yosemite and Sequoia-Kings Canyon. Mount Rainier, too, appears to be in this second series, perhaps as a result of its proximity to the Seattle-Tacoma population center, or perhaps partly as a consequence of its 1948 "mass" being underestimated in terms of data from only its Nisqually entrance. This division of these parks into two series, arbitrary as it may be, suggests the desirability of incorporating considerations of heterogeneity into any comprehensive sociological study of the National Park System. Some parks may lose their attractiveness as they become crowded; for other parks, crowds may not appreciably detract.

Another possible extension of the present study would depend on deriv-

FIGURE 6

ANNUAL TOTAL OF "VISITOR DAYS"
AS A FUNCTION OF THE "MASS" OF VARIOUS NATIONAL PARKS

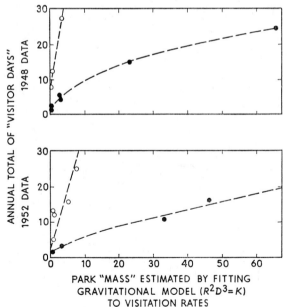

PARK "MASS" ESTIMATED BY FITTING
GRAVITATIONAL MODEL ($R^2D^3 = K$)
TO VISITATION RATES

ing estimates of the relative "mass" of all the other parks in the system. Then, on the assumption that national parks may be somewhat interchangable in the vacation behavior of their visitors, the hypothesis of intervening opportunities could be fitted to visitation rate data.[48] To the extent that it can be construed as a variant form of the gravitational model, this would be an important step.

Further studies of the growth of park "mass" would seem to be in order. In the case of at least one park in the present study there are clear indications that the visitation rate of each state has tended to grow logistically over the years, apart from such notable fluctuations as were caused by the great depression and World War II. It would be of considerable interest to see how the parameters of best-fitting logistic curves might vary from state to state. Also, would yearly estimates of the park's mass fit a logistic growth curve?

It seems to the author, however, that a host of conceptual implications arises from divorcing the concept of "mass" in "social physics" from sheer population size. Premature equating of these two variables may have been the major cause of the virtual sterility of physicalistic sociology.

If a little imaginative speculation be permitted, perhaps it can be suggested that the lesson of physics most cogent for sociology has been overlooked until now—by the "social physicists" themselves. Newton's great achievement rested on the "principle of proportionality," the empirical equality between inertial mass and gravitational mass. In the present century, Einstein went further and stated the "principle of equivalence": a *theoretical* assertion that inertial mass and gravitational mass are always equal *because they are the same thing*.[49] It hardly seems unreasonable to extend this "principle of equivalence" to sociology, where it would consist of the axiom that *a sociocultural element is valued* [50] *to the extent that it is regarded as sacred*. If this statement sounds tautological, it is neither more nor less so than the axioms of geometry (e.g., "A straight line is the shortest distance between two points"), or than the three laws of motion which provided the foundation for Newtonian physics.

The sociological principle of equivalence could be more than a mere exercise in reasoning by analogy. It might integrate previously disconnected

[48] Samuel A. Stouffer, "Intervening Opportunities: A Theory Relating Mobility and Distance," *American Sociological Review*, Vol. 5, No. 6, December, 1940, pp. 845–67. Since this writing, such a study has been carried out. See William R. Catton, Jr., and Lennart Berggren, "Intervening Opportunities and National Park Visitation Rates," *Pacific Sociological Review*, Vol. 7, No. 2, Fall, 1964, pp. 66–73.

[49] See George Gamow, "Gravity," *Scientific American*, Vol. 204, No. 3, March, 1961, pp. 94–106. Whether the principle of equivalence can be conceptually linked in sociology to anything analogous to the "curvature" of the space-time continuum by which Einstein explained it in physics remains a matter of speculation.

[50] "Valuing" has been defined as "actions which show a person's intensity of desire for various desiderata, or the amount of his 'motivation' to pursue them." William R. Catton, Jr., "A Theory of Value," *American Sociological Review*, Vol. 24, No. 3, June, 1959, p. 310.

bodies of research. Movement of people in geographical space may be explained by models that can also be applied to their motions in social-psychological space (as appropriate techniques of measurement become available). If the "mass" of a national park is created by a process of institutionalization, then it should be possible to ascertain the "mass" of a social norm, of a role or status, of a definition-of-the-situation, an attitude, or even of a self-conception. Each of these conventional sociological concepts refers to something which presumably has a property of inertia and a power of attraction. Heretofore these concepts have remained largely beyond the scope of "social physics," which has tended to deal mainly with demographic, ecological, or economic problems. If the "mass" of these sociological entities can be measured, it ought to be possible also to measure the *forces* which accelerate them. If the concept of "social forces" which so interested the early sociologists has since come to seem merely metaphorical, perhaps it is because it has been "operationally" defined in terms of the false identification of population with "mass." Must we assume that a theoretical framework which has been conspicuously fruitful in the study of other interacting inertial-attractive entities is inappropriate for the study of sociocultural interaction?

That the framework of physics *has* so far seemed to many sociologists to be irrelevant to their work is, we maintain, due in large part to the premature and misleading adoption of population size as the "social physicist's" analogue of mass. By correcting this misconception, social physics may yet make a genuine contribution to sociology. There will, of course, remain the difficult problem of developing standardized units of measurement.

Closer adherence to a framework intelligently adapted from physics might begin with the tentative generalization of Newton's three laws of motion so as to apply to sociology. Social change, rather than stability, would then be defined as problematic. And we might be more consistently committed to the study of *inter*action processes; is there any reason to suppose that there is *not* equal and opposite reaction for every *social* action?

Because the National Park System seems to epitomize, in institutional form, the cultural attribute of sacredness, further sociological study of this institution offers promise for consummation of the marriage between physicalistic and *verstehende* sociology. It also suggests an answer to the perennial question of the relative complexity of social and physical phenomena.[51]

---

[51] The alleged greater complexity of our subject matter has been offered both as an argument against the scientific pretensions of sociology and in extenuation of its scientific weakness. Lundberg has inverted the argument by asserting that "The complexity of human society . . . is largely a function of our ignorance of it." George A. Lundberg, *Social Research* (rev. ed.; New York: Longmans, Green, 1942), p. 18.

Complexity is not, he has argued, a characteristic that is inherent in the phenomena we study; it is a word that designates the inadequacies of both our responses and our communication of our responses. On this point, see his *Foundations of Sociology* (New York: Macmillan, 1939), p. 138.

Suppose there had been as many planets in the solar system as there were western states in the present study (only seven planets were known to Newton). Suppose their relative distances from the sun had not varied so widely but had been proportional to the relative distances of these states from a particular national park. Finally, suppose the planets' orbits were determined by the simultaneous gravitational attraction of a dozen scattered suns, as the wilderness-seeking residents of the several states are simultaneously attracted by more than two dozen national parks. In such a universe, physics would still be waiting for its Newton.

Clearly, then, the complexity of social data is such that it is prudent to grasp whatever advantage may be had by studying the earlier accomplishments of those who combined scientific ingenuity with the wisdom to begin by investigating phenomena of such relative simplicity as the solar system!

19

The Use of Gravity Models
in Social Research

DAVID L. HUFF *

THE GRAVITY CONCEPT of human interaction is based on the notion that the probability of interaction that is likely to occur between individuals and various potential destination sources varies directly with the size or attraction of each of these sources and inversely with the distance separating each of these sources from individuals' points of origination.

There are, however, several rather significant limitations associated with the use of models of this kind.

First, the gravity model is designed to account for the behavior of large groups of people. It rests on the assumption that group behavior is predictable on the basis of mathematical probability because the idiosyncracies of any one individual or small group tend to be cancelled out. As a result, the gravity model as presently formulated has not been able to account for individual or small group behavior with a high degree of accuracy.

Second, the gravity model has not been able to account for differences among various types of individual groups. Consequently, in making predictions the parameters of spatial interaction are assumed to be the same for all individuals. The only variations explicitly recognized are those associated with the differences generated by different trip types.

Third, the distance factor in the gravity model is generally raised to some power other than unity based on variations among types of trips. The assumption is that individuals are not willing to travel the same distances for all types of trips. Consequently, various exponents are used which are intended to reflect differences among various travel expeditions. However, there is fairly good evidence to indicate that the exponent may be a variable function related inversely to distance itself.[1]

Fourth, since the gravity model is essentially a static formulation, one must build into the variable inputs of the model anticipated future conditions; e.g., forecasts concerning the size and spatial distribution of em-

---

* University of California, Los Angeles.
[1] Gerald A. P. Carrothers, "An Historical Review of the Gravity Potential Concepts of Human Interaction," *Journal of the American Institute of Planners,* Vol. 22, No. 2, 1956, p. 94.

ployment, residential, and commercial sectors, and then one must calculate what the magnitude of future potential interactions is likely to be. However, when the gravity model is used to estimate future interactions based on such estimates, past evidence indicates quite clearly that the anticipated changes that have been calculated will in turn generate changes, the magnitude of which are almost impossible to anticipate.

Finally, the gravity concept is essentially an empirical notion. It tells nothing about *why* observed regularities occur as they do under various situations, and, as a consequence, it leaves one at a loss when discrepancies occur that cannot be accounted for. Yet, it is surprising to note how often gravity models pertaining to human interactions are loosely referred to as laws. These models are nothing more than tools that allow one to make short-cut approximations of the direction and magnitude of individual travel movements.

Furthermore, it is necessary to modify these tools (based on empirical evidence) as changes occur in the environment if they are to achieve a level of confidence that will permit a high degree of predictive value. Therefore, it is unrealistic to classify such tools as reflecting certain basic laws of human behavior. Exception to this last statement might be made on the grounds that the gravity model permits recognition of a basic tendency of human behavior; i.e., interaction declines with distance. However, the point being made is that while gross empirical regularities can be observed, the statistical properties of the gravity model are such that the actual values obtained from any given examination will not necessarily produce similar results when it is used to measure similar interaction phenomena under different environmental circumstances.[2]

The Uses of Analogy

The remarks cited above are not intended to imply that analogies drawn from the physical sciences cannot serve as important instruments of systematic social research. On the contrary, analogies not only serve as guides for establishing fundamental assumptions of a theory, they also can provide a carefully formulated operational structure for evaluating such assumptions. However, it is extremely important that social scientists be aware of the limits within which such analogies are valid.

For example, in developing concepts of human interaction based on an analogy to Newtonian physics of matter, it may be quite possible to account for such behavior using the gravity concept. But, if strict adherence is insisted upon concerning the parameters of such an explanatory structure, it is quite possible that the social scientist will defeat his own purpose.

---

[2] For example, see William L. Garrison, "Estimates of the Parameters of Spatial Interaction," *Papers and Proceedings of the Regional Science Association*, Vol. II, 1956, pp. 280–90.

Such a model merely provides a loosely formulated hypothesis for the formation of theoretical ideas. It would be naive to expect such an empirical formulation to apply in any absolute sense to all types of social interaction processes.

As another example, in the case of the distance exponent Newton found that for physical interaction processes the force of interaction between two concentrations of mass was directly proportional to the product of the masses, and inversely proportional to the *square* of the distance between them. Yet in human interaction processes it has been shown, as a result of empirical tests, that the distance exponent has ranged from one-half to over three. Such evidence would tend to indicate that differences among individuals, as well as variations in the environment, exert considerable influence in bringing about different forms of spatial behavior.

In Professor Catton's paper, "On the Concept of Mass in the Sociological Version of Gravitation," we have still another illustration that rigid adherence to the initial parameters of a "law" in the physical sciences does not produce expected results which exactly coincide with a particular human interaction situation. For example, Catton found that the relationship (derived from Kepler's Law) between expected park visitations and the actual park visitations obtained from survey data was close in some instances, while in others the fit was fairly poor. The latter condition was particularly true for the eastern states, where the model was found not to fit at all. Thus it does not appear that Professor Catton has demonstrated, from an operational standpoint, that his use of Kepler's explanatory structure is any better or any worse than Professor Cavanaugh's use of the interactance formula.

Consequently, it seems fallacious to expect a universal thread of continuity to exist between the *exact* values specified in formulations designed to account for the behavior of physical matter and formulations designed to examine human behavior. However, the conceptual framework provided by a physical science model may prove to be valuable. That is, such a conceptual framework may suggest ways in which the theory may be expanded, and, as a consequence, extend its range of application.

A Probabilistic Gravity Model

It would seem to me that a more fruitful approach in analyzing social interaction phenomena would be to formulate a general probabilistic type gravity model that would seek to determine the likelihood of movement *from* a given point of origin to various potential sources of destination for any type of spatial interaction. The properties of such a formulation might be as follows:

1. A set of alternative choices for a given type of spatial interaction, represented as set J;

2. A subset of choice alternatives, represented as J_o. This subset represents available alternatives which are in keeping with an individual's tastes and preferences. Any given alternative within the subset J_o is represented as j (where $j = 1, \ldots, n$);

3. A positive "payoff" function, u_j, associated with each choice alternative reflecting its "utility" to an individual.

Propositions

Given the preceding properties, the following testable propositions are set forth.

1. The probability, P, of a given choice alternative, j, being chosen from among all alternatives in the subset J_o is proportional to u_j. That is:

$$P_j = \frac{u_j}{\sum\limits_{j=1}^{n} u_j} ; \qquad (1)$$

such that:

$$\sum_{j=1}^{n} P_j = 1 \text{ and } 0 < P_j < 1.$$

2. The ratio between the probabilities of an individual's choosing any one of two particular choice alternatives does not depend on the existence of other alternatives. This ratio could be called the ratio of utilities of the two choice alternatives to an individual. That is:

$$\frac{P_{i_1}}{P_{i_2}} = \frac{u_{i_1}}{u_{i_2}}.$$

3. The properties of the pair (P_{j_1}, P_{j_2}) that determines the utility in (u_{j_1}, u_{j_2}) must be given empirical meaning in connection with a specific type of spatial interaction. In the case of Professor Catton's project, the properties might be:

a) The size, S_j, of a given park, measured in terms of the number of acres devoted to recreational purposes; and,

b) The distance, T_{ij}, in time units, from an individual's travel base i to j.

4. The utility, u_j, of a given park could be hypothesized as being directly proportional to the ratio S_j/T_{ij}^{λ} where λ is a constant which is to be determined empirically to reflect different types of recreational-trip purposes. Thus:

$$P_j = \frac{u_j}{\sum\limits_{j=1}^{n} u_j} = \frac{\dfrac{S_j}{T_{ij}^{\lambda}}}{\sum\limits_{i=1}^{n} \dfrac{S_j}{T_{ij}^{\lambda}}}. \qquad (2)$$

5. The expected number of individuals at a given place, i (e.g., a city,

county, state, etc.), and traveling to a park, j, would be equal to the number of people at i multiplied by the probability that an individual at i will select j for a recreational trip. Therefore:

$$E_j = P_j \cdot I_i = \frac{\dfrac{S_j}{T_{ij}^{\lambda}}}{\displaystyle\sum_{j=i}^{n} \dfrac{S_j}{T_{ij}^{\lambda}}} \cdot I_i \, , \qquad (3)$$

where E_j = the expected number of individuals at i that are likely to travel to park j,
and
I_i = the number of people at i.

20

A Class of Long_Tailed Probability Distributions and the Empirical Distribution of City Sizes *

BENOIT MANDELBROT †

IN OUR current investigations of the behavior of economic time-series [1] we repeatedly come across cases where simple stochastic formulas and models seem to account very well for certain observations, which, *a priori*, certainly appear to be in the exclusive province of causal explanations. Such theories yield such an abundance of riches that special consideration must be given to the question of whether they are acceptable as models of the real world.

---

* This research was supported in part by the Office of Naval Research under Contract No. Nonr 3775 (00) NR 047040. The substance of the present brief Note is further developed in our paper, "A Survey of Growth and Diffusion Models of the Law of Pareto," expected to appear in *Behavioral Science* (1965), and in the privately circulated notes on our Harvard University lectures on "The Statistics of Oligopoly and the Rank-Size Rule."

† International Business Machines Corporation, Thomas J. Watson Research Center, Yorktown Heights, New York.

[1] The following is a list of our published papers concerning Paretian phenomena, other than the Estoup-Zipf law of word frequencies: (1) "Variables et processus stochastiques de Pareto-Lévy et la repartition des revenus," *Comptes rendus de l'Académie des Sciences de Paris*, Vol. 249, 1959, pp. 613–15 and 2153–55; (2) "The Pareto-Lévy Law and the Distribution of Income," *International Economic Review*, Vol. 1, 1960, pp. 79–106, and Vol. 4, 1963, pp. 111–15; (3) "Stable Paretian Random Processes and the Multiplicative Variation of Income," *Econometrica*, Vol. 29, 1961, pp. 517–43; (4) "Paretian Distributions and Income Maximization," *Quarterly Journal of Economics*, Vol. 76, 1962, pp. 57–85; (5) "The Variation of Certain Speculative Prices," *The Journal of Business of the University of Chicago*, Vol. 36, 1963, pp. 394–419 (reprinted as pp. 307–32 of *The Random Character of Stock Market Prices*, Paul H. Cootner (ed.), M.I.T. Press); (6) "New Methods in Statistical Economics," *The Journal of Political Economy*, Vol. 71, 1963, pp. 421–40, or *Bulletin of the International Statistical Institute*, Vol. 40, 1964, pp. 699–720; (7) "Random Walks, Fire Damage Amount and Other Paretian Risk Phenomena," *Operations Research*, Vol. 12, 1964, pp. 582–85; (8) "Self-Similar Error-Clusters in Communications Systems and the Concept of Conditional Stationarity," *Institute of Electrical and Electronics Engineers Transactions on Communications Technology*, Vol. COM–13, 1965.

A number of other publications are in process and are available in the form of preprints or research reports.

More precisely, the empirical distributions which one observes in many contexts of behavioral science are characterized by the large number of values so removed from the mean, the median, and other "typical indicators of location" that they do *not* seem to be generated by the same mechanism as the values near the median: One rather considers them to be random or causal "outliers" and one tries somehow *first* to eliminate them, *then* to study the (hopefully Gaussian) random remainder.

However (*a*) in questions such as the distributions of incomes or of price changes, the far-removed values are of such enormous size, and are so numerous, that any theory that would exclude them would be too modest to be very useful. Moreover (*b*) even the very large price changes (those apparently due to radical and explainable changes of expectations) have a frequency distribution that happens to be perfectly well interpolated with the help of the simple analytic expression inferred from the not-so-far-removed data; in particular, there is no observable break or other discontinuity between the "causal" large values and the purely random "noise." Finally (*c*) the empirical formula, that covers the whole range of observable values of the changes of price, can be generated with the help of limit theorems of probability theory.

It seems, however, surprising that the conditions of validity of these theorems would hold in such a wide range of values of the variable. Hence, in terms both of description and "explanation," it seems that we can achieve more than we really "deserved to." It is clear that what this means is that one must reexamine carefully the relations between causal and random explanations in social science; we shall make a small beginning in that direction.

In presenting our comments we wish to avoid both a full restatement of our considerations about economics and too heavy a reliance upon references to previous publications. We shall therefore center our work around very similar questions of demography and sociology related to the distribution of a country's population among its various "cities." This example will also have the advantage of helping to coordinate the present work with the other papers collected in the present volume.

The Law of Auerbach (Zipf), or Representation of the Distribution of Populations by the Law of V. Pareto

The basic fact of observation is that, if one uses the Census definition of cities, their populations, U, follow the classical law of Pareto:

$$(^0) \qquad P(u) = 1 - F(u) = Pr(U > u) \sim (u/u^0)^{-\alpha},$$

where u^0 and α are constant over a wide range of values of u.[2] Alpha is not the same at different places and different periods. For example, in France it has decreased from 1.65 in 1851 to 1.15 in 1954.[3] However, in all cases we know of, alpha is in the range of from 0 to 2, and many empirical alphas are very close to the value 1 (e.g., see the 1960 U.S.A. data of Figure 1 and Auerbach's original data of Figure 2).

Naturally, the law of Pareto fails for very small u, necessarily so because the $P(u)$ given by the formula $(^0)$ tends to infinity as u tends to zero. Moreover, as one would expect, the very largest values of U are not always precisely represented by the formula; but one cannot go far in evaluating this divergence at the present time.

Before attempting to rationalize the law $(^0)$, we shall draw some of its consequences. To begin with, let us note that if one could extrapolate the expression $(^0)$ to all values of u, one would reach the interesting result that if $0 < \alpha < 2$, *the variable U has an infinite population second moment;* whenever $\alpha < 1$, U would not have a finite first moment either. This may seem to be a rather strange feature, and it is important to motivate its acceptance by stressing some of its implications.

First of all, city sizes all being finite, the same is true for all their sample moments. Moreover, there is no such thing as an infinite population from which the total number of cities would have been drawn; indeed, the sizes of samples are bounded by the total number of cities on the earth. From this it follows that the assumption that cities have an infinite "population" second moment can be only as useful as its implications concerning sample moments of increasing *subsets* of the total set of cities. The situation is, therefore, basically the following.

---

[2] The usual references concerning city populations are two books by G. K. Zipf: *National Unity and Disunity* (Bloomington, Ind.: Principia Press, 1941) and *Human Behavior and the Principle of Least Effort* (Reading, Mass.: Addison-Wesley Press, 1949). See also F. Auerbach, "Das Gesetz der Bevölkerungskonzentration," *Petermans Mitteilungen*, Vol. 59, 1913, pp. 74–76; and A. J. Lotka, *Elements of Physical Biology* (Baltimore, 1925), pp. 306–7, reprinted as *Elements of Mathematical Biology* (New York: Dover, 1956).

[3] Since these data may not be readily available, we shall reproduce the numbers of cities in various population ranges:

Range	1851	1876	1911	1946	1954
1–300	7,150	8,520	11,689	16,098	16,309
300–500	8,534	8,022	7,580	7,555	7,494
500–1000	11,955	10,867	9,406	7,818	7,594
1000–5000	8,779	8,137	6,895	5,623	5,617
5000–10,000	271	306	372	482	518
10,000–50,000	136	179	260	353	395
50,000–100,000	5	16	24	32	39
over 100,00	5	9	15	22	24

Let us also note the following values of alpha borrowed (without check) from M. Fréchet, *J. Soc. Stat.*, Paris, 1941, p. 122: Belgium, 1.65; India, 1.51; Bulgaria, 1.48; Hungary, 1.43; Switzerland, 1.35; Holland, 1.35; Japan, 1.23; Germany, 1.23; Ireland, 1.21; Scotland, 1.20. The values of alpha quoted by Zipf tend to be lower.

FIGURE 1

POPULATIONS OF U.S. CITIES IN 1960

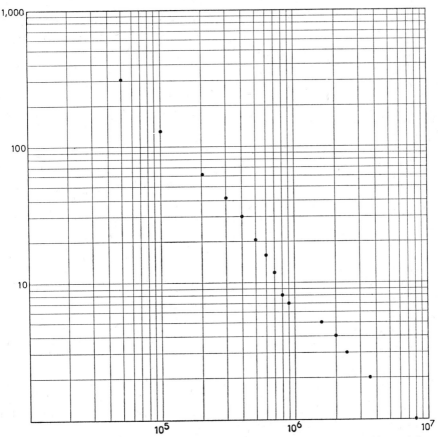

The abscissa gives the population u. The ordinate gives the number of cities for which the population is greater than u or equal to u; in other words, the ordinate is the "rank" of a city of population u, in the ordering of all cities by decreasing populations. Because of the use of logarithmic scales on both coordinates, a is measured by the slope of the best straight interpolate of the above graph.

Source: Information Please Almanac.

There could be no question that, if the sample second moment of city sizes were observed to rapidly "stabilize" around the value corresponding to the total set, it would be useful to take that value as an estimate of the population second moment of a conjectural infinite population from which cities could have been drawn. But it is easy to verify (see Figure 3) that the sample second moments, $V(M)$, corresponding to increasing subsets of M cities, continue to vary widely even when the sample size approaches the maximum imposed by the subject matter (also see Figure 4).

From the viewpoint of sampling, this should be interpreted as meaning that the distribution of city sizes is such that even the largest available

FIGURE 2

AUERBACH'S ORIGINAL DATA ON CITY SIZES

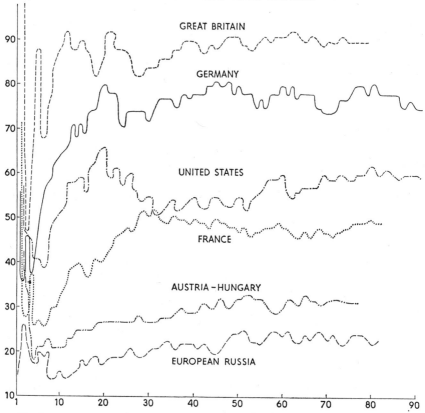

The abscissa represents the rank of a city and the ordinate represents the expression:
$S(r) = 100 \cdot (\text{rank}) \cdot (\text{population of the } r\text{th city}) / (\text{total population})$. $S(r)$ is not far from converging to a limit, which would correspond to the Pareto law with $a = 1$. There is, however, a tendency for $S(r)$ to increase, which indicates that a is rather slightly greater than 1. This graph shows the difficulty of accurately estimating the value of Pareto's exponent.

sample is too small for reliable estimation of the population second moment, or in other words that a wide range of values of the population second moment are equally compatible with the data. It turns out that this range of values of the moment happens to include the value "plus infinity." This means that facts can be equally well described by assuming that the "actual" moment is very large but finite, or by assuming that it is infinite. The first assumption is of course the more reasonable *a priori*, but it also happens to be by far the more cumbersome analytically. The second assumption, on the contrary, leads to simple analytical developments, and it could lead to absurd results only if one applied it to "infinite" samples; that is, if one raised problems devoid of concrete meaning. In other words, there is no

FIGURE 3

Variations of the Sample Second Moment, $V(M) =$
$$\frac{1}{M} \sum_{m=1}^{M} U_m^2 \text{ of the 1960 Populations of the 310 U.S. Cities}$$
with More than 50,000 Inhabitants (Linear Coordinates)

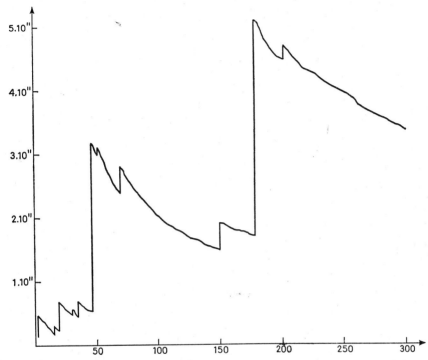

In principle, these 310 cities should have been picked at random; we have, however, assumed that an adequate approximation to randomness is provided by the ranking of these cities in their lexicographical order.

danger in assuming, as we shall do, that the intrinsically bounded set of city sizes was drawn at random from an infinite population having an infinite second moment.

As to the first moment, $A(M)$ (Figure 5), it is clear that it varies much less violently than the second, its final value. $A(310) = 204$ is, in fact, a reasonable approximation to all $A(M)$ for $M > 48$. However, the stabilization of $A(M)$ around this seeming limit is much slower than, for example, in the case of Gaussian variables; and this reflects the fact that the empirical value of $\alpha - 1$ is positive but very small (recall that $\alpha = 1$ is the value for which the population mean becomes infinite so that the sample mean $A(M)$ begins to increase without bound as $M \to \infty$).

One may add that Figures 3 and 4 would be hardly modified—except for the scales of the axes of coordinates—if, instead of the 310 largest cities, we considered the 3,100 largest. (If the law of Pareto could be interpolated

FIGURE 4

Reproduction of the Data of Figure 3 on Doubly Logarithmic Coordinates

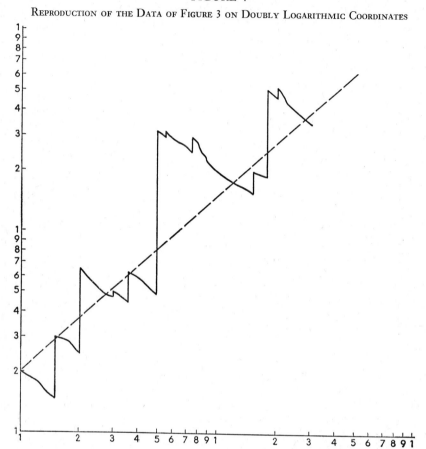

The dashed line is a free straight line interpolation. Its slope is .87, suggesting that city sizes follow the law of Pareto with an a such that $-1 + 2/a = .87$, or $a = 1.05$. This is as good an estimate as any of the exponent of city sizes.

that far, the $3,100^{st}$ city would have approximately 5,000 inhabitants.) One can indeed ascertain that the "new" graph could be obtained from Figures 3 or 4 by relabeling both coordinates to read 10 times as much as before.

To wind up this discussion, note that the third population moment of cities is also infinite, so that the skewness of their distribution cannot be measured by Karl Pearson's index of this name. Similarly, the "peakedness" cannot be measured by Pearson's index of kurtosis, which involves the fourth moment. The dependence of the sample kurtosis upon sample size is shown in Figure 6, and the theory suggests that the ordinate should increase proportionately to the abscissa, with great fluctuation on both sides; this is indeed the case. See reference (5) of footnote 1 for a description of how the exponent α replaces the kurtosis as a measure of peakedness.

FIGURE 5

$$\text{Variations of the Sample Average, } A(M) \;(1/M) \sum_{m=1}^{M} U_m, \text{ of the 1960}$$

Populations of the 310 U.S. Cities with More than 50,000 Inhabitants

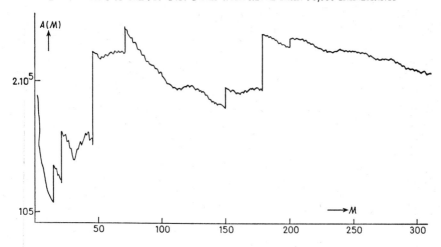

Having hopefully clarified the problem of moments, let us proceed to sketch a model of the law of Pareto, which translates into terms of city sizes certain well known considerations concerning physical random walks. We shall then note that the idea of random walk implies that the largest quantity of interest is negligible in relative size. Hence, after we develop our model, we shall have to investigate the consequences of the failure of one of its fundamental assumptions.

Random Walks of the Logarithm of Population, with Downward Trend and with Immigration at a Constant Rate

If the Pareto-Auerbach-Zipf law is written in terms of $V = \log U$, it takes the form:

$$Pr(\log U = V > v) = \exp(-\alpha v)\, \exp(\alpha v^0).$$

This is of course the exponential distribution, one of the most fundamental of probability theory, and it can be generated in many ways (having obvious counterparts in physics).

In particular, the following classical generation was first applied in this context by Champernowne, who was concerned with incomes.[4] Let $W(t)$ be the deflated population of a city at time t, i.e., the ratio of its population

---

[4] D. G. Champernowne, "A model of income distribution," *Economic Journal*, Vol. 63, 1953, pp. 318–51. Unfortunately, this author does not begin his paper by giving any simple example exhibiting the gist of his argument. Therefore his paper is cumbersome and has not attracted much attention.

FIGURE 6

VARIATION OF THE SAMPLE KURTOSIS
OF THE 1960 POPULATIONS OF THE 310 U.S. CITIES WITH MORE
THAN 50,000 INHABITANTS (LINEAR COORDINATES)

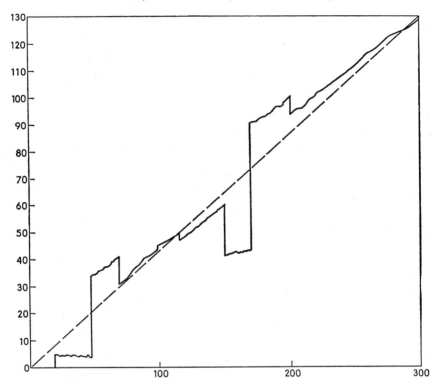

to the sum of the populations of the 100 largest cities (100 being chosen just for the sake of explicitness). Assume the principle of *random* proportionate effect, according to which $W(t+1)$ is the product of $W(t)$ by some random quantity, the distribution of which is independent of the value $w(t)$ of $W(t)$. To make things simplest, suppose that W has been quantized so as to be an integral multiple of some quantity c, and suppose that only three things can happen to log W between the times t and $t+1$:

a) Log W can increase by the quantity c; the probability of such a relative growth for the city will be p;

b) Log W can decrease by c; this relative decline will have the probability q;

c) Log W can remain invariant; this relative stagnation has the probality $1 - p - q$.

For the invariance of the probability distribution of log W, it is clearly necessary that the following identity be satisfied:

expected number of cities for which log W goes from kc to $(k+1)c =$
expected number of cities for which log W goes from $(k+1)c$ to kc.

This necessary condition of invariance can be written:

$$\frac{Pr\big(\log W > (k+1)c\big) - Pr(\log W > kc)}{Pr(\log W > kc) - Pr\big(\log W > (k-1)c\big)} = p/q.$$

Hence, there must exist a constant, H, such that:

$$Pr(\log W > kc) = H \exp\left[-k \log (q/p)\right].$$

Such a distribution can be applied to all u's only if $q > p$; in that case, writing $\alpha = (1/c) \log (q/p)$, one obtains the law of Pareto for u:

$$\text{Prob } (U > u) = (u/u^0)^{-\alpha} \text{ Q.E.D.}$$

(The condition $q > p$ is a demographical counterpart of the physical condition that expresses the presence of "gravity.")

We shall not bother to prove that the above necessary condition for invariance is also sufficient, nor to prove that, if one starts from a non-Paretian initial distribution of U, successive applications of Champernowne's transformation will lead to the law of Pareto.

On Collective Models

Many social scientists resent any reference to physics in the study of behavior phenomena, but such reference is unavoidable in the case of the preceding model, which is an obvious adaptation of physical random walk. In other words, we are quite prepared to yield to the irresistible temptation, already followed by Pareto and many of his successors, of considering that the exchanges of persons between cities are somewhat similar to the exchanges of energy in the interaction between gas molecules.

However, great differences appear immediately. In physics, the quantity of interest is energy, which, in the notation of our last section, was designated V. The usual Gaussian limit laws apply to this exponential random variable, so that the energy of even the most energetic molecule remains negligible with respect to the total energy of a reservoir. It seems therefore quite reasonable to use a random walk model, which treats each molecule "as if" its fate would hardly influence that of the whole and "as if" it were influenced only by its nearest neighbors; i.e., as if no molecule had a particularly wide range of influence as a result of having a particularly high energy.

A similar argument would seem to be quite adaptable to those "collectives" encountered in social sciences, for which the size of the largest contributor is negligible as compared to the total "size." In other words, if "size" is interpreted as the population of a city, the random walk argument would be adaptable with little further argument if the largest U were negligible with respect to the sum of all U's. If, however, the variance of U is infinite, there is no way of weighting the sum $\Sigma_{m=1}^{M} U_n$ so that it converges to the usual Gaussian limit as M tends to infinity. Moreover, the size of the largest of M independent U_m is not at all negligible in comparison with their sum (in fact, the population of the largest city is often of the order of magnitude of one-tenth of the total population). As a result, it seems *a priori* absurdly far-fetched to assume that the populations of small or medium-sized cities can evolve independently of those of the largest ones. And still one gets correct results by assuming that they do!

We know, of course, that it is common to find that stochastic models yield results more reasonable than any of their assumptions: somehow, various small errors seem to cancel out. But in the present case the situation is different because the contributing errors are *not* small, either absolutely or relatively.

Therefore, let us resume our original discussion by recalling that the predictivity of the model based upon random walk is hardly more unexpected than the very existence of a single analytic expression (^{0}): one would think the rules governing population change would be very dependent upon present size; for medium-size cities, one would accept random explanations, but for the largest ones, one would immediately look for "causes." In a quite similar fashion, small price changes are readily considered as being random, while one attempts to explain causally the larger changes. And yet the same law (^{0}) holds over all the data!

All these considerations suggest that one should not underestimate the scope of laws based upon curve-fitting when they are explainable by stochastic models. That is, one need not consider *a priori* that the largest and most important phenomena are different *in nature* from the small "noise." Quite the contrary, one may argue that the same mechanisms act all through the range of city sizes (or incomes or price changes). If a city, income, or price change is large, one can *a posteriori* track back its causes; but if it is small, such tracking is impossible, so that a quantity *will seem "random"* *precisely because it is small*. Of course, nothing could guarantee *a priori* that stochastic arguments would predict the overall structure of the set of *all* city sizes, but one need not consider this as being impossible.

Finally, let us note that we consider the random walk of the logarithm of population as being a very primitive model: the considerations of reference 6 in note 1 give a deeper insight into the role of the law of Pareto, and the results of references 2 and 3 can be translated into a model of the distribution of population among various cities and between various socioeconomic functions.[5]

---

[5] This distribution has been empirically studied by D. D. Bourland, Jr., "The Distribution of Professions within Cities in the United States," *The American Journal of Psychology*, Vol. 63, 1950, pp. 244–49.

21

The Application of Latent Structure Analysis to Quantitative Ecological Data

PAUL F. LAZARSFELD and NEIL W. HENRY [*]

IN the social sciences the formation of basic variables is a continuing challenge. On an observational level, the social world is more fluid than the physical world, and does not offer such "natural" units as centimeters, grams, and hours. At the same time we do not have any extensive theories from which we can derive basic concepts, such as absolute temperature and kinetic energy. As a result we try to develop "measurement models," which are efforts to formalize what the social scientist does when he constructs indices, scales, or whatever he might call his classificatory instruments.

A major purpose of these measurement models is to bring out clearly the assumptions implied by a specific technique. The model itself does not permit a decision as to which of several techniques is more desirable; this can be established only through empirical studies or through substantive theoretical considerations. It is, however, possible to examine whether a given model is of broad enough generality to adapt itself to a large number of existing techniques.

In recent years the desirable tendency has prevailed to derive quantitative measurements from elementary qualitative operations. Two of the most common approaches to this quantification have been the method of *paired comparisons*, which makes use of the subject's preference between two alternatives to determine a measure of "distance" between the alternatives, and the analysis of *itemized tests*, which are observations of responses to discrete variables. These observations may be of certain characteristics of the subject, of whether he agrees with a given statement, or, generally, of anything which has a finite number of possible alternatives. Latent Structure Analysis is a model which was developed for tests in which the items are all dichotomous: yes or no responses to questions, presence or absence of specified traits, etc.

* Columbia University.

The Origins of Latent Structure Analysis

We do not intend to give the logical foundations of latent structure analysis here, as they have been discussed in a considerable number of publications (e.g., Lazarsfeld, 1954, 1959). It is, however, worthwhile to consider briefly the origin of latent structure analysis. Louis Guttman first emphasized that traditional psychometric procedures should not be applied to qualitative data. For instance, we are usually not justified in applying factor analysis to a set of dichotomous variables, since the results of a factor analysis may be quite different, according to what we use as a measure of the correlations between items (e.g., phi-coefficients, tetra-chorics, etc.). More important, however, is the fact that factor analysis neglects the relationships among more than two items: if scores on three items are symbolized, respectively, by X, Y and Z, the notion of the expected value of (XYZ) never enters the analysis. With dichotomous data, however, such "higher order correlations" are of practical importance; for example, in high educated strata, men and women are about equally likely to vote; in low educated strata women go to the polls much less frequently than men. We therefore have to use all the response patterns (in this example, the eight combinations of male-female, high-low education, and voting-not voting) to completely understand the situation. The task of a model such as latent structure analysis is to provide a rationale for ordering these response patterns ("response" may refer to the observation of any kind of dichotomous item).

Guttman's first solution was what is known as perfect scale. He stipulated that the items which formed his famous hierarchy could be combined into a "one-dimensional measurement." The assumption, however, is rather restrictive. Latent structure analysis generalized Guttman's model by introducing notions of probability. The model introduced the idea that subjects were located in a hypothetical *latent space*. At each point of this space, every item of the test has a certain probability of being observed. (Guttman himself subsequently broadened these ideas even further.)

Other authors soon considered the relation between such a model and the conventional model of factor analysis. As a result, a curious inversion took place. Originally, the latent structure analysis was developed as a procedure to deal with qualitative material. It then turned out that it could also be applied to quantitative data, or at least to the averages of quantitative variables. But, instead of yielding factors, the latent structure analysis model yields *typologies*, each type being represented by a specific average score on each of the variables involved in the investigation.

We will present in this paper the basic algebra of the latent profile model as developed by W. A. Gibson (1959). We will then apply the model, using as data demographic information about the 88 counties of the state of Ohio. For simplicity's sake only five quantitative variables will be introduced. The general idea can be applied to the analysis of as many as 15 variables with the help of a high-speed computer.

Two Discrete Class Models

A. The Discrete Class Model of Latent Structure Analysis. In the discrete class model of latent structure analysis the population is assumed to be clustered into homogeneous latent classes: the division is not directly observable. The manifest (observable) data are the proportions of the population who respond positively to the items and to combinations of the items. Thus p_i, p_{ij}, p_{ijk} denote first, second, and third order positive proportions, respectively. The *latent parameters* are the relative class sizes: v^1, v^2 ... v^q; and the probability of positive response for each item (i) within a class (x) is p_i^x.

The assumption of local independence is made. That is, within a particular class, a response to any item is independent of the response to any other item. Thus the equations relating the manifest and latent parameters are as follows:

$$1 = \sum_x v^x ;$$

$$p_i = \sum_x v^x p_i^x \quad , \text{ for all items } i;$$

$$p_{ij} = \sum_x v^x p_i^x p_j^x \quad , \text{ for all distinct } i,j;$$

$$p_{ijk} = \sum_x v^x p_i^x p_j^x p_k^x , \text{ for all distinct } i,j,k; \tag{1}$$

etc., where all the summations are over the q latent classes. p_{ij} and other terms having repeated subscripts are not observable quantities, and are defined implicitly in terms of the latent parameters.

A solution of this model is any method which enables us to estimate the latent parameters, (v^x, p_i^x), given a set of observable manifest data. Anderson (1954) and Lazarsfeld (1961) have worked out one solution for the latent class model, which we will use in this paper. (Another solution, that of Green (1951) requires the estimation of terms with repeated subscripts, e.g., p_{jj}, unlike the Anderson method.) Problems arise in the solution due to the fact that there are more independent equations than unknown parameters. When we are considering a real problem, when the data are subject to sampling error and may not fit the model *exactly*, it is possible to obtain several different solutions (sets of latent parameters). Each solution would fit some of the data very well, and some of the data less well, depending on how the manifest data were used in that solution of the model. A study of the variability of latent parameters was made by Anderson and

Carleton (n.d.), and ways of finding a "best" solution have been studied.

B. *Latent Profile Analysis.* Let us suppose that q different quantitative characteristics of N individuals have been observed. i's score on variable j will be denoted by $y_{j,i}$. The average score on variable j is $\bar{Y}_j$ and the variance is:

$$(s_j)^2 = \frac{1}{N}\sum_i (Y_{j,i} - \bar{Y}_j)^2.$$

We standardize each of these scores by subtracting the mean and dividing by the standard deviation. The resulting scores:

$$Z_{j,i} = (Y_{j,i} - \bar{Y}_j)/s_j, \tag{2}$$

have mean zero and variance equal to one.

The equations:

$$\frac{1}{N}\sum_i Z_{j,i} = m_j = 0,$$

$$\frac{1}{N}\sum_i Z_{j,i}\, Z_{k,i} = r_{jk},$$

$$\frac{1}{N}\sum_i Z_{j,i}\, Z_{k,i}\, Z_{m,i} = r_{jkm}, \tag{3}$$

etc., where summations are over all N individuals, serve to *define* the *manifest parameters* of latent profile analysis (*LPA*). r_{jk} is simply the ordinary product moment correlation between tests j and k; r_{jkm} is the "average triple product" or third order correlation. Higher order correlations are similarly defined. Latent profile analysis thus uses the same manifest parameters as the ordinary factor analysis model, with the *addition* of newly defined higher order correlations, e.g., r_{123}.

The latent profile model is similar to the latent structure model in that the population is assumed to be divided into several homogeneous groups. The latent parameters are v^x, the relative size of class x, and m_j^x, the *average score on variable j for members of class x*. The accounting equations, analogous to equations 1, are:

$$1 = \sum_x v^x,$$

$$m_j = 0 = \sum_x v^x m_j^x,$$

$$r_{jk} = \sum_x v^x m_j^x m_k^x,$$

$$r_{ijk} = \sum_x v^x m_j^x m_k^x m_i^x, \tag{4}$$

etc., for higher order correlations.

In order to obtain the accounting equations (*1*) we had to assume within-class independence of items. The same assumption must be made in order to arrive at the LPA equations (4). Each class is homogeneous in the sense that within any class the items are independent, all the correlations among items being zero. Equations (4) are derived using only this assumption of "local independence."

Since equations (4) are algebraically identical with the equations of the latent structure model (1), the solution derived for that model can be applied to the latent profile model. Table 1 shows the corresponding symbols of the two models.

TABLE 1

SYMBOL SUMMARY

Manifest Parameters	LSA	LPA
1st order	p_i: proportion positive to item i	m_i: mean standard score on item i
2nd order	p_{ij}: proportion positive to i and j	r_{ij}: correlation between items i and j
3rd order	p_{ijk}: proportion positive to i, and j, and k	r_{ijk}: third order correlations
Latent parameters	v^x: proportion in latent class x	v^x: proportion in class x
	p_i^x: probability of positive response to item i for someone in class x	m_i^x: mean standard score on item (test, dimension) i within class x

An Application of Latent Profile Analysis to Real Data

A. The Data and the Solution. Gibson (1959), in both his exposition and his examples, referred to latent profile analysis as applied to scores on psychological tests. Rather than apply the model to psychological variables and attributes, however, we will consider ecological variables, with the "subject" or unit of analysis being a county. C. T. Jonassen (1959 and 1960) compiled a total of 82 variables, some of them census figures, such as population and income, and others derived indices, such as socioeconomic status, for each of the 88 counties in Ohio. He then proceeded with a factor analysis of the entire 82 by 82 correlation matrix to obtain dimensions of community systems.

As an example of the potentialities of the latent profile model, five of Jonassen's variables were chosen. These variables, numbered 1–5 (Jonassen's numbering is in parentheses) are:

1. Weekly local newspaper circulation per capita, 1950 (9).
2. Percent of persons 25 years or over who completed high school, 1950 (34).
3. Local educational expenditures per pupil, 1953 (41).

4. Socioeconomic status (SES), 1950 (62).[1]
5. Per capita retail sales, 1954 (77).

We are interested in dividing the 88 counties into several classes by applying the latent profile model to this set of five variables. A different set of variables would, of course, lead to a different grouping of the counties. The five variables we have chosen are all oriented toward the economic level of the counties; another set of variables might measure some dimension or dimensions less related to the economy.

The means and the standard deviations of the five variables were computed from the raw data given by Jonassen (1959, pp. 73–155), and are included in Table 2.

TABLE 2

Observed Means and Standard Deviations of Five Items

	Mean	Standard Deviation
1. Newspaper circulation/capita/week	1.445	0.99
2. Percent high school graduates	33.4	6.55
3. Local education $/pupil	111.5	39.7
4. Socioeconomic status index	178	76.6
5. Retail sales/capita	990	260.6

The second-order correlations, r_{jk}, were taken directly from Jonassen (1960, Table 4). These are given in our Table 3. Preliminary inspection of the data indicated that two latent classes would not be sufficient to account for the observed correlations, so a three-class model was postulated.

TABLE 3

Second Order Correlations: r_{jk}

	Matrix of Correlations				
	1	2	3	4	5
Newspaper 1	—	.366	.547	.545	.402
High school 2	.366	—	.616	.835	.405
Education $ 3	.547	.616	—	.746	.459
SES 4	.545	.835	.746	—	.505
Retail sales 5	.402	.405	.459	.505	—

The Anderson-Lazarsfeld solution for the latent parameters is not symmetric. That is, one item is chosen to be the *stratifier*, and the only third-order data used in the solution are those in which this item appears. In this

---

[1] Variable 4, socioeconomic status, is derived by Jonassen from the rank orderings of the counties on the following four items: "Family Income," "Home Value," "Professional Workers" and "Unskilled Workers." A high value of the index means that the county has high SES. Since this is a rank order measure, no comparisons can be made to counties outside Ohio.

case, variable 5 was chosen as stratifier, so, for the solution, $r_{135}, r_{145}, r_{235}$ and r_{245} had to be computed from the raw data according to the definition, equations (3). All of the second-order correlations are used in the solution. The basic matrices (B and B_5) used in the solution are given in Table 4. B is called the *unstratified*, and B_5 the *stratified* basic matrix.

TABLE 4

BASIC MATRICES OF MANIFEST DATA

$$B: \begin{pmatrix} 1 & m_1 & m_2 \\ m_3 & r_{13} & r_{23} \\ m_4 & r_{14} & r_{24} \end{pmatrix} = \begin{pmatrix} 1 & 0 & 0 \\ 0 & .547 & .616 \\ 0 & .545 & .835 \end{pmatrix}$$

$$B_5: \begin{pmatrix} m_5 & r_{15} & r_{25} \\ r_{35} & r_{135} & r_{235} \\ r_{45} & r_{145} & r_{245} \end{pmatrix} = \begin{pmatrix} 0 & .402 & .405 \\ .459 & .1089 & -.1995 \\ .505 & .0511 & -.2573 \end{pmatrix}$$

The first step in the Anderson-Lazarsfeld solution is to solve the determinantal equation $|tB - B_5| = 0$, the roots being the three class means of item 5. The remainder of the solution procedure is included in the appendix. The latent parameters obtained by this method are given in Table 5 in standard units; e.g., $m_1' = 1.19$ means that this group mean is 1.19 standard deviations above the overall mean for variable 1. Table 6 gives these group means in terms of the original measures.

TABLE 5

LATENT PROFILE SOLUTION; CLASS MEANS IN STANDARD UNITS

	Classes		
	I	II	III
1. Newspaper	1.19	— .26	— .64
2. High school	.32	1.16	−1.23
3. Education $	1.03	.22	— .95
4. SES	.95	.56	−1.17
5. Retail sales	.76	.10	— .63
Relative Class Sizes	.282	.332	.386

TABLE 6

LATENT CLASS MEANS IN ORIGINAL UNITS

	I	II	III	Units
1. Newspaper	2.62	1.19	0.81	Circulation/week/capita
2. High school	36	41	25	Percent of adult population
3. Education $	153	120	74	Dollars/pupil
4. SES	250	220	89	SES index
5. Retail sales	1188	1016	826	Dollars/capita

Fit of the Model. Once we have found the latent parameters we can substitute them into equations *(4)* to obtain the fitted manifest parameters. Comparison of the actual data with these fitted means and correlations indicated that the three-class model agreed quite well with the population characteristics. These comparisons of real and fitted data are shown in Table 7.

TABLE 7

COMPARISON OF REAL AND FITTED MEANS AND CORRELATIONS

Item:	1	2	3	4	5
Fitted Means:	.0022	.0006	−.0032	.0022	.0043
		Fitted Correlations above Diagonal, Residuals below			
1. Newspaper	—	.311	.561	.559	.402
2. High school	−.055	—	.629	.857	.406
3. Education $	.014	.013	—	.746	.459
4. SES	.014	.022	.000	—	.507
5. Retail sales	.000	.001	.000	.002	—

	Third-Order Correlations				
	r_{135}	r_{145}	r_{235}	r_{245}	r_{345}
Actual:	.1089	.0511	−.1995	−.2573	−.0428
Fitted:	.1130	.0534	−.2051	−.2632	−.0565

Because of the difficulty involved in computing the higher order correlations from the data, only five of the third-order correlations were computed.

B. Interpretation of Results. The latent structure solution presented in Tables 5 and 6 shows that it is possible to divide the 88 counties of Ohio into three groups, each having a mean score on each of the five variables as indicated in the tables. There would be approximately 25 counties in class I, 29 in class II, 34 in class III, and the items would be uncorrelated in each class. Of course, even though we know what the size of each class is, and what the item means are for each class, we cannot make a definite assignment of counties to classes. (We will discuss this classification problem in a subsequent section.) The only way in which we can speak with confidence about the characteristics of the classes is to find certain counties whose profiles of scores are very similar to one of the class mean profiles (Figure 1). By considering these to be "typical" of the classes, we can proceed to draw conclusions about the classes.

We found that Stark and Erie counties were typical of class I, Delaware and Knox of class II, and Brown and Hocking of class III. The "typical" class I county is a strongly urban area, highly industrialized, ranking high in family income. In contrast, the typical class III counties are very low on the economic ladder, being either rural areas or poor industrial areas with a high concentration of unskilled workers. In marked contrast with the rest

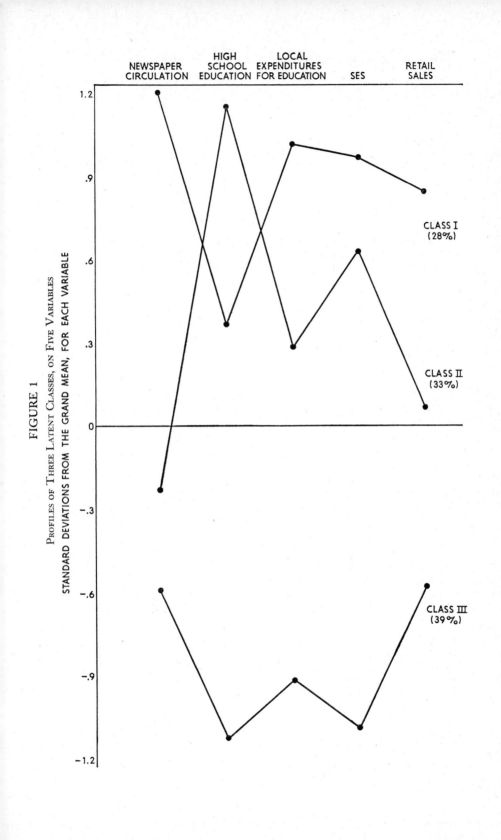

FIGURE 1

PROFILES OF THREE LATENT CLASSES, ON FIVE VARIABLES

STANDARD DEVIATIONS FROM THE GRAND MEAN, FOR EACH VARIABLE

NEWSPAPER CIRCULATION
HIGH SCHOOL EDUCATION
LOCAL EXPENDITURES FOR EDUCATION
SES
RETAIL SALES

1.2
.9
.6
.3
0
-.3
-.6
-.9
-1.2

CLASS I (28%)

CLASS II (33%)

CLASS III (39%)

of the state, these class III counties showed little increase in population from 1940 to 1950, and some had decreased in size. Class II can be characterized as fairly prosperous areas, without, however, the massive urban concentration of class I counties. Urban areas of 10–20,000 persons—trading centers rather than industrial centers, with a large proportion of professional people and skilled workers—are typical of class II counties.

High local newspaper circulation is an urban phenomenon, occurring where the great majority of papers are published; and this explains the large gap between class I and class II on item 1. The SES index and the retail sales are tied very closely to the economic level of the county, as is the local expenditure for education, which is probably strongly correlated with the amount of taxable industrial activity there. We thus see that our classification can best be described as a two-dimensional process: first there is an economic barrier separating class III from the other two classes, and then classes I and II are separated by urbanization. Figure 1, the class profiles, indicates that a simple rule for classifying the 88 counties might be to use SES, item 4, to get the class III counties, and then to use item 1, newspaper circulation, to separate class I from class II, since these items are good discriminators.

The behavior of item 2, high school education, is quite interesting. We usually think of education as being correlated positively with SES or with the amount people are willing to spend on education, and the manifest correlations support this view. Yet the latent profiles of the three classes (Figure 1) show that class II ranks highest on item 2, while falling below class I on the other four variables. The reason for this relationship among the items is clear when we recall that the major difference between classes I and II is in the degree of urbanization of the counties. The class I counties have higher average incomes than the class II counties, but also contain a slightly higher proportion of unskilled workers, who undoubtedly contribute the most to the non-high-school-graduate category.[2]

Our *typical* class I counties are by no means the most urban in Ohio, although Stark County contains the city of Canton, and Erie contains Sandusky. Counties such as Hamilton, which includes Cincinnati, and Cuyahoga, which contains Cleveland, might be called *extreme* class I counties, rather than typical. They would surely be assigned to class I, since they rank much higher than the class I averages on items 1, 3, 4 and 5, while their profiles show the characteristic drop for item 2. (Cuyahoga is higher than the class I average on item 2, but is slightly below the class II average.) See Figure 2 for the profiles of these counties.

---

[2] We must remember that these statements are based on data collected in the early 1950s. It would be interesting to repeat the analysis using data from the 1960s to see whether the "suburban boom" of the '50s will be reflected by a change in the latent profiles of the classes. For instance, we might expect the class II counties to be spending more on education today.

FIGURE 2

Profiles of Two Large, Urban Counties Compared with the
Profile of Latent Class I

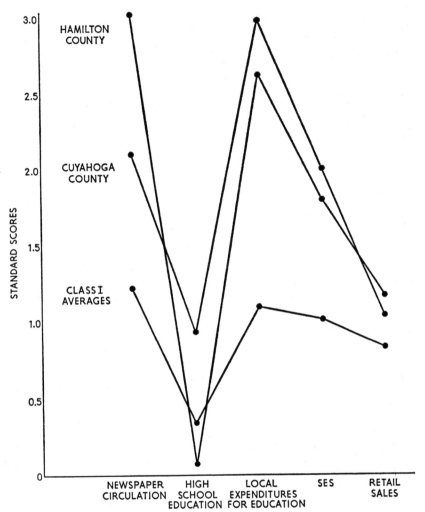

Classification in the Latent Profile Model

For any latent profile model the latent class means and the class frequencies can be obtained from manifest correlations by a straightforward
application of the latent structure solution developed for dichotomous
data. This is of little practical value, however, if we cannot assign the
members of the population to one or another of these classes. The classification procedure generally used in the case of the LSA model makes use
of the fact that the latent parameters are *probabilities*, and assigns an indi-

vidual to that class to which it is *most probable* he belongs on the basis of his response pattern (see Lazarsfeld, 1954, pp. 379–83). Such a procedure cannot be applied to the latent profile model since the parameters are means and not probabilities.

If there are n items under analysis, each individual can be thought of as a point in an n dimensional Euclidean space, the coordinates of that point being the scores on each of the items. There is also a point representing each of the latent classes. We propose to assign each individual to the class to which he is *closest*, using the usual Euclidean measure of distance. In our example, for instance, we had a five-item, three-class model. We have computed the within-class averages, m_i^x, $i = 1, \ldots 5$, $x = 1, 2, 3$. (These means are in standard form; so that all of the five dimensions have comparable units.) Consider a county which has standardized scores of $(Y_1, Y_2, Y_3, Y_4, Y_5)$ on the five items. We compute the three statistics:

$$A = \sum_{i=1}^{5} (Y_i - m_i^1)^2,$$

$$B = \sum_{i=1}^{5} (Y_i - m_i^2)^2,$$

$$C = \sum_{i=1}^{5} (Y_i - m_i^3)^2,$$

which are, of course, the squares of the distances from the county to each of the three class points. If A is smallest, it is assigned to class I, if B is smallest, to class II, and if C is smallest it is assigned to class III.

What we are doing is dividing the five-dimensional-item space into three regions, so that all the counties in a region belong to the same class. We carried out the above classification scheme for our example, getting 22 counties in class I, 32 counties in class II, and 34 counties in class III. This division compares favorably with the theoretical division result of 25/29/34, based on the latent class sizes of Table 5. The counties assigned to class III are mostly from southern Ohio, in the poorer section of the state. Class I counties generally contain the main industrial centers of the state: Dayton, Akron, Sandusky, etc., as well as Cleveland and Cincinnati. The class II counties could be called suburban areas, as they are nearly always adjacent to a class I county. This assignment of counties to classes is given in Table 8.

We must remember, however, that this assignment is only approximately accurate. The model assumes that, within a latent class, the correlations among items vanish. Since we cannot with certainty assign a county to the proper class, we cannot expect that the correlations will be zero when computed for the groups formed by applying this procedure. In fact, the correlations which we have computed for these three groups are fairly low,

TABLE 8

CLASSIFICATION OF 88 COUNTIES OF OHIO ON THE BASIS
OF A LATENT PROFILE ANALYSIS (See Table 3)

Class I	Class II	Class III
1. Ashtabula	1. Allen	1. Adams
2. Butler	2. Ashland	2. Belmont
3. Clark	3. Athens	3. Brown
4. Cuyahoga	4. Auglaize	4. Carroll
5. Erie	5. Champaign	5. Clermont
6. Franklin	6. Clinton	6. Columbiana
7. Hamilton	7. Crawford	7. Coshocton
8. Hancock	8. Defiance	8. Darke
9. Jefferson	9. Delaware	9. Fayette
10. Lorain	10. Fairfield	10. Gallia
11. Lucas	11. Fulton	11. Guernsey
12. Mahoning	12. Geauga	12. Harrison
13. Marion	13. Greene	13. Highland
14. Montgomery	14. Hardin	14. Hocking
15. Muskingum	15. Henry	15. Holmes
16. Richland	16. Huron	16. Jackson
17. Sandusky	17. Knox	17. Lawrence
18. Shelby	18. Lake	18. Madison
19. Stark	19. Licking	19. Meigs
20. Summit	20. Logan	20. Monroe
21. Van Wert	21. Medina	21. Morgan
22. Wayne	22. Mercer	22. Morrow
	23. Miami	23. Noble
	24. Ottawa	24. Paulding
	25. Portage	25. Perry
	26. Preble	26. Pickaway
	27. Seneca	27. Pike
	28. Trumbull	28. Putnam
	29. Union	29. Ross
	30. Williams	30. Scioto
	31. Wood	31. Tuscarawas
	32. Wyandot	32. Vinton
		33. Warren
		34. Washington

and definitely lower than the manifest correlations. The fact that a few are comparatively large indicates that there are problems either of classification, or else of fit, which have not been satisfactorily solved.

We note that this method of classification does not possess any desirable statistical properties, such as consistency. It is not a maximum likelihood assignment, and it does not seem possible to carry out any maximum likelihood procedure unless we make some *a priori* assumptions about the distribution of the counties within the classes. We are still investigating classification procedures that might be more efficient than the one used here.[3]

Conclusion

We have not, in this paper, touched on a number of computational problems that are inherent to the latent structure solution. For instance, in applying the solution we chose item 5 to be the "stratifier." Since we are analyzing data which fit the model only approximately, using another of the items as stratifier in the solution would lead to a set of latent parameters slightly different from the one found here. Experimentation with many numerical examples has shown that if the overall fit of the data to the model is fairly good, the variation in the latent item means (latent probabilities in the LSA model) is not too great, but that there may be a large variation in the estimates of the class sizes obtained using different arrangements of the same data. There are various ways of obtaining average or "best" estimates in some sense (e.g., maximum likelihood), but these will not be discussed here.[4]

In summary, we have found that latent profile analysis allows us to characterize the latent classes by the mean score of each variable for each class. In addition, the variables are uncorrelated within each class. Thus we can speak meaningfully of "social types" within a population; as here the types were the three kinds of counties. Although Jonassen's factor analysis of 82 variables is certainly a more elaborate study than ours, we believe that the ability of the latent profile approach to consider the correlations among several (more than two) items may prove very useful in many situations.

APPENDIX: SOLUTION OF THE LATENT PROFILE MODEL

As indicated in the section "An Application of Latent Profile Analysis to Real Data," the first step in the Anderson-Lazarsfeld solution is to solve the equation $\mid tB - B_5 = 0$, the basic matrices B and B_5 as defined in that section. The three roots of this equation are the latent parameters of the stratifier, m_5^1, m_5^2, m_5^3. Next we form three matrices G^1, G^2, G^3, as follows:

---

[3] W. A. Gibson, in the 1962 *Journal of Applied Psychology*, has derived the maximum likelihood assignment procedure assuming that within-class observations are normally distributed and that the within-class variance of a variable is the same in each class.

[4] Computer programs for estimating the parameters of latent class models have been developed at the Bureau of Applied Social Research. One program, following the Anderson solution described herein, can be applied to the latent profile model. A program which computes maximum likelihood estimates for the latent class parameters has proven useful, but cannot be applied to the continuous variables of latent profile analysis.

$$G^x = \begin{pmatrix} \overset{m_x}{5} & -r_{15} & -r_{25} \\ -r_{35} & m_5^x\, r_{13} - r_{135} & m_5^x\, r_{23} - r_{235} \\ -r_{45} & m_5^x\, r_{14} - r_{145} & m_5^x\, r_{24} - r_{245} \end{pmatrix} = \begin{pmatrix} g_{11}^x & g_{12}^x & g_{13}^x \\ g_{21}^x & g_{22}^x & g_{23}^x \\ g_{31}^x & g_{32}^x & g_{33}^x \end{pmatrix} \;;$$

$x = 1, 2, 3.$

Define C_0^x, C_1^x, C_2^x as the signed cofactors of the first row of G^x, and $C_0^x, C_3^x,$ and $C_4^x,$ as the signed cofactors of the first column of G^x. That is, the Cs are the determinants:

$$C_0^x = \begin{vmatrix} g_{22}^x & g_{23}^x \\ g_{32}^x & g_{33}^x \end{vmatrix} ; \quad C_1^x = - \begin{vmatrix} g_{21}^x & g_{23}^x \\ g_{31}^x & g_{33}^x \end{vmatrix} ; \quad C_2^x = \begin{vmatrix} g_{21}^x & g_{22}^x \\ g_{31}^x & g_{32}^x \end{vmatrix} ;$$

$$C_3^x = - \begin{vmatrix} g_{12}^x & g_{13}^x \\ g_{32}^x & g_{33}^x \end{vmatrix} ; \quad C_4^x = \begin{vmatrix} g_{12}^x & g_{13}^x \\ g_{22}^x & g_{23}^x \end{vmatrix} .$$

Lazarsfeld (1961) has shown that:

$$m_j^x = \frac{r_{1j}\, C_1^x + r_{2j}\, C_2^x}{C_0^x} \qquad \text{when } j = 3 \text{ or } 4, \text{ and}$$

$$m_i^x = \frac{r_{3i}\, C_3^x + r_{4i}\, C_4^x}{C_0^x} \qquad \text{when } i = 1 \text{ or } 2.$$

Once we have obtained all the latent class means, the latent class frequencies v^1, v^2 and v^3 can be estimated in a number of ways. We choose to solve the five linear equations:

$$\sum_{x=1}^{3} m_j^x\, v^x = 0 \quad \text{and} \quad j = 1,2,3,4,5,$$

by least squares, subject to the condition that $v^3 = 1 - v^1 - v^2$. In this way we are able to fit the first order data (means) quite well.

Since the derivation of this solution is beyond the scope of this paper, we have not attempted to prove any of the assertions made here. Proofs may be found in the papers by Anderson and Lazarsfeld.

REFERENCES

ANDERSON, T. W.   "On Estimation of Parameters in Latent Structure Analysis," *Psychometrika*, Vol. 19, 1954.

———— and CARLETON, R. O.   "A Sampling Experiment and Its Implications" (Dittoed). New York: Bureau of Applied Social Research, Columbia University.

GIBSON, W. A.   "Three Multivariate Models: Factor Analysis, Latent Structure Analysis, and Latent Profile Analysis," *Psychometrika*, Vol. 24, 1959.

GREEN, B. F.   "A General Solution for the Latent Class Model of Latent Structure Analysis," *Psychometrika*, Vol. 16, 1951.

JONASSEN, C. T.   *The Measurement of Community Dimensions and Elements.* Columbus, O.: Center for Educational Administration, Ohio State University Press, 1959.

—— and PERES, S.   *Interrelationships of Dimensions of Community Systems.* Columbus, O.: Ohio State University Press, 1960.

LAZARSFELD, P. F.   "A Conceptual Introduction to Latent Structure Analysis," Chapter 7 in *Mathematical Thinking in the Social Sciences*, P. F. LAZARSFELD (ed.). Glencoe, Ill.: Free Press, 1954.

——.   "An Extended Solution of the Discrete Class Case," Memorandum No. 1, *New Developments in Latent Structure Analysis*. New York: Bureau of Applied Social Research, Columbia University, 1961.

——.   "Latent Structure Analysis," in *Psychology: A Study of a Science*, S. KOCH, (ed.). New York: McGraw-Hill, Inc., 1959.

The Economic Implications of Learning by Doing*

22

Kenneth J. Arrow [†]

IT IS by now incontrovertible that increases in per capita income cannot be explained simply by increases in the capital-labor ratio. Though doubtless no economist would ever have denied the role of technological change in economic growth, its overwhelming importance relative to capital formation has perhaps only been fully realized with the important empirical studies of Abramovitz [1] and Solow.[2]

These results do not directly contradict the neoclassical view of the production function as an expression of technological knowledge. All that has to be added is the obvious fact that knowledge is growing in time. Nevertheless, a view of economic growth that depends so heavily on an exogenous variable, let alone one so difficult to measure as the quantity of knowledge, is hardly intellectually satisfactory. From a quantitative, empirical point of view, we are left with time as an explanatory variable. Now trend projections, however necessary they may be in practice, are basically a confession of ignorance, and, what is worse from a practical viewpoint, they are not policy variables.

Further, the concept of knowledge which underlies the production function at any moment needs analysis. Knowledge has to be acquired. We are not surprised, as educators, that even students subject to the same educational experiences have different bodies of knowledge, and we may therefore be prepared to grant, as has been shown empirically (see Arrow, Chenery, Minhas and Solow [3]), that different countries, at the same mo-

* Subsequent to presentation at the Cambria Pines Conference, this paper was published in *Review of Economic Studies*, Vol. 29, No. 3, pp. 155–73.

† Stanford University.

[1] M. Abramovitz, "Resource and Output Trends in the United States Since 1870," *American Economic Review, Papers and Proceedings of the American Economic Association*, Vol. 46, May, 1956, pp. 5–23.

[2] R. M. Solow, "Technical Change and the Aggregate Production Function," *Review of Economics and Statistics*, Vol. 39, 1957, pp. 312–20.

[3] K. J. Arrow, H. B. Chenery, S. Minhas, and R. M. Solow, "Capital-Labor Substitution and Economic Efficiency," *Review of Economics and Statistics*, Vol. 43, 1961, Part III, pp. 225–50.

ment of time, have different production functions even apart from differences in natural resource endowment.

I would like to suggest here an endogenous theory of the changes in knowledge which underlie intertemporal and international shifts in production functions. The acquisition of knowledge is what is usually termed "learning," and we might perhaps pick up some clues from the many psychologists who have studied this phenomenon (for a convenient survey, see Hilgard [4]). I do not think that the picture of technical change as a vast and prolonged process of learning about the environment in which we operate is in any way a far-fetched analogy; exactly the same phenomenon of improvement in performance over time is involved.

Of course, psychologists are no more in agreement than economists, and there are sharp differences of opinion about the processes of learning. But one empirical generalization is so clear that all schools of thought must accept it, although they interpret it in different fashions: Learning is the product of experience. Learning can only take place through the attempt to solve a problem, and therefore takes place only during activity. Even the Gestalt and other field theorists, who stress the role of insight in the solution of problems (Köhler's famous apes), have to assign a significant role to previous experiences in modifying the individual's perception.

A second generalization that can be gleaned from many of the classic learning experiments is that learning associated with repetition of essentially the same problem is subject to sharply diminishing returns. There is an equilibrium response pattern for any given stimulus, toward which the behavior of the learner tends with repetition. To have steadily increasing performance, then, implies that the stimulus situations must themselves be steadily evolving rather than merely repeating.

The role of experience in increasing productivity has not gone unobserved, though the relation has yet to be absorbed into the main corpus of economic theory. It was early observed by aeronautical engineers, particularly T. P. Wright [5], that the number of labor-hours expended in the production of an airframe (airplane body without engines) is a decreasing function of the total number of airframes of the same type previously produced. Indeed, the relation is remarkably precise; to produce the Nth airframe of a given type, counting from the inception of production, the amount of labor required is proportional to $N^{-1/3}$. This relation has become basic in the production and cost planning of the United States Air Force (for a full survey, see Asher [6] and Hirsch [7], and other works cited). Hirsch

[4] E. R. Hilgard, *Theories of Learning* (2d ed., New York: Appleton-Century-Crofts, 1956).

[5] T. P. Wright, "Factors Affecting the Cost of Airplanes," *Journal of the Aeronautical Sciences*, Vol. 3, 1936, pp. 122–28.

[6] H. Asher, *Cost-Quantity Relationships in the Airframe Industry*, R-291 (Santa Monica, Calif.: The RAND Corporation, 1956).

[7] W. Z. Hirsch, "Firm Progress Radios," *Econometrica*, Vol. 24, 1956, pp. 136–43.

has shown the existence of the same type of "learning curve" or "progress ratio" (as it is variously termed) in the production of other machines, though the rate of learning is not the same as for airframes.

Lundberg [8] has given the name "Horndal effect" to a very similar phenomenon. The Horndal iron works in Sweden had no new investment (and therefore presumably no significant change in its methods of production) for a period of 15 years, yet productivity (output per man-hour) rose on the average close to 2 percent per annum. We find again steadily increasing performance which can only be imputed to learning from experience.

I advance the hypothesis here that technical change in general can be ascribed to experience; that it is the very activity of production which gives rise to problems for which favorable responses are selected over time. The evidence so far cited, whether from psychological or from economic literature, is of course, only suggestive. The aim of this paper is to formulate the hypothesis more precisely and to draw from it a number of economic implications. These should enable the hypothesis and its consequences to be confronted more easily with empirical evidence.

The model set forth will be very much simplified in some other respects to make clearer the essential role of the major hypothesis; in particular, the possibility of capital-labor substitution is ignored. The theorems about the economic world presented here differ from those in most standard economic theories: profits are the result of technical change; in a free-enterprise system, the rate of investment will be less than the optimum; net investment and the stock of capital become subordinate concepts, with gross investment taking a leading role.

In the first section, the basic assumptions of the model are set forth. In the second section, the implications for wage earners are deduced; in the third section, implications for profits, the inducement to invest, and the rate of interest. In the fourth section, the behavior of the entire system under steady growth with mutually consistent expectations is taken up. In the fifth section, the divergence between social and private returns is studied in detail for a special case (where the subjective rate of discount of future consumption is a constant). Finally, in the sixth section, some limitations of the model and needs for further development are noted.

The Model

The first question is that of choosing the economic variable which represents "experience." The economic examples given above suggest the possibility of using cumulative output (the total of output from the beginning of time) as an index of experience, but this does not seem entirely satis-

---

[8] E. Lundberg, *Produktivitet och räntabilitet* (Stockholm: P. A. Norstedt and Söner, 1961), pp. 129–33.

factory. If the rate of output is constant, then the stimulus to learning presented would appear to be constant, and the learning that actually takes place is a gradual approach to equilibrium behavior. I therefore take instead cumulative gross investment (cumulative production of capital goods) as an index of experience. Each new machine produced and put into use is capable of changing the environment in which production takes place, so that learning is taking place with continually new stimuli. This at least makes plausible the possibility of continued learning in the sense, here, of a steady rate of growth in productivity.

The second question is that of deciding where the learning enters the conditions of production. I follow here the model of Solow[9], and Johansen[10], in which technical change is completely embodied in new capital goods. At any moment of new time, the new capital goods incorporate all the knowledge then available, but, once built, their productive efficiency cannot be altered by subsequent learning.

To simplify the discussion we shall assume that the production process associated with any given new capital good is characterized by fixed coefficients, so that a fixed amount of labor is used and a fixed amount of output obtained. Further, it will be assumed that new capital goods are better than old ones in the strong sense that, if we compare a unit of capital goods produced at time t_1 with a unit produced at time $t_2 > t_1$, the first requires the cooperation of at least as much labor as the second, and produces no more product. Under this assumption, a new capital good will always be used in preference to an older one.

Let G be cumulative gross investment. A unit capital good produced when cumulative gross investment has reached G will be said to have *serial number* G. Let:

$\lambda(G) =$ amount of labor used in production with a capital good of serial number G,

$\gamma(G) =$ output capacity of a capital good of serial number G,

$x =$ total output,

$L =$ total labor force employed.

It is assumed that $\lambda(G)$ is a non-increasing function, while $\gamma(G)$ is a non-decreasing function. Then, regardless of wages or rental value of capital goods, it always pays to use a capital good of higher serial number before one of lower serial number.

It will further be assumed that capital goods have a fixed lifetime, T. Then capital goods disappear in the same order as their serial numbers. It follows that, at any moment of time, the capital goods in use will be all

---

[9] R. M. Solow, "Investment and Technical Progress," in K. J. Arrow, S. Karlin, and P. Suppes (ed.), *Mathematical Methods in the Social Sciences, 1959* (Stanford, Calif.: Stanford University Press, 1960), pp. 89–104.

[10] L. Johansen, "Substitution vs. Fixed Production Coefficients in the Theory of Economic Growth: A Synthesis," *Econometrica*, Vol. 27, 1959, pp. 157–76.

those with serial numbers from some G' to G, the current cumulative gross investment. Then:

$$x = \int_{G'}^{G} \gamma(G)dG, \tag{1}$$

$$L = \int_{G'}^{G} \lambda(G)dG. \tag{2}$$

The magnitudes x, L, G, and G' are, of course, all functions of time, to be designated by t, and they will be written $x(t)$, $L(t)$, $G(t)$, and $G'(t)$ when necessary to point up the dependence. Then $G(t)$, in particular, is the cumulative gross investment up to time t. The assumption about the lifetime of capital goods implies that:

$$G'(t) \geqq G(t - \bar{T}). \tag{3}$$

Since $G(t)$ is given at time t, we can solve for G' from (1) or (2) or the equality in (3). In a growth context, the most natural assumption is that of full employment. The labor force is regarded as a given function of time and is assumed equal to the labor employed, so that $L(t)$ is a given function. Then $G'(t)$ is obtained by solving in (2). If the result is substituted into (1), x can be written as a function of L and G, analogous to the usual production function.

To write this, define:

$$\Lambda(G) = \int \lambda(G)dG, \tag{4}$$
$$\Gamma(g) = \int \gamma(G)dG.$$

These are to be regarded as indefinite integrals. Since both $\lambda(G)$ and $\gamma(G)$ are positive, $\Lambda(G)$ and $\Gamma(G)$ are strictly increasing, and therefore have inverses, $\Lambda^{-1}(u)$ and $\Gamma^{-1}(v)$, respectively. Then (1) and (2) can be written, respectively:

$$x = \Gamma(G) - \Gamma(G'), \tag{1'}$$
$$L = \Lambda(G) - \Lambda(G'). \tag{2'}$$

Solve for G' from (2'):

$$G' = \Lambda^{-1}[\Lambda(G) - L]. \tag{5}$$

Substitute (5) into (1'):

$$x = \Gamma(G) - \Gamma\{\Lambda^{-1}[\Lambda(G) - L]\}, \tag{6}$$

which is thus a production function in a somewhat novel sense. Equation (6) is always valid, but, under the full employment assumption, we can regard L as the labor force available.

A second assumption, more suitable to a depression situation, is that in which demand for the product is the limiting factor. Then x is taken as given; G' can be derived from (1) or (1'), and employment can then be found from (2) or (2′). If this is less than the available labor force, we have Keynesian unemployment.

A third possibility, which, like the first, may be appropriate to a growth analysis, is that the solution (5), with L as the labor force, does not satisfy (3). In this case, there is a shortage of capital due to depreciation. There is again unemployment, but due now to structural discrepancies rather than to demand deficiency.

In any case, except by accident, there is either unemployed labor or unemployed capital; and there could be both in the demand deficiency case. Of course, a more neoclassical model, with substitution between capital and labor for each serial number of capital good, would permit full employment of both capital and labor, but this remains a subject for further study.

In what follows, the full-employment case will chiefly be studied. The capital shortage case, the third one, will be referred to only parenthetically. In the full-employment case, the depreciation assumption no longer matters; obsolescence, which occurs for all capital goods with serial numbers below $G′$, becomes the sole reason for the retirement of capital goods from use.

The analysis will be carried through for a special case. To a very rough approximation, the capital-output ratio has been constant while the labor-output ratio has been declining. It is therefore assumed that:

$$\gamma(G) = a, \tag{7}$$

a constant, while $\lambda(G)$ is a decreasing function of G. To be specific, it will be assumed that $\lambda(G)$ has the form found in the study of learning curves for airframes:

$$\lambda(G) = bG^{-n}, \tag{8}$$

where $n > 0$. Then:

$$\Gamma(G) = aG, \Lambda(G) = cG^{1-n}, \text{ where } c = b/(1 - n) \text{ for } n \neq 1.$$

Equation (6) then becomes:

$$x = aG\left[1 - \left(1 - \frac{L}{cG^{1-n}}\right)^{1/(1-n)}\right] \text{ if } n \neq 1. \tag{9}$$

Equation (9) is always well defined in the relevant range, since, from (2′):

$$L = \Lambda(G) - \Lambda(G′) \leq \Lambda(G) = cG^{1-n}.$$

When $n = 1$, $\Lambda(G) = b \log G$ (where the natural logarithm is understood), and:

$$x = aG(1 - e^{-L/b}) \text{ if } n = 1. \tag{10}$$

Although (9) and (10) are, in a sense, production functions, they show increasing returns to scale in the variables G and L. This is obvious in (10) where an increase in G, with L constant, increases x in the same proportion; a simultaneous increase in L will further increase x. In (9), first suppose that $n < 1$. Then a proportional increase in L and G increases L/G^{1-n}, and therefore increases the expression in brackets which multiplies G. A similar argument holds if $n > 1$. It should be noted that x increases more than proportionately to scale changes in G and L in general, not merely for the special case defined by (7) and (8). This could be verified by careful examination of the behavior of (6), when it is recalled that $\lambda(G)$ is non-increasing and $\gamma(G)$ is non-decreasing, with the strict inequality holding in at least one. It is obvious intuitively, since the additional amounts of L and G are used more efficiently than the earlier ones.

The increasing returns do not, however, lead to any difficulty with distribution theory. As we shall see, both capital and labor are paid their marginal products, suitably defined. The explanation is, of course, that the private marginal productivity of capital (more strictly, of new investment) is less than the social marginal productivity since the learning effect is not compensated in the market.

The production assumptions of this section are designed to play the role assigned by Kaldor to his "technical progress function," which relates the rate of growth of output per worker to the rate of growth of capital per worker.[11] I prefer to think of relations between rates of growth as themselves derived from more fundamental relations between the magnitude involved. Also, the present formulation puts more stress on gross rather than on net investment as the basic agent of technical change.

Earlier, Haavelmo had suggested a somewhat similar model.[12] Output depended on both capital and the stock of knowledge; and investment depended on output, the stock of capital, and the stock of knowledge. The stock of knowledge was either simply a function of time, or, in a more sophisticated version, the consequence of investment—the educational effect of each act of investment decreasing exponentially in time.

Wages

Under the full employment assumption, the profitability of using the capital good with serial number G' must be zero; for if it were positive, it would be profitable to use capital goods with higher serial number, and if it were negative, capital good G' would not be used, contrary to the definition of G'.

Let w = wage rate with output as numéraire. From (1') and (7):

$$G' = G - (x/a), \tag{11}$$

[11] N. Kaldor, "Capital Accumulation and Economic Growth," in F. A. Lutz and D. C. Hague (eds.), *The Theory of Capital* (New York: St. Martin's Press, 1961), Section VIII, pp. 177–222.

[12] T. Haavelmo, *A Study in the Theory of Economic Evolution* (Amsterdam: North Holland, 1954), sections 7.1 and 7.2.

so that:

$$\lambda(G') = b\left(G - \frac{x}{a}\right)^{-n}.\tag{12}$$

The output from capital good G' is $\gamma(G')$, while the cost of operation is $\lambda(G')w$. Hence:

$$\gamma(G') = \lambda(G')w,$$

or from (7) and (8):

$$w = a\left(G - \frac{x}{a}\right)^{n}/b.\tag{13}$$

It is interesting to derive labor's share, which is wL/x. From (2'), with $\Lambda(G) = cG^{1-n}$, and G' given by (11):

$$L = c\left[G^{1-n} - \left(G - \frac{x}{a}\right)^{1-n}\right],$$

for $n \neq 1$; and therefore:

$$wL/x = a\left[\left(\frac{G}{x} - \frac{1}{a}\right)^{n}\left(\frac{G}{x}\right)^{1-n} - \left(\frac{G}{x} - \frac{1}{a}\right)\right]/(1 - n) \text{ for } n \neq 1,\tag{14}$$

where use has been made of the relation $c = b/(1-n)$. It is interesting to note that labor's share is determined by the ratio G/x.

Since, however, x is determined by G and L, which, at any moment of time, are data, it is also useful to express the wage ratio, w, and labor's share, wL/x, in terms of L and G. First, G' can be found by solving for it from (2'):

$$G' = \left(G^{1-n} - \frac{L}{c}\right)^{1/(1-n)} \text{ for } n \neq 1.\tag{15}$$

We can then use the same reasoning as above, and derive:

$$w = a\left(G^{1-n} - \frac{L}{c}\right)^{n/(1-n)}/b,\tag{16}$$

$$\frac{wL}{x} = \frac{\left[\left(\frac{L}{G^{1-n}}\right)^{(1-n)/n} - \frac{1}{c}\left(\frac{L}{G^{1-n}}\right)^{1/n}\right]^{n/(1-n)}}{b\left[1 - \left(1 - \frac{L}{cG^{1-n}}\right)^{1/(1-n)}\right]}.\tag{17}$$

Labor's share thus depends on the ratio L/G^{1-n}; and it can be shown to decrease as the ratio increases.

For completeness, I note the corresponding formulas for the case $n = 1$. In terms of G and x, we have:

$$w = (aG - x)/b,\tag{18}$$

$$wL/x = \left(\frac{aG}{x} - 1\right)\log\frac{G/x}{(G/x) - (1/a)}.\tag{19}$$

In terms of G and L, we have:

$$G' = Ge^{-L/b},\tag{20}$$

$$w = \frac{aG}{be^{L/b}},\tag{21}$$

$$wL/x = \frac{L}{b(e^{L/b} - 1)}.\tag{22}$$

In this case, labor's share depends only on L, which is indeed the appropriate special case ($n = 1$) of the general dependence on L/G^{1-n}.

The preceding discussion has assumed full employment. In the capital shortage case there cannot be a competitive equilibrium with positive wage, since there is necessarily unemployment. To complete the model, it would be necessary to add an assumption about the behavior of wages. The most natural one would be that (real) wages steadily decline. This should increase the inducement to invest and therefore eventually lead to the ending of the capital shortage. But the matter is somewhat complex, since, as seen in more detail in the next section, the willingness to invest depends on expectations of future wages, and it would be necessary to make appropriate assumptions about these also.

Profits and Investment

The profit at time t from a unit investment made at time $v \leq t$ is:

$$\gamma[G(v)] - w(t)\lambda[G(v)].$$

In contemplating an investment at time v, the stream of potential profits depends upon expectations of future wages. We will suppose that, looking ahead at any given moment of time, each entrepreneur assumes that wages will rise exponentially from the present level. Thus the wage rate, expected at time v to prevail at time t, is:

$$w(v)e^{\theta(t-v)},$$

and the profit, expected at time v to be received at time t, is:

$$\gamma[G(v)]\,[1 - W(v)e^{\theta(t-v)}],$$

where

$$W(v) = w(v)\lambda[G(v)]/\gamma[G(v)],\tag{23}$$

the labor cost per unit output at the time the investment is made. The dependence of W on v will be made explicit only when necessary. The profitability of the investment is expected to decrease with time (if $\theta > 0$) and to reach zero at time $T^* + v$, defined by the equation:

$$W e^{\theta T^*} = 1.\tag{24}$$

Thus T^* is the expected economic lifetime of the investment, provided it does not exceed the physical lifetime, T. Let:

$$T = \min(\overline{T}, T^*).\tag{25}$$

Then the investor plans to derive profits only over an interval of length T, either because the investment wears out or because wages have risen to the point where it is unprofitable to operate. Since the expectation of wage rises, which causes this abandonment, derives from anticipated investment and the consequent technological progress, T^* represents the expected date of obsolescence. Let:

$$\rho = \text{rate of interest.}$$

If the rate of interest is expected to remain constant over the future, then the discounted stream of profits over the effective lifetime, T, of the investment is:

$$S = \int_0^T e^{-\rho t}\, \gamma[G(v)]\, (1 - W e^{\theta t})\,dt, \tag{26}$$

or

$$\frac{S}{\gamma[G(v)]} = \frac{1 - e^{-\rho T}}{\rho} + \frac{W(1 - e^{-(\rho-\theta)T})}{\theta - \rho}. \tag{27}$$

Let:

$$V = e^{-\theta T} = \max\,(e^{-\bar\theta T}, W), \quad \alpha = \rho/\theta. \tag{28}$$

Then:

$$\frac{\theta S}{\gamma[G(v)]} = \frac{1 - V^\alpha}{\alpha} + \frac{W(1 - V^{\alpha-1})}{1 - \alpha} = R(\alpha). \tag{29}$$

The definitions of $R(\alpha)$ for $\alpha = 0$ and $\alpha = 1$, needed to make the function continuous, are:

$$R(0) = -\log V + W(1 - V^{-1}), \quad R(1) = 1 - V + W \log V.$$

If all the parameters of (26), (27) or (29) are held constant, S is a function of ρ, and, equivalently, R of α. If (26) is differentiated with respect to ρ, we find:

$$dS/d\rho = \int_0^T (-t)e^{-\rho t}\gamma[G(v)]\, (1 - W e^{\theta t})\,dt < 0.$$

Also:

$$S < \gamma[G(v)]\int_0^T e^{-\rho t}dt = \gamma[G(v)]\,(1 - e^{-\rho T})/\rho < \gamma[G(v)]/\rho.$$

Since, obviously, $S > 0$, S approaches 0 as ρ approaches infinity. And, since R and α differ from S and ρ, respectively, only by positive constant factors, we conclude:

$$dR/d\alpha < 0, \quad \lim_{\alpha \to +\infty} R(\alpha) = 0.$$

To examine the behavior of $R(\alpha)$ as α approaches $-\infty$, write:

$$R(\alpha) = -\frac{(1/V)^{1-\alpha}}{(1 - \alpha)^2}\,[(1 - \alpha)V + \alpha W]\left(\frac{1 - \alpha}{\alpha}\right) + \frac{1}{\alpha} + \frac{W}{1 - \alpha}.$$

The last two terms approach zero. As α approaches $-\infty$, $1 - \alpha$ approaches $+\infty$. Since $1/V > 1$, the factor:

$$\frac{(1/V)^{1-\alpha}}{(1-\alpha)^2}$$

approaches $+\infty$, since an exponential approaches infinity faster than any power. From (28), $V \geqq W$. If $V = W$, then the factor:

$$(1-\alpha)V + \alpha W = \alpha(W - V) + V,$$

is a positive constant; if $V > W$, then it approaches $+\infty$ as α approaches $-\infty$. Finally

$$\frac{1-\alpha}{\alpha}$$

necessarily approaches -1. Hence:

> $R(\alpha)$ is a strictly decreasing function, approaching
> $+\infty$ as α approaches $-\infty$ and 0 as α approaches $+\infty$.   (30)

The market, however, should adjust the rate of return so that the discounted stream of profits equals the cost of investment; i.e., $S = 1$, or, from (29):

$$R(\alpha) = \theta/\gamma[G(v)].   (31)$$

Since the right-hand side of (31) is positive, (30) guarantees the existence of an α which satisfies (31). For a given θ, the equilibrium rate of return, ρ, is equal to $\alpha\theta$; it may indeed be negative. The rate of return is thus determined by the expected rate of increase in wages, current labor costs per unit output, and the physical lifetime of the investment. Further, if the first two are sufficiently large, the physical lifetime becomes irrelevant, since then $T^* < T$, and $T = T^*$.

The discussion of profits and returns has not made any special assumptions as to the form of the production relations.

Rational Expectations in a Macroeconomic Growth Model

Assume a one-sector model so that the production relations of the entire economy are described by the model shown earlier in this paper. In particular, this implies that gross investment at any moment of time is simply a diversion of goods that might otherwise be used for consumption. Output and gross investment can then be measured in the same units.

The question arises, can the expectation assumed to govern investment behavior in the preceding section actually be fulfilled? Specifically, can we have a constant relative increase of wages and a constant rate of interest which, if anticipated, will lead entrepreneurs to invest at a rate which, in conjunction with the exogenously given rate of increase of the labor force, cause wages to rise at the given rate and the rate of interest to remain at the given level? Such a state of affairs is frequently referred to as "perfect foresight," but a better term is "rational expectations," a term introduced by J. Muth.[13]

We study this question first for the full employment case. For this case to occur, the physical lifetime of investments must not be an effective constraint. If, in the notation of the last section, $T^* > \overline{T}$, and if wage expectations are correct, then investments will disappear through depreciation at a time when they are still yielding positive current profits. As seen in the "wages" section of their paper, this is incompatible with competitive equilibrium and full employment. Assume therefore that:

$$T^* \leqq \overline{T}; \tag{32}$$

then, from (28), $W = V$, and, from (29) and (31), the equilibrium value of ρ is determined by the equation:

$$\frac{1 - W^\alpha}{\alpha} + \frac{W - W^\alpha}{1 - \alpha} = \frac{\theta}{a}, \tag{33}$$

where, on the right-hand side, use is made of (7).

From (16) it is seen that, for the wages to rise at a constant rate θ, it is necessary that the quantity:

$$G^{1-n} - \frac{L}{c},$$

rise at a rate $\theta(1-n)/n$. For θ constant, it follows from (33) that a constant ρ (and therefore a constant α) requires that W be constant. For the specific production relations (7) and (8), (23) shows that:

$$W = \frac{a\left(G^{1-n} - \dfrac{L}{c}\right)^{n/(1-n)}}{b} \frac{bG^{-n}}{a} = \left(1 - \frac{L}{cG^{1-n}}\right)^{n/(1-n)},$$

and therefore the constancy of W is equivalent to that of L/G^{1-n}. In combination with the preceding remark, we see that:

$$L \text{ increases at rate } \theta(1 - n)/n, \; G \text{ increases at rate } \theta/n. \tag{34}$$

Suppose that:

$$\sigma = \text{rate of increase of the labor force}$$

is a given constant. Then:

$$\theta = n\sigma/(1 - n), \text{ and} \tag{35}$$

$$\text{the rate of increase of } G \text{ is } \sigma/(1 - n). \tag{36}$$

Substitution into the production function (9) yields:

$$\text{the rate of increase of } x \text{ is } \sigma/(1 - n). \tag{37}$$

From (36) and (37), the ratio G/x is constant over time. However, the value at which it is constant is not determined by the considerations so

---

[13] See J. Muth, "Rational Expectations and the Theory of Price Movements," *Econometrica*, 29 (1961), pp. 315–35.

far introduced; the savings function is needed to complete the system. Let the constant ratio be:

$$G(t)/x(t) = \mu. \tag{38}$$

Define:

$$g(t) = \text{rate of gross investment at time} = dG/dt.$$

From (36), $g/G = \sigma/(1-n)$, a constant. Then:

$$g/x = (g/G)(G/x) = \mu \, \sigma/(1 - n). \tag{39}$$

A simple assumption is that the ratio of gross saving (equals gross invest-ment) to income (equals output) is a function of the rate of return, ρ; a special case would be the common assumption of a constant savings-to-income ratio. Then μ is a function of ρ. On the other hand, we can write W as follows, using (23) and (13):

$$W = \frac{a\left(G - \frac{x}{a}\right)^n}{b} \quad \frac{bG^{-n}}{a} = \left(1 - \frac{x}{aG}\right)^n = \left(1 - \frac{1}{a\mu}\right)^n. \tag{40}$$

Since θ is given by (35), (31) is a relation between W and ρ, and by (40), between μ and ρ. We thus have two relations between μ and ρ, so they are determinate.

From (38), μ determines one relation between G and X. If the labor force, L, is given at one moment of time, the production function (9) con-stitutes a second such relation, and the system is completely determinate.

As in many growth models, the rates of growth of the variables in the system do not depend on savings behavior; however, their levels do.

It should be made clear that all that has been demonstrated is the exis-tence of a solution in which all variables have constant rates of growth, correctly anticipated. The stability of the solution, however, requires further study.

The growth rate for wages implied by the solution has one paradoxical aspect; it increases with the rate of growth of the labor force (provided $n < 1$). The explanation seems to be that, under full employment, the in-creasing labor force permits a more rapid introduction of the newer ma-chinery. It should also be noted that, for a constant saving ratio, g/x, an increase in σ decreases μ [from (39)], from which it can be seen that wages at the initial time period would be lower.

This solution is however admissible only if the condition (32), that the rate of depreciation not be too rapid, be satisfied. We can find an explicit formula for the economic lifetime, T^*, of new investment. From (24), it satisfies the condition:

$$e^{-\theta T*} = W.$$

If we use (35) and (40) and solve for T^*, we find:

$$T^* = \frac{-(1 - n)}{\sigma} \log \left[1 - \frac{1}{a\mu}\right], \tag{41}$$

and this is to be compared with $\bar{T}$; the full employment solution, with rational expectations of exponentially increasing wages and constant interest, is admissible if $T^* \leq \bar{T}$.

If $T^* > \bar{T}$, then the full employment solution is inadmissible. One might ask if a constant-growth solution is possible in this case. The answer depends on assumptions about the dynamics of wages under this condition.

We retain the two conditions, that wages rise at a constant rate θ, and that the rate of interest be constant. With constant θ, the rate of interest, ρ, is determined from (31); from (29), this requires that

$$W \text{ is constant over time.} \tag{42}$$

From the definition of W, (23), and the particular form of the production relations, (7) and (8), it follows that the wage rate, w, must rise at the same rate as G^n, or:

$$G \text{ rises at a constant rate } \theta/n. \tag{43}$$

In the presence of continued unemployment, the most natural wage dynamics in a free market would be a decreasing or, at best, constant wage level. But since G can never decrease, it follows from (43) that θ can never be negative. Instead of making a specific assumption about wage changes, it will be assumed that any choice of θ can be imposed—perhaps by government or union or social pressure—and it is asked what restrictions on the possible values of θ are set by the other equilibrium conditions.

In the capital shortage case, the serial number of the oldest capital good in use is determined by the physical lifetime of the good; i.e., $G' = G(t - \bar{T})$. From (43):

$$G(t - \bar{T}) = e^{-\theta \bar{T}/n} G.$$

Then, from (1') and (7):

$$x = aG(1 - e^{-\theta \bar{T}/n}),$$

so that the ratio, G/x, or μ, is a constant:

$$\mu = 1/a(1 - e^{-\theta \bar{T}/n}). \tag{44}$$

From (43), $g/G = \theta/n$; hence, by the same argument as that leading to (39):

$$g(x) = \theta/na(1 - e^{-\theta \bar{T}/n}). \tag{45}$$

There are three unknown constants of the growth process, θ, ρ, and W. If, as before, it is assumed that the gross savings ratio, g/x, is a function of the rate of return, ρ, then, for any given ρ, θ can be determined from (45). Note that the right-hand side of (45) is a strictly increasing function of θ for $\theta \geq 0$, so that the determination is unique, and the rate of growth is an increasing function of the gross savings ratio, contrary to the situation in the full employment case. Then W can be solved for from (31) and (29).

Thus the rate of return is a freely disposable parameter whose choice determines the rate of growth and W, which, in turn, determines the initial wage rate. There are, of course, some inequalities which must be satisfied to insure that the solution corresponds to the capital shortage rather than the full employment case; in particular, $W \leq V$, and the labor force also must be sufficient to permit the expansion. From (2'), this means that the labor force must at all times be at least equal to:

$$cG^{1-n} - c(G')^{1-n} = cG^{1-n}(1 - e^{-\theta(1-n)\overline{T}/n}),$$

if σ is the growth rate of the labor force. We must then have:

$$\sigma \geq \theta(1 - n)/n, \tag{46}$$

which sets an upper bound on θ (for $n < 1$). Other constraints on ρ are implied by the conditions $\theta \geq 0$ and $W \geq 0$ (if it is assumed that wage rates are non-negative). The first condition sets a lower limit on g/x; it can be shown, from (45), that:

$$g/x \geq 1/a\overline{T}; \tag{47}$$

i.e., the gross savings ratio must be at least equal to the amount of capital goods needed to produce one unit of output over their lifetime. The constraint $W \geq 0$ implies an interval in which ρ must lie. The conditions under which these constraints are consistent (so that at least one solution exists for the capital shortage case) have not been investigated in detail.

Divergence of Private and Social Product

As has already been emphasized, the presence of learning means that an act of investment benefits future investors, but this benefit is not paid for by the market. Hence it is to be expected that the aggregate amount of investment under the competitive model of the last section will fall short of the socially optimum level. This difference will be investigated in detail in the present section under a simple assumption as to the utility function of society. For brevity, I refer to the *competitive solution* of the last section, to be contrasted with the *optimal* solution. Full employment is assumed. It is shown that the socially optimal growth rate is the same as that under competitive conditions, but the socially optimal ratio of gross investment to output is higher than the competitive level.

Utility is taken to be a function of the stream of consumption derived from the productive mechanism. Let:

$$c = \text{consumption} = \text{output} - \text{gross investment} = x - g.$$

It is in particular assumed that future consumption is discounted at a constant rate, β, so that utility is:

$$U = \int_0^{+\infty} e^{-\beta t} c(t) dt = \int_0^{+\infty} e^{-\beta t} x(t) dt - \int_0^{+\infty} e^{-\beta t} g(t) dt. \tag{48}$$

Integration by parts yields:

$$\int_0^{+\infty} e^{-\beta t} g(t) dt = e^{-\beta t} G(t) \Big|_0^{+\infty} + \beta \int_0^{+\infty} e^{-\beta t} G(t) dt.$$

From (48):

$$U = U_1 - \lim_{t \to +\infty} e^{-\beta t} G(t) + G(o), \tag{49}$$

where:

$$U_1 = \int_0^{+\infty} e^{-\beta t} [x(t) - \beta G(t)] dt. \tag{50}$$

The policy problem is the choice of the function $G(t)$, with $G'(t) \geqq 0$, to maximize (49), where $x(t)$ is determined by the production function (9), and:

$$L(t) = L_0 e^{\sigma t}. \tag{51}$$

The second term in (49) is necessarily non-negative. It will be shown that, for sufficiently high discount rate, ρ, the function $G(t)$ which maximizes U_1 also has the property that the second term in (49) is zero; hence it also maximizes (49) since $G(0)$ is given.

Substitute (9) and (51) into (50):

$$U_1 = \int_0^{+\infty} e^{-\beta t} G(t) \left[a - \beta - a \left(1 - \frac{L_0 e^{\sigma t}}{cG^{1-n}} \right)^{1/(1-n)} \right] dt.$$

Let $\bar{G}(t) = G(t) e^{-\sigma t/(1-n)}$; then:

$$U_1 = \int_0^{+\infty} e^{-\left(\beta - \frac{\sigma}{1-n}\right)t} \bar{G}(t) \left[a - \beta - a \left(1 - \frac{L_0}{c\bar{G}^{1-n}} \right)^{1/(1-n)} \right] dt.$$

Assume that:

$$\beta > \frac{\sigma}{1 - n}; \tag{52}$$

otherwise an infinite utility is attainable. Then, to maximize U_1, it suffices to choose $\bar{G}(t)$ so as to maximize, for each t:

$$\bar{G} \left[a - \beta - a \left(1 - \frac{L_0}{c\bar{G}^{1-n}} \right)^{1/(1-n)} \right]. \tag{53}$$

Before actually determining the maximum, it can be noted that the maximizing value of $\bar{G}$ is independent of t and is therefore a constant. Hence the optimum policy is:

$$G(t) = \bar{G} e^{\sigma t/(1-n)}, \tag{54}$$

so that, from (36), the growth rate is the same as the competitive. From (52), $e^{-\beta t} G(t) \to 0$ as $t \to +\infty$.

To determine the optimal $\bar{G}$, it will be convenient to make a change of variables. Define:

$$v = \left(1 - \frac{L_0}{c\bar{G}^{1-n}} \right)^{n/(1-n)},$$

so that:

$$\bar{G} = \left[\frac{L_0}{c(1 - v^{(1-n)/n})}\right]^{1/(1-n)}.$$ (55)

The analysis will be carried through primarily for the case where the output per unit capital is sufficiently high, more specifically, where:

$$a > \beta.$$ (56)

Let:

$$\gamma = 1 - \frac{\beta}{a} > 0.$$ (57)

The maximizing $\bar{G}$, or v, is unchanged by multiplying (53), the function to be maximized, by the positive quantity, $(c/L_0)^{1/(1-n)}/a$ and then substituting from (55) and (57). Thus, v maximizes:

$$(1 - v^{(1-n)/n})^{-1/(1-n)} (\gamma - v^{1/n}).$$

The variable v ranges from 0 to 1. However, the second factor vanishes when $v = \gamma^n < 1$ (since $\gamma < 1$), and becomes negative for larger values of v. Since the first factor is always positive, it can be assumed that $v < \gamma^n$ in searching for a maximum, and both factors are positive. Then v also maximizes the logarithm of the above function, which is:

$$f(v) = -\frac{\log (1 - v^{(1-)n/n})}{1 - n} + \log (\gamma - v^{1/n}),$$

so that:

$$f'(v) = \frac{v^{\frac{1}{n}-2}}{n}\left[\frac{\gamma - v}{(1 - v^{(1-n)/n})(\gamma - v^{1/n})}\right].$$

Clearly, with $n < 1$, $f'(v) > 0$ when $0 < v < \gamma$ and $f'(v) < 0$ when $\gamma < v < \gamma^n$, so that the maximum is obtained at:

$$v = \gamma.$$ (58)

The optimum $\bar{G}$ is determined by substituting γ for v in (55).

From (54), L/G^{1-n} is a constant over time. From the definition of v and (58), then:

$$\gamma = \left(1 - \frac{L}{cG^{1-n}}\right)^{n/(1-n)}$$

for all t along the optimal path, and, from the production function (9):

$$\gamma = \left(1 - \frac{x}{aG}\right)^n \quad \text{for all } t \text{ along the optimal path.}$$ (59)

This optimal solution will be compared with the competitive solution of steady growth studied in the last section. From (40), we know that:

$$W = \left(1 - \frac{x}{aG}\right)^n \quad \text{for all } t \text{ along the competitive path.}$$ (60)

It will be demonstrated that $W < \gamma$; from this it follows that *the ratio G/x*

is less along the competitive path than along the optimal path. Since, along both paths:

$$g/x = [\sigma/(1 - n)] \, (G/x),$$

it also follows that *the gross savings ratio is smaller along the competitive path than along the optimal path.*

For the particular utility function (48), the supply of capital is infinitely elastic at $\rho = \beta$; i.e., the community will take any investment with a rate of return exceeding β and will take no investment at a rate of return less than β. For an equilibrium in which some, but not all, income is saved, we must have:

$$\rho = \beta. \tag{61}$$

From (35), $\theta = n\sigma/(1-n)$; hence, by definition (28):

$$\alpha = (1 - n)\beta/n\sigma. \tag{62}$$

Since $n < 1$, it follows from (62), and the assumption (52), that:

$$\alpha > 1. \tag{63}$$

Equation (33) then becomes the one by which W is determined. The left-hand side will be denoted as $F(W)$.

$$F^1 \, (W) = \frac{1 - W^{\alpha - 1}}{1 - \alpha}.$$

From (63), $F^1(W) < 0$; for $0 \leq W < 1$ is the relevant range since the investment will never be profitable if $W \geq 1$. To demonstrate that $W < \gamma$, it suffices to show that $F(W) > F(\gamma)$ for that value of W which satisfies (33); i.e., to show that:

$$F(\gamma) < \theta/a. \tag{64}$$

Finally, to demonstrate (64), note that $\gamma < 1$ and $\alpha > 1$, which imply that $\gamma^\alpha < \gamma$, and therefore:

$$(1 - \alpha) - \gamma^\alpha + \alpha\gamma > (1 - \alpha)(1 - \gamma).$$

Since $\alpha > 1$, $\alpha(1-\alpha) < 0$. Dividing both sides by this magnitude yields:

$$\frac{1 - \gamma^\alpha}{\alpha} + \frac{\gamma - \gamma^\alpha}{1 - \alpha} < \frac{1 - \gamma}{\alpha} = \frac{\theta}{a},$$

where use is made of (57), (28), and (61); but from (33), the left-hand side is precisely $F(\gamma)$, so that (64) is demonstrated.

The case $a \leq \beta$, excluded by (56), can be handled similarly; in that case the optimum v is 0. The subsequent reasoning follows in the same way, so that the corresponding competitive path would have $W < 0$, which is, however, impossible.

Some Comments on the Model

1. Many writers, such as Theodore Schultz, have stressed the improvement in the quality of the labor force over time as a source of increased

productivity. This interpretation can be incorporated in the present model by assuming that σ, the rate of growth of the labor force, incorporates qualitative as well as quantitative increase.

2. In this model, there is only one efficient capital-labor ratio for new investment at any moment of time. Most other models, on the contrary, have assumed that alternative capital-labor ratios are possible both before the capital good is built and after. A still more plausible model is that of Johansen,[14] according to which alternative capital-labor ratios are open to the entrepreneur's choice at the time of investment but are fixed once the investment is congealed into a capital good.

3. In this model, as in those of Solow [15] and Johansen,[16] the learning takes place, in effect, only in the capital goods industry; no learning takes place in the use of a capital good once built. Lundberg's Horndal effect suggests that this is not realistic. The model should be extended to include this possibility.

4. It has been assumed here that learning takes place only as a by-product of ordinary production. In fact, society has created institutions—education and research—whose purpose it is to enable learning to take place more rapidly. A fuller model would take account of these as additional variables.

---

[14] *Op. cit.*
[15] *Op. cit.*
[16] *Op. cit.*

Indexes

In ancient days
        (As in Part One)
The search for order
        Had begun:

To look at man's
        Most mortal soul
By finite lens
In bits, or whole:

*** the journey has no end:

                F.M.

Index of Names

Index of Subjects

*This book has been set in 10 point Janson,
leaded 2 points, and 9 point Janson, leaded 1
point. Part numbers and chapter titles are in 18
point Caslon True Cut italic; part titles and
chapter numbers are in 24 point Caslon True
Cut italic. The size of the type page is 27 by
46½ picas.*